VERTEBRATE ANIMALS
OF THE
UNITED STATES
(Exclusive of Birds)

PRATT

A MANUAL OF
LAND AND FRESH WATER

VERTEBRATE ANIMALS
OF THE
UNITED STATES
(Exclusive of Birds)

BY

HENRY SHERRING PRATT, Ph.D.

PROFESSOR OF BIOLOGY IN HAVERFORD COLLEGE, PA.
AUTHOR OF "A MANUAL OF THE COMMON
INVERTEBRATE ANIMALS," ETC.

SECOND EDITION
WITH 184 ILLUSTRATIONS
AND A GLOSSARY

PHILADELPHIA
P. BLAKISTON'S SON & CO., INC.
1012 WALNUT STREET

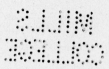

71745

TO THE MEMORY OF

ISAAC SHARPLESS

(President of Haverford College 1887–1917)

a Lover of Nature and a Good Man

PREFACE TO THE SECOND EDITION

The main purpose of the revision of this Manual has been to reflect in it the numerous changes in the nomenclature of the Vertebrate animals of the United States which have been made in the past few years, and to define more precisely their known ranges of distribution. In the accomplishment of this purpose the author has freely utilized all the published sources of information at his command. For the group of Fishes he has followed in the main the *Check List of the Fishes and Fishlike Vertebrates of North and Middle America* by Jordan, Evermann and Clark (1930), and for the group of Mammals Anthony's *Field Book of North American Mammals* (1928). In both these groups Jordan's *Manual of the Vertebrate Animals of the Northeastern United States, Thirteenth Edition* (1929) has often been followed, the section on Fishes in this work having been revised by Dr. C. L. Hubbs and that on Mammals by Dr. H. H. T. Jackson.

Dr. Emmett Reid Dunn, Professor of Biology in Haverford College and the author's colleague, has thoroughly revised the sections on Amphibians and Reptiles, and the author is under a great obligation to him for this valuable service. The author is also under obligation to Joshua L. Baily Jr., San Diego, California, for reading and correcting the proof.

HAVERFORD COLLEGE,
HAVERFORD, PA.

PREFACE TO THE FIRST EDITION

This Manual was written to furnish students of Zoology, students of the Geographical Distribution of animals, and Nature students, with diagnostic descriptions of the land and fresh water vertebrate animals of the United States, together with analytical keys by means of which they can be readily identified and their affinities determined. Many excellent hand-books for the identification of birds already exist, and their number is constantly being added to, and it is for this reason that this large Class has not been included in the present book. There is, however, a very real need of a general modern manual of the fishes, amphibians, reptiles and mammals of the country which shall give the accepted scientific names of species, as well as of the larger groups to which they belong, and also reflect the recent advances in our knowledge of their systematic and structural relationships, their manner of life and their geographical distribution.

The region covered by this work is the whole of the United States between the Canadian and Mexican borders, neither Alaska nor the West Indian or Hawaiian Islands being included; the southern portion of Canada, however, is included, as it belongs to the same geographical region as the northern portion of the United States. With certain exceptions, all the species, as well as the geographic subspecies, of the four Classes of vertebrates above mentioned which are found in this large region, are described, the exceptions being those species which are of doubtful validity, those which are very rare, and certain Mexican species, chiefly of reptiles, which have been observed but a few times north of the boundary. Great care has been taken to state precisely the geographic limits, so far as known, of these species and subspecies.

In compiling this work the author has utilized every source of information at his command, and is consequently under obligations to very many persons; to all of these he extends his heartiest thanks. The section on Fishes is based upon Jordan and Evermann's "Fishes of North and Middle America," and one of the authors of this fundamental work, Dr. Barton Warren Evermann, Director of the Museum of the California Academy of Sciences, San Francisco, has read this portion of the manuscript critically. Large use has also been made of "American Food and Game Fishes" by the same authors, and of Jordan's "Guide to the Study of Fishes" and "Manual of Vertebrates," and also of Forbes and Richardson's "Fishes of Illinois," the general arrangement of the main subdivisions of the Class being based on the last-named work. Smith's "Fishes of North Carolina," Bean's "Fishes of New York," and the various papers in the Bulletins of the Fish Commission and the Bureau of Fisheries, as well as numerous other publications, have also been used. In the arrangement of the Lampreys the recent revision of Creaser and Hubbs published by the Museum of Zoology of the University of Michigan has been followed.

The arrangement of the Amphibians and Reptiles has been based upon Stejneger and Barbour's "Check List of North American Amphibians and Reptiles" and the descriptions and keys upon Cope's "Batrachia of North America" and Cope's "Crocodilians, Lizards and Snakes of North America." Extensive use has also been made of many other works, especially Miss Dickerson's "Frog Book," Ditmar's "Reptile Book," and the State Reports of several States. The author is under an especial obligation to the important Smith college group of Herpetologists for bringing his arrangement and descriptions down to date, the morphological studies of Professor H. H. Wilder and Professor I. W. Wilder and the systematic studies of Professor E. R. Dunn having contributed to this end. The latter author, especially, has revised the sections on the caudate Amphibians and the Snakes and Turtles, the synopsis of the larvæ of the Plethodontidæ, which is largely new matter, being wholly by him. Dr. G. Kingsley Noble of the American Museum of Natural History, New York, has revised the section on Frogs and Toads, and Karl P. Schmidt of the Field Columbian Museum, Chicago, that on Lizards and Crocodilians. The synopsis of the eggs and larvæ of Frogs and Toads has been taken from A. H. Wright's "Life History of the Anura of Ithaca, New York."

The arrangement of the Mammals is based upon Gerrit S. Miller, Jr.'s "List of the North American Land Mammals in the United States National Museum, 1911." For the description and keys full use has been made of the various numbers of "The North American Fauna" prepared under the direction of C. Hart Merriam, former Director of the United States Biological Survey, the publication of which has been of epochal importance in the study of American mammals. Many other works have been useful, especially Elliot's "Synopsis of the Mammals of North America and adjacent Seas," which is a work of fundamental importance. For accounts of the life and habits of mammals, Stone and Cram's "American Animals," Nelson's "Wild Animals," Seton's "Northern Animals," and Audubon and Bachman's

"Quadrupeds of North America" have been used. The senior author of the first named work, Dr. Witmer Stone, of the Academy of Natural Sciences, Philadelphia, has been so good as to read critically the whole manuscript of Mammals.

The figures which have been introduced are intended to illustrate and explain the most important diagnostic features of the various groups of animals and to illuminate the keys and make them more easy to comprehend, and have been copied mostly from monographs, special treatises and textbooks; the author here extends his thanks to the authors of these figures and the publishers of the books in which they are found for the privilege of using them.

In the use of scientific names of animals of the laws of priority established by the International Commission of Nomenclature have been followed. The name of the author of each species, subspecies and genus follows the first mention of it in the descriptions, as is customary, and in those cases in which an author originally placed his species in some other genus than the one here given, his name is in parentheses. Wherever an author's name appears more than once in the same genus it is usually abbreviated after the first occurrence. No other abbreviations of the names of authors' appear except in the case of Linnæus, whose name is always shortened to "L" wherever he appears as the author of a scientific name.

Much of the labor of compiling this work has been done at Cold Spring Harbor, Long Island, and the author wishes to express his great obligation to his friend and colleague, Dr. Charles B. Davenport, for his constant support and encouragement during its progress. He also wishes to thank his publishers, P. Blakiston's Son and Company, for their many courtesies and their readiness in meeting his wishes.

HAVERFORD COLLEGE,
HAVERFORD, PA.

CONTENTS

PAGE

VERTEBRATE ANIMALS
OF THE
UNITED STATES

VERTEBRATES

Vertebrates are bilaterally symmetrical animals with an interna cartilaginous or bony skeleton; with usually two pairs of locomotory appendages, the fore and hind limbs; with pharyngeal respiration; with a tubular dorsal central nervous system; with a ventral heart, a closed circulatory system consisting of arteries, capillaries, and veins, and red blood.

The vertebrates are characterized as a group among animals by their large size and the high degree of specialization of many of their parts, and also by their general distribution over the earth. Every part of the surface of the globe, as well as the ground and the waters beneath and the air above it in which animals can in any way satisfy the need of all life of food and oxygen, is inhabited by them. The fishes and other aquatic forms abound in fresh and salt water, while the terrestrial and flying vertebrates inhabit all the continents, even the coldest and most inclement.

External Characters.—The vertebrate body is in most cases more or less cylindrical in form, and is made up of four regions, the head, the neck, the trunk and the tail. The *head*, being the anterior portion of the body, bears the principal organs of orientation, which are the special sense organs, and the organs of prehension—the mouth with the lips and teeth where these are present; it also contains the large brain, which innervates these essential organs, enclosed, for its protection, in the skull. The *neck* is absent or unimportant in fishes and other aquatic vertebrates, but in most of the land forms is of great importance inasmuch as it is the flexible body region which gives the head the wide range of movement necessary to it in a rapidly moving terrestrial animal. In fishes the head and anterior portion of the body forms a wedge which must be pushed by the locomotory movements of the tail-fin through a resistant medium, and it is greatly to the advantage

I

of the animal that the head be joined solidly with the trunk and without
the interposition of a flexible body region, which would lessen the driving power of the caudal fin.   Fishes, also, in their watery environment,
do not depend so much on the sense of sight and the other special
senses located in the head to orient themselves as do the land animals,
because the density of the medium in which they live limits the carrying
power of these senses, but they depend rather upon the lateral line sense
and other special senses which reside in the skin over the whole body
and are affected directly by the water surrounding it.   Fishes are,
consequently, often sufficiently oriented with regard to their environment without moving, and may be observed to lie motionless in the
water for long periods of time.

The *trunk* contains the principal viscera and is the largest and
bulkiest body region; in it also are the places of attachment of the
two pairs of limbs.   In the terrestrial vertebrates the trunk may be
subdivided into two or three subregions, the thoracic subregion which
with the fore limbs forms the anterior portion, the sacral subregion,
forming with the hind limbs the posterior portion, and, in four-footed
vertebrates, the lumbar subregion which lies between the other two and
forms the pivot where the body bends when the direction of movement
is changed.

The paired limbs are wanting in the cyclostomate fishes, the most
primitive vertebrates, and also in snakes and certain species of lizards.
The anterior pair is wanting in certain species of fishes, and the posterior
pair in many fishes and also in *Siren* among the amphibians and
in the *Cetacea* and *Sirenia* among the mammals.   The paired appendages of fishes are the pectoral and ventral fins, which are flattened
swimming organs stiffened by radiating bony and cartilaginous rods.
In the other classes of vertebrates they are more or less cylindrical
in form and each is made up of three main divisions.   The proximal
division projects directly from the trunk and articulates with it;
the distal division of the appendages is applied to the substratum or
medium on or in which the animal is moving, and is the most complex
of the three in structure, terminating typically in the five digits.   This
number has, however, undergone a reduction in very many vertebrates
—in extreme cases, like that of the horse, only one digit being present on
each foot.   In the four-footed vertebrates, also, the fore and hind pairs
differ, in most cases, in the number of their digits and the essential
uses to which they are put, the hinder pair having a smaller number
than the forward pair, as is the case, for instance, in cats and dogs;
inasmuch as the hinder pair principally propels the animal, the fewer

its points of contact with the ground the greater will be its effectiveness. In the *Primates* the digits may be used for prehensile purposes; in the flying vertebrates, the birds and bats, the fore limbs become wings.

The *tail* of vertebrates is the postanal portion of the body, and is the principal organ of locomotion in most aquatic forms. In the terrestrial representatives it has lost its primitive significance and varies much among the various groups in relative length as well as in function, and may be rudimentary or absent altogether.

The *integument* of vertebrates, which forms the outer covering of the body, consists of two distinct layers, the outer epidermis and the inner dermis, and its effectiveness as a protective envelope is increased by the growth of additional characteristic coverings, such as the bony dermal scales of fishes and the horny epidermal scales and plates of reptiles, feathers of birds and hair of mammals. The epidermal layer of the integument is soft and slimy in fish and amphibians, which live in or near the water, while in terrestrial vertebrates, whose bodies are exposed to the air, it becomes more or less hard and horny and the special integumental coverings of the land forms just mentioned appear as specializations of it.

One of the most conspicuous of the external characters of vertebrates, as well as of other animals, and consequently important in the classification of them, is their coloration. This is also a feature of great importance to the animal itself in its relation to its environment, inasmuch as in a large class of cases the coloration of an animal tends to render it inconspicuous to its enemies and to its prey, and perhaps to increase the absorption of heat from the atmosphere or to prevent the too great radiation of bodily heat to it. The same color pattern, however, in numerous cases does not characterize all the individuals of a species, the males being often colored differently from the females and the young individuals from the adults. The summer coat is also often different from the winter coat in color and markings. The practical purposes of these differences is sometimes hard to explain, but can often be correlated with the habits of animals and the need of concealment and protection at different times of the year and during different periods of growth. A few species are dichromatic, there being two color phases which may characterize individuals. The gray squirrel and the black bear are familiar examples, gray and black squirrels appearing in the same litter and black and brown (cinnamon) individuals in the same family of bears. Metachrosis, or the rapid change in color under the influence of external stimuli, is common among fishes, amphibians and lizards. Brown and green tones may alternate with each other in frogs and toads, mainly under the stimulus of light; the so-called chameleon of our southern States and many other lizards have a still more remarkable range of color change. Very old individuals in all the classes of vertebrates often show differences in coloration and markings which are due to wear and the fading of colors or loss or injury of parts.

Internal Characters.—Characteristic of vertebrates, and often of importance in classifying them, is the *internal skeleton*, which forms the supporting framework of the body. In the most primitive fishes this framework is composed entirely of cartilage and the ligaments and membranes which serve to bind its various parts together; in the higher fishes and all the other vertebrates it is formed principally of bone. The ratio of the cartilage to the bone that forms the skeleton varies much among vertebrates in the classes above fishes, it being the largest in the amphibians and the smallest in the birds. The backbone, the main skeletal axis of the body, is a flexible segmented column consisting of a succession of the similar disk-like or cylindrical vertebræ which grow around the unsegmented embryonic rod-like notochord and are bound together by intervertebral ligaments. The vertebræ forming the column may vary in number in the various classes of vertebrates, ranging from 6 in certain amphibians to 300 in some snakes; they fall into groups which correspond to the main subdivisions of the body of the animal. The skull, or anterior portion of the axial skeleton, is composed of two parts, the cranium, which encloses and protects the brain and the organs of special sense, and the visceral skeleton, which surrounds the mouth and forms the framework of the face, the jaws, the tongue and the gills, where they are present. These two portions of the skull, which protect and support such diverse organs, develop quite distinct from each other, and are but loosely bound together in fishes, and more or less so in all other vertebrates in which the mouth is employed mainly in seizing the food and not in masticating it. In the mammals, however, which masticate their food, the need of a solid base to chew against has brought about a firm union of the visceral with the cranial portions of the skull, which is thus given the compact character which distinguishes it.

The other internal organs in vertebrates are usually of less importance in classification, although the entire inner structure of the vertebrate body bears the characteristic stamp of the group. This is especially true of the *circulatory system*—the ventrally situated heart, the closed system of blood tubes and the red blood corpuscles. The heart is made up primarily of two portions, an anterior and a posterior, into the former of which the blood is poured by the veins, while from the latter it is discharged through the arteries and distributed to the respiratory organs and throughout the body. In mammals and birds, whose bodies maintain a constant, relatively high temperature, without regard to that of the medium in which they are living or the time of year, each of these portions of the heart is subdivided by a septum, so that the heart in these animals is composed of two pairs of chambers, the anterior pair forming the right and left auricles and the posterior pair the right and left ventricles; the right chamber in each pair contains venous blood which has been brought exhausted of oxygen and charged with carbon dioxide from the various organs of the body and the left chamber contains arterial blood brought purged of carbon dioxide and with oxygen renewed directly from the lungs. It is this complete separation of the venous from the arterial sides of the heart which results in the distribution of pure unmixed oxygenated blood over the body and the consequent maintenance in it of a relatively high and also constant temperature.

In reptiles and amphibians, on the other hand, the ventricle is not thus divided into two completely separated chambers, but there is a communication of greater or less extent between its venous and arterial sides, and in consequence the freshly oxygenated blood in the left division is more or less diluted by the venous and vitiated blood in the right division before it is pumped through the arteries over the body. Metabolism, consequently, which bears a direct relation to the oxygen content of the blood, cannot be so active as in birds and mammals; the body temperature is not maintained at a constant level but is dependent to a certain extent on the temperature of the surrounding medium and varies with it.

The heart of fishes contains venous blood only, the auricle and ventricle not being divided into right and left halves (except partially so in the *Dipnoi*); the blood is sent to the gills from the heart, where it is oxygenated, and then distributed directly throughout the body without first returning to the heart.

The process of *respiration*, by which an animal or plant takes in oxygen from the surrounding medium and gives off carbon dioxide, is performed by a radically different body surface in vertebrates than in invertebrates. Being a transfusion process it requires a moist surface, and consequently while it may be performed by an aquatic animal through the outer surface it must be carried on by land animals in the interior of the body. The aquatic invertebrates, with the exception of the chordate forms, respire directly with the integument or with organs derived from it. The vertebrate, on the other hand, in common with all chordate animals, respires directly with the pharynx, the anterior portion of the digestive tract, and with structures derived from the pharynx; the medium in which the animal lives, whether water or air, must be drawn through the mouth into the respiratory organs by an incessently repeated muscular effort, the interruption of which, only for a few moments, will often kill the animal. In fishes the gills are paired lateral pockets of the pharynx which open through the integument to the outside; through these the breathing motions of the animal maintain never ceasing streams of water from which the thin-walled, delicately branched gill filaments absorb the respiratory air.

In amphibians the larval forms, and to a large extent the adults as well, respire after the manner of invertebrates, by means of the integument. All amphibians, however, in the adult condition, respire also directly with the surface of the pharynx, and also in most species with the lungs, which arise as a ventral diverticulum of it, as well. The importance of direct pharyngeal respiration is shown by the rapid and regular respiratory movements of the throat of salamanders and frogs when in the air, which affect the pharynx alone and do not serve to introduce air into the lungs, and also by the total lack of lungs in a large group of salamanders. Amphibians are the oldest and most primitive terrestrial vertebrates; direct pharyngeal respiration was probably the earliest method among vertebrates of utilizing the atmospheric air for respiratory purposes, and may have grown out of the habit, not uncommon among fishes, of rising to the surface of the water and swallowing air. The lungs, in the earliest amphibians, were probably primarily hydrostatic organs like the air-bladder of fishes, a function they still retain in many primitive salamanders, and to a certain extent probably in all amphibians.

In the amniotic vertebrates respiration is exercised by the lungs exclusively rather than by the pharynx directly, and the complexity of their structure in each group of such animals bears a direct relation to the intensity of the metabolism in that group. The cold-blooded, sluggish reptiles have sack-like lungs with relatively large and relatively few lung vesicles. The lungs of the warm-blooded vertebrates, on the other hand, which maintain a constant temperature in their bodies without reference to the surrounding medium, contain a dense mass of minute vesicles which represent a very much larger relative absorptive surface and gives the lungs the spongy texture characteristic of them, the birds with their higher temperature possessing lungs with smaller vesicles and consequently a larger relative surface than the mammals.

The union of the *digestive tract* in vertebrates with the respiratory, just alluded to, is peculiar to them and to chordates. The paired gill clefts in the lateral walls of the pharynx and the paired visceral arches which form their skeletal support are universal throughout the group and are not found in other animals. The character and position of the mouth and the jaws and their relation to the gill system are especially noteworthy. In the great group of *Arthropoda* the organs of mastication are modified limbs and are lateral in position; in the *Mollusca* these organs, where they are present, are cuticular or calcareous thickenings on the surface of the mouth or pharynx, and the same is true of other invertebrate groups. In vertebrates, however, the jaws have a dorso-ventral position, and they and the slit-like mouth have had their origin respectively from the foremost pair of visceral arches and the foremost pair of primitive gill-clefts. The fact that the cyclostomate fishes, the most primitive vertebrates, are without jaws seems to indicate that the earliest vertebrates, like them, possessed a circular jawless mouth armed with cuticular teeth and with a series of about seven pairs of gill-clefts supported by cartilaginous arches posterior to it. When the true fishes, the ancestors of all other vertebrates, developed from a cyclostomate stock, the foremost two pairs of cartilaginous arches and the foremost two pairs of gill-clefts lost their primitive functions and were transferred from the respiratory to the digestive system of organs. The foremost pair of gill-clefts became the mouth while the foremost pair of arches reinforced by dermal bones formed the upper and lower jaws; the second pair of clefts became the spiracles in the elasmobranch fishes and the Eustachian tubes in the terrestrial vertebrates, while the second pair of arches formed the skeletal support of the tongue. The remaining five pairs of arches are gill-bearing in the fishes and support the gill-clefts; in the terrestrial vertebrates, however, they undergo a change of function during the embryonic period and lose their primary significance, being transformed into the cartilages of the larynx and trachea.

The teeth of all vertebrates are identical in structure, being composed of dentine overlaid with enamel, and the identity of this structure with that of the placoid scales of the lowest of the true fishes shows that vertebrate teeth are directly derived from these scales. The actual form of the teeth in each group has been determined by the service they are expected to perform. In most fishes, amphibians and reptiles the teeth are employed only for grasping and holding the prey; they are conical in shape like a placoid scale and are usually more or less loosely attached in the oral cavity. In mammals, which use their teeth not only for grasping but for chewing their food, the teeth are firmly set in alveoli—deep cavities in the jaw bone—and have a variety of forms which fit them for grasping, cutting, gnawing or chewing. The teeth of alligators and the extinct toothed birds occupy a mid-way position, being elongated cones in form and set in alveoli.

The digestive canal in vertebrates is characterized in general by great length and by the presence of two digestive glands of large size, the liver and pancreas, which originate as outgrowths of it, also by the mesenteries in the body cavity which support its various divisions. The intestine opens at the hinder end either directly to the outside through the anus, or into a cloaca which receives also the discharges of the excretory and reproductive organs.

The *excretory* and *reproductive systems* are closely associated in vertebrates, often possessing ducts in common through which their products find a way to the outside. Reproduction is in all cases sexual; with a few exceptions among fishes the sexes are separate; sexual dimorphism is universal.

The *central nervous system* of vertebrates, the spinal chord and brain, has no homologue among invertebrates. It originates in the embryo as a middorsal ectodermal groove, which sinks beneath the surface and forms a tube. The anterior portion of this tube widens and forms a series of five vesicles the walls of which become thick and folded, and the brain comes into existence; the posterior portion becomes the spinal chord. The cranial and spinal nerves proceeding from the brain and spinal chord to the special sense organs and the muscles of the trunk and appendages have a metameric arrangement; the same is true also of the sympathetic nervous system, which is intimately joined with them and controls the activities of many of the viscera.

The characteristic *special senses* of vertebrates are smell, taste, sight and hearing. The sensory perceptions of aquatic vertebrates, especially fishes, are in many respects sharply different from those of animals which live in so attenuated a medium as the air, vibrations of the water being the most important stimulating agents which cause their sensory reactions. Vibrations of very low frequency, such as are produced by impacts on the water, currents and surface waves, undoubtedly affect the skin over the whole surface of the fish's body; the lateral line, which is a specialized portion of the skin, is sensitive to vibrations of higher frequency, such as slight oscillations of the whole mass of the water, which are, however, too slight to stimulate the skin itself; the ear, which is a modified portion of the lateral line, is attuned to vibrations of still higher frequency, such as cause the sensation of sound. The ears of the lowest fishes, however, notably the cyclostomes and selachians, have not reached a development high enough to be stimulated by tonal vibrations, although they may be by noises sufficiently loud to produce vibrations which affect the skin or lateral line; the ear of such fishes is apparently merely an organ of equilibrium, the maintenance of which is probably the primitive function of the vertebrate ear.

In aquatic vertebrates taste and smell are similar senses, causing similar reactions and having a similar purpose, which is the detection of food. Taste buds, in many fishes, especially bottom feeders, are not only present in the mouth, but are distributed over the skin, so that such fishes may be conscious of the presence of food which is near any part of the body, the pectoral fins and barbels being especially sensitive. Smell is probably perceived by fishes with the nostrils alone, and enables the animal to scent its food at a distance.

The eyes of fishes and amphibians are adapted to near vision only, inasmuch as they have a spherical lens and lack the ciliary muscles by means of which the land animals accommodate their vision to the perception of distant objects. In many fishes the whole skin is also sensitive to light, independently of the eyes, the head and tail being more so than the trunk.

The change in their sensory reactions which took place in vertebrates when the terrestrial forms first developed from the aquatic is well illustrated in the transformation of the tadpole into the frog. The tadpole has the sensory equipment of a bottom fish, and undoubtedly depends largely on vibrations of the water for its means of orientation; the lateral line is well developed, the ear does not appear at the surface of the head, there being no tympanum, and the eye is small and sunken. The frog, on the other hand, depends upon sight and hearing for its knowledge of its surroundings; it has very large projecting eyes, the tympanum is at the surface of the head and no lateral line is present. Thus, in the terrestrial vertebrates the general or contact sense, so important to fishes, falls into the background as a means of orientation. In frogs, toads and reptiles, generally, which are the lowest of them, sight is apparently the best developed special sense, and the one most depended upon for information of the surroundings; also in frogs and many lizards, and undoubtedly in others too, the whole skin is sensitive to light, independently of the eyes. Hearing, smell and taste are all poorly represented.

Birds also depend largely upon sight, and this sense has attained an extraordinary development in many species. The accurate vision of birds during swift flight and over great distances, and the instantaneous accommodation of it to their rapid manœuvres in the air, seem to indicate that birds have the best eyes among vertebrates. Hearing is also highly developed in birds; smell and taste, however, are apparently in a backward condition.

In mammals all the special senses have reached a very high development. As the bird is essentially a creature of the air and must be able to see far and accurately, so the mammal belongs on or near the ground and in most cases finds its greatest security and advantage in its remarkable sense of smell. But its habit of life, which gives the mammal the most varied environment among vertebrates, makes all the special senses important to it, and has brought about the high state of perfection which characterizes all of them.

The *muscular system* of vertebrates has but few distinctive features. The body or somatic muscles of fishes and salamanders, which, being aquatic animals, move through the water by alternate to-and-fro movements of the trunk and tail, have a strictly metameric arrangement and longitudinal fibres, and the appendicular muscles of all vertebrates, although not metameric, are directly derived from them; both are striated in structure and voluntary in character. The body muscles of terrestrial vertebrates, however, especially those whose locomotory movements are carried on exclusively by the appendages, have mostly lost their primitive character, although it is still indicated in several of them, notably the *rectus abdominis*. The attachment of a muscle to a bone by a single tendon, by which the action of all the fibres is concentrated on a single point, is a peculiarly vertebrate character. The visceral muscles, which are involuntary and, with a few exceptions, unstriated, are present in the walls of the various tubular internal organs to which they impart the peristaltic movements characteristic of them.

Distribution.—The United States covers an area of continental extent containing the greatest possible variety of conditions which may surround the lives of the animals living within it. Certain physical features of this area strike the attention of the observer as of especial importance. Of these the following may be mentioned; the great extent and number of the fresh water lakes in the northern portion of the country, the great river basins which characterize almost every part of it and especially that of the Mississippi, the mountain systems in the East and the West, the extensive coastal plains bordering the Atlantic

Ocean and the Gulf of Mexico, the great forested regions in both the eastern and western States, the well-watered, treeless prairies, the high, dry Great Plains, and the arid and mountainous Great Basin. Climatic conditions vary from the tropical heat and constant temperature of southern Florida and the Mexican border to the Arctic cold and violent and sudden changes of the Canadian border and the high mountain regions, and conditions of moisture from the excessively wet western slopes of the Cascades which look towards the Pacific to the deserts of the Great Basin and the extreme southwest.

The actual extent of territory occupied by any species of animal is determined by several factors, of which the most important are probably temperature and amount of moisture, both of which tend to check the migration of species and to confine them within certain more or less definite boundaries. The United States Biological Survey, has formulated the following two fundamental Laws of Temperature Control of Distribution: First, the northward distribution of terrestrial animals and plants is governed by the total quantity of heat during the season of growth and reproduction; Second, the southward distribution is governed by the mean temperature of a brief period during the hottest part of the year. The meaning of these laws is that each species requires a certain minimum total quantity of heat during the period of the year when growth and reproduction are going on, which is the summer season in temperate regions, and that this factor establishes the northern limit of its distribution; also, that excess of heat through a sufficiently long portion of this period tends to check or stop growth and reproduction, and consequently the mean temperature of the mid-summer weeks, when the heat is the greatest, is the factor which establishes the southern limit of distribution of a species.

On the basis of these laws the North American continent has been divided into three Life Regions, the *Boreal*, *Austral* and *Tropical*, the first two of which have been subdivided each into three Life zones. The *Boreal Region* is the portion of the continent north of the Canadian boundary, and is composed of the *Arctic*, *Hudsonian* and *Canadian zones*, each transcontinental in extent. The *Arctic zone* is the circumpolar region north of the northern limit of forests; it is the home of the muskox, polar bear, Arctic fox, wolf and hare and barren-ground caribou. The *Hudsonian zone* is the region of firs and spruces which extends as a wide belt between Labrador and Alaska, and southwards along the main ridge of the Rockies into the United States, and occurs also in limited areas in several high mountain regions in the Rockies and Cascades; it is the home, in Canada, of the woodland caribou, moose and wolverine. The *Canadian zone* is the region of the great coniferous forests and occupies southern Canada, extending extensively into the eastern and central northern United States, the higher Alleghanies and the mountains of the West.

The *Austral Region* comprises the greater part of the United States, and is composed of the *Transition, Upper Austral* and *Lower Austral zones*, each transcontinental in extent, the limits of which may be seen by reference to the frontispiece. The life conditions of the eastern and western portions of these three zones are greatly affected by the differences in the precipitation of moisture in them. The one-hundredth meridian represents the approximate boundary between the well-watered prairies and the arid Great Plains, to the eastward of which the annual rain-fall is greater than 25 inches and to the westward it is less than that amount, except on the Pacific coast. The eastern divisions of the three Austral zones are also called the *Alleghanian, Carolinian* and *Austroriparian*, respectively, and the two most southerly western divisions are also called the *Upper Sonoran* and *Lower Sonoran*.

The *Tropical Region* comprises the southern portion of the continent and occupies only a small part of this country, being limited to the southern end of Florida, south of Lake Worth, and perhaps the valley of the lower Colorado.

History.—The first person in modern times to unite the different classes of vertebrates in a single phylum was the French naturalist Lamarck, who, near the beginning of the 19th century, divided all animals into the two groups of those with vertebræ and those without. Aristotle, in his time, pointed to the same fundamental subdivision of the animal kingdom when he contrasted the several classes possessing red blood with those apparently without blood, their blood being color-less. The Swedish naturalist Linnæus, the founder of the modern system of classifying animals and plants, who lived in the generation immediately preceding Lamarck, did not take notice of the interrela-tionship of the classes of vertebrates notwithstanding the example of Aristotle, but gave each of these classes equal rank in his system with the invertebrate groups. Cuvier, who was a younger contemporary and fellow-countryman of Lamarck, adopted the term *Vertebrata* introduced by him as one of the four fundamental types into which he divided the Animal Kingdom, and the group maintained this rank in the zoological system of classification until about the seventh decade of the last century. At that time the epoch-making researches of Kowalevsky and others having shown the relationship of vertebrates with ascidians, Amphioxus and Balanoglossus, a new phylum was formed, first by the

German zoologist Hæckel, to include these groups, which received the name *Chordata*, under which the *Vertebrata* are now commonly rated a subphylum.

The primary subdivisions of this subphylum was first made by Aristotle, who recognised four groups, namely, fishes, oviparous tetrapodous and apodous vertebrates (amphibians and reptiles), birds, and viviparous vertebrates (mammals). Linnæus recognised the same four groups and named them classes in his system, giving them the modern names of *Pisces*, *Amphibia*, *Aves* and *Mammalia*, but he did not unite them in a single phylum. In Cuvier's system the same classes were also recognised, but for the name of the second class the term *Reptilia* was employed in place of *Amphibia*. This system was maintained in the classification and the amphibians and reptiles placed in a common class until about the year 1850, when the French zoologist Milne-Edwards called attention to the fundamental subdivision of all vertebrates into two great groups, the *Anamia* and the *Amniota*, and also to the fact that inasmuch as the *Amphibia* belong to one and the *Reptilia* to the other of these groups these two subdivisions of the *Vertebrata* should each constitute an independent class. Of the five classes of vertebrates thus formed the English naturalist Huxley in 1871 formed three divisions, the *Ichthyopsida* or fish-like vertebrates, the *Sauropsida* or reptile-like vertebrates and the *Mammalia*.

Classification.—Over 60,000 species and subspecies of vertebrates have been described, grouped in 5 classes, of which about 30,000 species and subspecies are fishes, 1,700 are amphibians, 5,500 are reptiles, 15,000 are birds and 10,000 are mammals. The primary grouping of these classes gives the following subdivisions:

A. *Anamia or Ichthyopsida.*—Vertebrates whose eggs are deposited in most cases in the water and are without a shell; and whose embryos are protected only by an albuminous envelope and the water and not by an amnion; which respire by means of gills either during the whole or a part of life; and which have a slimy epidermis lacking special epidermal coverings (Fishes and Amphibians).

B. *Amniota.*—Vertebrates whose eggs (in the oviparous species) are laid on the land and have the protection of a shell; whose embryos have the additional protection of an amnion and respire by means of an allantois; which respire after birth by means of lungs; and have special epidermal coverings in form of scales, feathers or hair.

1. *Sauropsida.*—Vertebrates which produce a very large egg and are either oviparous or ovoviviparous; which have a single median occipital condyle, and epidermal coverings in form of scales or feathers (Reptiles and Birds).

2. *Mammalia.*—Vertebrates which produce a minute egg (except the Monotremata), and are viviparous with uterine embryonic development; which nourish the young by means of mammary glands; which have a pair of occipital condyles, and an epidermal covering in form of hair (Mammals).

Key to the Classes of Vertebrates

a_1 Aquatic vertebrates whose locomotory appendages are fins...1. *Fishes* (p. 15).

a_2 Aquatic or land vertebrates with legs or wings as locomotory appendages, or without them.

b_1 Body naked (in American species), being without special integumentary coverings; toes without claws or nails......................................2. *Amphibians* (p. 134).

b_2 Body not naked, but with special integumentary coverings; toes with claws or nails.

c_1 Body covered with horny scales or plates.........3. *Reptiles* (p. 177).

c_2 Body covered with feathers (not included in this book).......................................4. *Birds.*

c_3 Body covered with hair......................5. *Mammals* (p. 243).

CLASS 1. FISHES

Aquatic, cold-blooded vertebrates which have an integumentary covering of dermal scales or plates, and which breathe by means of pharyngeal gills. Median and paired fins are in most cases present, the latter being homologous to the limbs of the higher vertebrates. The heart has but one ventricle and one auricle, and contains only venous blood. The head is joined with the trunk without articulation, and there is no neck. No external ear-opening is present. With a few exceptions all fishes lay eggs, which develop without an amnion.

On the Identification of Fishes.—The body of most species of fishes is more or less lenticular in shape and compressed laterally. In many species, however, the anterior portion is cylindrical, as it is in the eel, or more or less depressed (flattened), as in the catfish. The head forms the anterior end of the body, the hinder margin of the opercles marking the boundary between it and the trunk. The caudal or tail fin forms the posterior end, the caudal peduncle being the slenderer portion of the body from which it projects, the caudal fin and peduncle being postanal in position.

Measurements (Fig. 1).—The *length* of a fish, as given in this book, is the distance between the tip of the snout and the base of the caudal fin, expressed in millimeters; the caudal fin is not included. The measurements of the *head* and of the *depth* (*i.e.*, the greatest dorso-ventral measurement) of the body are not given in millimeters or by any other absolute scale, but are relative, being the number of times the length of the body is greater than that of the head or the depth of the body, respectively. Thus, the expression "head 3, depth 5" means that the length of the body is 3 times the length of the head and 5 times its own depth.

Fins (Fig. 1).—The fins of fishes are of two kinds, the *median* or *vertical fins* and the *paired fins.* The *median fins* are the *dorsal, caudal* and *anal fins:* they are the more primitive of the two kinds, and alone occur in cyclostomate fishes. The *dorsal fin* lies in the middorsal plane and in many fishes is divided, so that there are two or even three or more of them. The *caudal* or *tail fin* is usually the largest and the principal organ of locomotion; its hinder margin may be either forked, concave, emarginate (slightly forked or notched), straight or rounded.

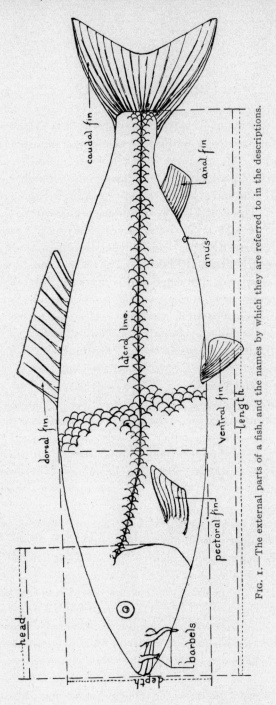

FIG. 1.—The external parts of a fish, and the names by which they are referred to in the descriptions.

In the sturgeon and many other primitive fishes the backbone takes an upward turn at the base of the caudal fin and continues in the fin to near its hinder end, so that the greater part of the fin is ventral to the backbone; such a tail is called *heterocercal* (Fig. 2). In most fishes, however, the caudal fin is *homocercal*, that is, the backbone extends only to the base of the fin, which projects fan-shaped back of it. The *anal fin* lies in the midventral plane behind the anus; it is in most cases single, but in some species is divided.

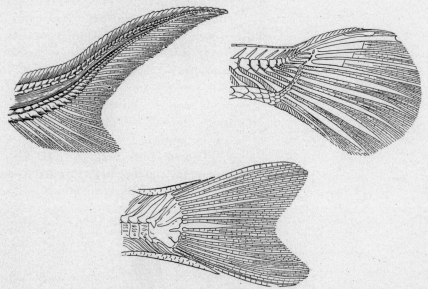

FIG. 2.—Types of tail fins of fishes: heterocercal tail of sturgeon (*upper left-hand figure*); heterocercal tail of garpike (*upper right-hand figure*); homocercal tail of pike-perch (*lower figure*) (*from Fishes of Illinois*).

The *paired fins* are the *pectoral fins*, which are anterior in position, and the *ventral fins*, which are posterior. The pectoral fins are immediately back of the head, either on the side of the body or on the breast. The ventral fins (Fig. 3) lie on the belly in front of the anus in the more primitive fishes, in which case they are said to be *abdominal* in position; in the more specialized fishes they are situated nearer the head, and are said to be *thoracic* in position when they are immediately beneath the pectoral fins and *jugular* when they are in front of the pectoral fins.

The fins are stiffened and supported by slender bony rods called *the fin-rays* (Fig. 4). These are of two kinds, the *soft rays*, which are jointed and have divided or split terminal ends, and the *spiny rays*, which are stiff and not jointed and have undivided and sharp-pointed ends.

The position of the fins and the number of soft and spiny rays are of great importance in descriptions of fishes. The number of the soft rays is expressed by Arabic and that of the spiny rays by Roman numerals: thus, the expression "rays of dorsal fin VI, 12" means that the dorsal fin has 6 spiny and 12 soft rays. Where two dorsal fins are present the number of the rays of the anterior fin is separated from that of the posterior one by a dash. Thus the expression "rays of dorsal fins XI-III, 5" means that the anterior dorsal fin has 11 spiny rays and the posterior dorsal has 3 spiny and 5 soft rays. In certain groups of soft-rayed fishes, such as the trout, catfish and others, the posterior dorsal fin is a fleshy structure without rays of any kind, and is consequently not mentioned in such descriptions; it is called the *adipose fin*.

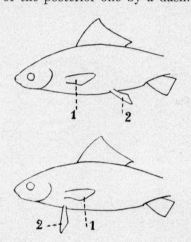

Lateral Line (Fig. 1).—In most fishes the lateral line appears as a longitudinal series of modified scales

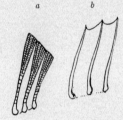

FIG. 4.—Soft fin-rays (*a*); spiny fin-rays (*b*) (*from Süssw, Fauna. Deut.*).

FIG. 3.—Position of the ventral fins: (*top figure*), the ventral fins in an abdominal position; (*middle figure*), in a thoracic position; (*bottom figure*), in a jugular position: 1, pectoral fins; 2, ventral fins (*from Süssw, Fauna. Deut.*).

extending along the side of the body between the head and the caudal fin. In the lower, soft-rayed fishes it tends to run parallel to the line of the belly, and in the higher, spiny-rayed fishes to the line of the back. In many fishes it is not complete or is altogether wanting, at least so far as any external appearance is concerned.

Scales (Fig. 5).—In some species of fishes, the catfish for example, the skin is naked and without any hard skeletal covering. In most fishes, however, the skin is protected by a layer of scales, and in a few groups by bony plates, prickles, or other skeletal structures. By far the greatest number of species have scales of one of two types, the *cycloid* or the *ctenoid scales*. These are thin rounded plates which cover the body more or less completely and are imbricated, that is, arranged in overlapping rows like the shingles on a roof, the free ends being directed backwards. Cycloid scales characterize the more primitive of the bony fishes, as the trout and salmon, and have a smooth hinder margin. Ctenoid scales have a more or less roughened surface and a dentate, serrate or spiny free hinder margin; they characterize the more specialized bony fishes, as the perch and the bass. In some species both types of scales are present, and in some species scales which are intermediate between the two. Certain ganoid fishes, as the garpike, have

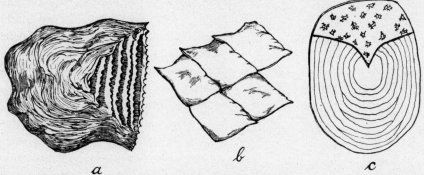

a   *b*   *c*

FIG. 5.—Scales of fishes: *a*, ctenoid scale (hinder end of scale at the right); *b*, ganoid scales; *c*, cycloid scale (hinder end of scale above) (*modified from Cambridge Natural History and Jordan's Guide to the Study of Fishes*).

ganoid scales, which are rhombic in form and are not imbricated, while certain ganoids, as the sturgeon, and certain teleosts, as the sticklebacks, have bony plates on the sides of the body.

In the description of a fish the average number of scales (Fig. 6) occurring in the lateral line between the head and the caudal fin is given. The number, also, occurring in a dorso-ventral series, between the lateral line and the back and the lateral line and the belly, is usually given. Thus the expression "scales 5-46-11" means that 46 scales occur in the lateral line, or if no lateral line is present in a lateral series between the head and the caudal fin, that 5 scales occur in a dorso-ventral series between the forward end of the dorsal fin and the lateral line and 11 scales between the lateral line and the anus or the forward end of the anal fin. These figures are never absolute for all the individuals of a species, but are liable to vary a sixth from the average given.

Color.—Fishes are among the brightest of animals. Their colors cover a wide range, and a statement of the markings of a specimen is usually an important part of a description.   It must be remembered, however, that there is often a considerable variation in the coloration of a species in different individuals and at different times of the year, that the two sexes are often colored differently, the female being duller than the male, and that bright colors, especially reds and blues, often fade after the death of the animal or when it has lain in a preserving fluid.

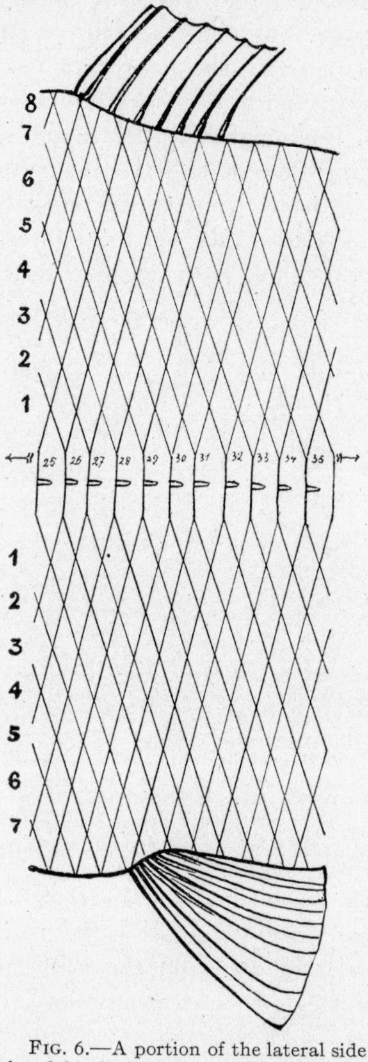

Head (Fig. 7).—The portion of the head in front of the eyes is the *snout*. The mouth may be either terminal in position, inferior, subinferior or superior, and may also be either horizontal or oblique (Fig. 8). The *nostrils* are four in number, two on each side immediately in front of the eye. The upper jaw contains the paired *premaxillary* bones which support its anterior portion, and also often the lateral portions as well, and the paired *maxillaries*, which lie above and behind the lateral portions of the premaxillary, on each side. The premaxillaries are, in many fishes, protractile, that is, they can be thrust forward. In certain fishes a *supplementary maxillary* lies above the posterior portion of the maxillary, on each side.

Many species of fishes, catfish for instance, have one or more pairs of elongated tentacles called *barbels* extending from one or both jaws (Fig. 1).

Below and behind the eyes on each side of the head is the *cheek*.

Fig. 6.—A portion of the lateral side of a fish's body between the dorsal fin (above) and the anal fin (below) to illustrate the count of the scales, the lateral line series of which is in the middle, and the dorso-ventral series above and below it (*from Süssw. Fauna Deut.*).

Behind the cheek is the *preopercle*, and behind it the *opercle;* beneath them lies the *interopercle* and the *subopercle;* these structures form the gill-covers.   Ventral to them lies the *branchiostegal membrane* supported by the *branchiostegal rays*, or as they are usually called, the *branchio-stegals*. The gills lie beneath the gill-covers, borne on four *gill-arches* (Fig. 9); posterior to these arches is a fifth arch which rarely bears gills but is usually massively built and bears teeth; it is called the *pharyngeal arch*. On the inner surface of the opercle near its anterior margin are,

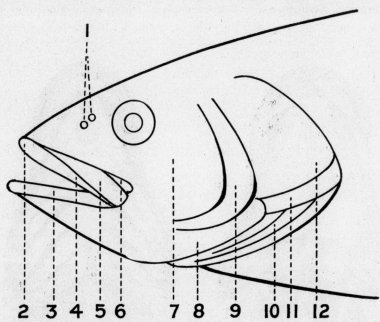

FIG. 7.—Head of a fish: 1, nostrils; 2, premaxillary; 3, mandible; 4, lateral portion of premaxillary; 5, maxillary; 6, supplementary maxillary; 7, cheek; 8, interopercle; 9, pre-opercle; 10, branchiostegals; 11, subopercle; 12, opercle.

in most fishes, small gills called the *pseudobranchiæ*. In most fishes from the pharyngeal margins of each gill-arch a double series of car-tilaginous or bony rods project towards the gill-cleft; these are the *gill-*

FIG. 8.—Position of the mouth: *a*, mouth terminal in position; *b*, mouth superior; *c*, mouth inferior (*from Süssw. Fauna Deut.*).

rakers and they serve as a sieve to prevent particles of food from passing through the gill-clefts with the respiratory water.

Teeth.—A few species of fish are without teeth. They are, however, usually present, and may be found, in the various species, on the pre-maxillaries, dentaries (lower jaw), vomer, palatines, pterygoids, sphenoids, gill-arches, tongue and pharyngeals (Fig. 9). Short, slender, close-set teeth are called *villiform;* long, sharp teeth which project beyond the level of the others are called *canine;* teeth with blunt tips used for crushing shells are called *molar;* flat, mosaic-like teeth are called *paved* or *tessellated;* front teeth with cutting edges are called *incisor.*

Internal Structures.—A knowledge of the internal anatomy of a fish is usually not necessary in order to make a systematic description

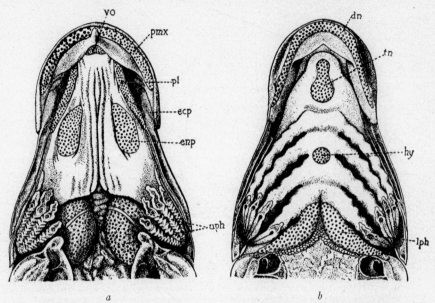

a   *b*

FIG. 9.—The inside of the mouth (of the rock bass, *Ambloplites rupestris*) showing the dentition and the gill-arches: *a,* the roof of the mouth; *b,* the floor of the mouth: *dn,* dentary; *ecp,* ectopterygoid; *enp,* entopterygoid; *hy,* hyoid; *lph,* lower pharyngeal arch; *pl,* palatine; *pmx,* premaxillary; *tn,* tongue; *uph,* upper pharyngeal arch; *vo,* vomer (*from Fishes of Illinois*).

of it. The following features, however, are occasionally referred to in the descriptions in this book: the shape of the stomach; the number and character of the pyloric appendages or cæca of the stomach; the length and character of the intestine; the presence or absence of the air bladder, and its character when present; the character of the four anterior vertebræ, whether they are coössified and have some of their elements detached to form the Weberian ossicles which connect the air bladder with the ear; the unossified portion of the top of the skull in certain fishes known as the fontanelle.

History.—Fishes, conspicuous and abundant animals as they are and important in the dietary of all peoples, have attracted the interest of naturalists from time immemorial. The modern scientific study of them is based upon the classifications of Peter Artedi and Linnæus, who wrote in the 18th century, and Cuvier, who wrote in the early part of the 19th. In recent times the most important single work is Günther's *"Catalogue of the Fishes of the British Museum,"* published in 1859–70. This work and Boulenger's continuation of it published in 1898–1900 are fundamental for the modern systematic study of fishes. The fishes of America have attracted many brilliant students, the most eminent of the earlier ones being Louis Agassiz, who first placed the study of American fishes on a sound scientific basis. Since his death in 1873 the school of ichthyologists founded by him has been directed and carried on by David Starr Jordan, one of his pupils, who together with his pupils and associates has made the fishes of North America better known than perhaps those of any other equally large area. The *"Fishes of North and Middle America"* by Jordan and Evermann (1896–1900), the *Check List* of Jordan, Evermann and Clark (1930) and the *Manual of Vertebrates* (1929), revised as to Fishes by C. L. Hubbs, are the foundation of the descriptions of fishes in this book.

Number of Species and Distribution.—The Class, *Fishes*, includes over 30,000 described species and subspecies, grouped, as described in this book, in 2 subclasses. Over 600 species live in the fresh waters of the United States, grouped in about 36 families. The largest of these families are the *Cyprinidæ* with 311 species and the *Etheostomidæ* with 115 species, as given in the *Check List* of the *Fishes of North and Middle America* of Jordan, Evermann and Clark (1928). The *Catostomidæ* with 83 species and the *Cyprinodontidæ* with 61 species are the next in rank; and these four families include two-thirds of all the species of fresh water fishes in the country.

The fresh waters of the United States are very rich in species of fishes, as will be seen by a comparison with those of Europe, which, although having a land area of about the same extent and with a very varied surface, contains only about 125 species. It is the very large hydrographical basins of our country joined with its varied character and the relatively high temperature of the middle and southern portions of it which have brought about the multiplication of species of fishes within its borders. The Mississippi basin contains about 200 species and that of the Great Lakes about 150 species.

Key to the Subclasses of Fishes

a_1 Mouth without jaws; no paired fins; nostril median..1. *Cyclostomata* (p. 24).
a_2 Mouth with true jaws; paired fins present; nostrils
    paired ....2. *Pisces* (p. 28).

Subclass 1. Cyclostomata.—Fish-like vertebrates with a cylindrical, eel-like body, without scales, paired fins, gill-arches or jaws; skeleton cartilaginous and without ribs; skull imperfectly developed and not separate from the vertebral column; nostril single, median; mouth suctorial; gills sac-like, 6 to 14 in number, opening to the outside through paired pores; no genital ducts, sympathetic nervous system, arterial bulb, pancreas, spleen or air bladder; median fins on posterior half of body: about 20 species, mostly parasitic on fishes in both fresh and salt water, grouped in 2 orders. The first of these orders, with 2 American species, the Californian hagfish, *Polistotrema stouti* (Lockington) and the Atlantic hagfish, *Myxine glutinosa* L., is exclusively marine.

Key to the Orders of Cyclostomata

a_1 Gill openings not near head; hagfish, all marine, and not included
in this book..1. *Hyperotreta.*
a_2 Gill openings immediately back of head; lampreys.............2. *Hyperoartia.*

Order 2. Hyperoartia.—The lampreys. Body cylindrical anteriorly, compressed posteriorly; fins median and well developed, the

FIG. 10.—Buccal funnel of *Reighardina unicolor* (*from Jordan's Guide to the Study of Fishes, after Gage*).

dorsal fin being more or less completely separated by a median notch into two fins; nostril just in front of the eyes and opening into a blind sac which does not communicate with the pharynx; eyes well developed in the adult; mouth suctorial, in the middle of a depressed, funnel-shaped oral plate, called the *buccal funnel* (Fig. 10), which has a fringed margin and is set with sharp, horny teeth or toothlike tubercles; tongue with sharp rasping teeth; bordering the mouth anteriorly and posteriorly, respectively, are the so-called *supraoral* and *infraoral laminæ*, horny plates each with 2 or more teeth; intestine with spiral valve; 7 pairs of gill-sacs, the external openings forming a row immediately back of the eyes: about 15 species, in fresh and salt water; 1 family, the *Petromyzonidæ*, with about 8 species in the United States.

Adult lampreys, in the case of most of the species, feed by attaching themselves to fishes and sucking their blood and rasping away the flesh, often killing them, and causing large sores and scars on those they do not kill; they are often destructive to fisheries. The marine species ascend the streams to breed. The young animals, which are called *Ammocœtes*, are without functional paired eyes, suctorial mouth or teeth and pass through a metamorphosis; they live in this larval condition two to six years, during which they burrow in muddy bottoms in the streams where they are born, feeding on minute organic particles which the current brings them. Several of the smaller species have apparently a very short adult life; the intestine is degenerate and nonfunctional and the buccal teeth are weak, blunt and more or less obsolescent; such species are probably not parasitic.

Key to the United States Genera of Petromyzonidæ

a_1 Buccal funnel with numerous teeth which radiate from the mouth in all directions (Fig. 10).

   b_1 Dorsal fin continuous; Great Lakes and Mississippi Valley.

      c_1 Expanded buccal funnel much broader than body.......1. *Icthyomyzon*.

      c_2 Expanded buccal funnel narrower than body...........2. *Reighardina*.

   b_2 Two separated dorsal fins; Atlantic slope.................3. *Petromyzon*.

a_2 Buccal funnel with teeth which do not radiate from the mouth but lie in several groups (Fig. 12).

   b_1 A posterior row of small teeth connect the posterior pair of enlarged lateral teeth (Fig. 12).

      c_1 Pacific Coast and Slope forms........................4. *Entosphenus*.

      c_2 Atlantic Slope forms.................................5. *Lethenteron*.

   b_2 No such row of teeth present (Fig. 13).

      c_1 Pacific Slope forms.................................6. *Lampetra*.

      c_2 Atlantic Slope forms...............................7. *Okkelbergia*.

1. **Ichthyomyzon** Girard. Small fresh water lampreys with a single dorsal fin which has a broad notch in the middle and is joined with the caudal fin; muscle segments between gill and anus less than 60: 1 species.

I. concolor (Kirtland). Silver lamprey. Length 300 mm.; color silvery; a small dark spot above each gill pore; supraoral lamina with 1 to 4 (usually 2) approximated cusps; buccal funnel, when expanded, much wider than the body, and with a double row of marginal fringes: valleys of the Great Lakes and St. Lawrence River; southward and westward into the Ohio, Missouri and upper Mississippi valleys; northwards to Hudson Bay; common on the sturgeon and other large fishes.

2. **Reighardina** Creaser and Hubbs. Similar to *Icthyomyzon*, but with a narrow buccal funnel: 1 species.

R. unicolor (DeKay) (Fig. 10). Length 150 mm.; supraoral lamina with 2 separated cusps; buccal funnel, when expanded, not wider than the body, and with weak or obsolescent teeth; intestine degenerate in the adult: basin of the Great Lakes; often abundant.

3. Petromyzon L.   Marine and fresh water lampreys with 2 separated dorsal fins: several species, 1 in the United States.

P. marinus L.   Lamprey eel; great sea lamprey (Fig. 11).   Length up to 1,000 mm.; color blackish, more or less mottled; buccal funnel large, with strong, pointed teeth, the innermost lateral teeth being enlarged and usually bicuspid; supraoral lamina with 2 approximated cusps; infraoral lamina with 7 to 9 strong cusps; muscle segments between gills and anus about 70: North Atlantic along the American, European and African coasts; southward to Florida, ascending the streams to breed; common in the interior lakes of New York and Lake Ontario.

Fig. 11.—*Petromyzon marinus* (*from Jordan's Guide to the Study of Fishes*).

4. Entosphenus Gill.   Marine and fresh water lampreys with 2 separate dorsal fins; teeth in groups, there being a marginal series bordering the edge of the buccal disc, several enlarged teeth on each lateral border of the mouth, a group on the anterior and one on the posterior part of the disc: 3 species, 1 in Mexico.

E. tridentatus (Gairdner).   Length 450 mm. or more; color dark brown; 4 enlarged lateral teeth on a side, the first and last bicuspid, the middle two tricuspid; infraoral lamina with 4 to 6 cusps; supraoral lamina tricuspid: Pacific Ocean, from Unalaska to southern California, ascending the streams, in the Columbia as far as Walla Walla.

E. ciliatus (Ayres).   Muscle segments between gills and anus 57 to 67: streams of northern California.

5. Lethenteron Creaser and Hubbs.   Similar to *Entosphenus:* 1 species.

L. appendix (DeKay) (*E. wilderi* Jordan & Evermann) (Fig. 12). Length 200 mm.; color bluish black; enlarged lateral teeth 3 on a side, all bicuspid; infraoral lamina with 8 to 11 cusps; supraoral lamina bicuspid; muscle segments between gills and anus 67 to 73; intestine of adult degenerate: in streams from southern New England to Maryland; westward to Wisconsin and Iowa; northward into Canada; in eastern Asia.

6. Lampetra Gray. Teeth very few, there being usually 3 enlarged two-cusped laterals on each side of the mouth; supraoral lamina with 2 separated cusps, joined by a bridge: 3 American species.

L. ayresii (Günther). Length 350 mm.; dorsal fins separated; 63 to 70 muscle segments between gills and anus; teeth strong and sharp; infraoral lamina with 6 to 9 cusps; anterior portion of buccal disc with many teeth: coasts and streams of Europe, Asia and western North America from San Francisco to Puget Sound.

7. Okkelbergia Creaser and Hubbs. Similar to *Lampetra:* 1 species.

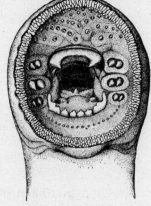

FIG. 12.—Buccal funnel of *Lethenteron appendix (from Fishes of Illinois).*

O. lamotteni (LeSueur) (*L. œpyptera* Abbott) (Fig. 13). Length 120 mm.; teeth much reduced in number and size; infraoral lamina with a crenulated crest and without distinct cusps; lateral teeth sometimes unicuspid and more or less obsolescent; anterior portion of buccal disc with

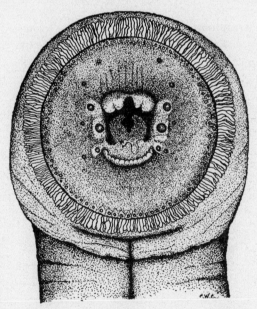

FIG. 13.—Buccal funnel of *Okkelbergia lamotteni (from Creaser & Hubbs).*

usually 4 teeth; 54 to 60 muscle segments between gills and anus: in the Ohio and Potomac River basins.

Subclass 2.   Pisces.—The true fishes.   Aquatic vertebrates with gills which are attached to bony or cartilaginous gill-arches; with true jaws; with median fins and usually two pairs of paired fins; in most cases with scales; with paired nostrils: 3 divisions.

Key to the Divisions of Pisces

a_1 Skeleton cartilaginous; skull without membrane bones; sharks;
     skates; (all marine, not included in this book)...............1. *Selachii.*
a_2 Skeleton in most cases bony; skull with membrane bones.
   b_1 Paired fins each with a segmented cartilaginous axis; respiration
      by gills and lungs (no American species and hence not
      included in this book)....................................2. *Dipnoi.*
   b_2 Fins supported by fin-rays and without central axes.........3. *Teleostomi.*

Division 3.   Teleostomi.—Skeleton usually bony; skull covered with membrane bones separated by sutures; a single gill opening on each side, the gills being supported by 4 pairs of arches in most cases, and covered by the opercles; air bladder mostly present: 2 series.

Key to the Series of Teleostomi

a_1 Skeleton cartilaginous or bony........................1. *Ganoidei* (p. 28).
a_2 Skeleton bony..2. *Teleostei* (p. 33).

Series 1.   Ganoidei.—The ganoid fishes.   Fishes with either cartilaginous or bony skeleton; with heterocercal or homocercal caudal fin; with either ganoid or cycloid scales or bony dermal plates; with an air bladder provided with an open duct connecting it with the pharynx or the œsophagus; with an arterial bulb with several pairs of valves; and with an intestinal spiral valve: 2 American orders, with about 13 American species.

Key to the American Orders of Ganoidei

a_1 Ganoids without scales, with the body either naked or
     with bony plates; skeleton cartilaginous.............1. *Chondrostei* (p. 28).
a_2 Ganoids with the body covered either with ganoid or
     cycloid scales; skeleton bony.......................2. *Holostei* (p. 31).

Order 1.   Chondrostei.—Cartilaginous ganoids.   Fish of large size and with the skeleton cartilaginous; notochord persistent; branchiostegal rays weak or wanting; mouth ventral beneath a long snout; body naked or with bony plates; tail heterocercal: 2 suborders.

Key to These Suborders

a_1 Body naked...1. *Selachostomi.*
a_2 Body more or less covered with bony plates.................2. *Glaniostomi.*

Suborder 1. Selachostomi.—Skin naked: 1 family.

Family Polyodontidæ.—The paddle-fishes. Body without scales and smooth; snout spatulate and very long; teeth minute, present only in the young; opercles rudimentary, prolonged behind on each side to form a long flap; spiracles present; 1 branchiostegal ray; air bladder cellular: 2 species and genera, 1 in China (*Psephurus gladius*).

Polyodon Lacépède. Gill-rakers very fine and numerous: 1 species.

P. spathula (Walbaum). Spoonbill; paddle-fish. Extreme length 1,800 mm.; extreme weight 150 lbs.; color olivaceous; head, with opercle, more than half the length of the body; spatula one-third the total length: Mississippi Valley; French Broad, North Carolina; Lake Erie; often common in the larger streams and lakes, where it feeds on small organisms in the mud; used for food and the roe made into caviar.

Suborder 2. Glaniostomi.—Skin with bony scales; sturgeons: 1 family.

Family Acipenseridæ.—Sturgeons. Large fish with 5 longitudinal rows of keeled bony plates on the body, a middorsal series and a lateral and an abdominal series on each side, between which are small plates or granules; mouth ventral and toothless, in front of which projects a long snout; 4 barbels in a transverse row in front of the mouth; gill-slits 4, with an accessory opercular gill; no branchiostegal rays; ventral fins posterior; median fins with spine-like projections called fulcra: about 20 species; 7 species and 3 genera in America.

Key to the Genera of Acipenseridæ

a_1 Spiracles present.....................................1. *Acipenser.*
a_2 Spiracles absent.
  b_1 Belly covered with subrhombic plates..............2. *Scaphirhynchus.*
  b_2 Belly naked.....................................3. *Parascaphirhynchus.*

1. Acipenser L. Snout subconical; a small spiracle above the eye; tail subcylindrical and not mailed; pseudobranchiæ present: cosmopolitan, in northern waters, both fresh and salt; 5 species in America; the marine species ascend the rivers to breed; the flesh is used for food, the eggs are made into caviar and the air bladder into isinglass; the food of sturgeons consists of small fishes, crayfish, snails, etc.

Key to the American Species of Acipenser

a_1 In the eastern and central States.
  b_1 In the Atlantic Ocean and its tributaries.
    c_1 Space between dorsal and lateral plates with 5 to 10
      rows of small plates...............................*A. oxyrhynchus.*

c_2 Space between dorsal and lateral plates with very many
    series of minute plates..........................*A. brevirostrum.*
  b_2 In the Great Lakes and upper Mississippi Valley........*A. fulvescens.*
a_2 On the Pacific slope.
  b_1 Lateral plates about 44.............................*A. transmontanus.*
  b_2 Lateral plates 26 to 30.............................*A. acutirostris.*

A. oxyrhynchus Mitchill. Common sturgeon. American sturgeon.
Extreme length 3,600 mm.; extreme weight 550 lbs.; head 3.5; depth
5.75; color olive gray, lighter below; dorsal plates 10 to 14; laterals
27 to 29; ventrals 8 to 11; rays of dorsal fin 38; anal 27; snout long and
sharp, almost as long as the head: Atlantic Ocean and its tributary
streams from Main to South Carolina; often common; a valuable food
fish.

FIG. 14.—*Acipenser fulvescens (from Jordan & Evermann).*

A. brevirostrum LeSueur. Short-nosed sturgeon. Length 800 mm.;
head 4; depth 5.5; color dusky; snout very short, about a quarter the
length of the head; dorsal plates 8 to 11; laterals 22 to 33; ventrals 6 to
9; rays of dorsal fin 41; anal 22: Cape Cod to Florida; not common.

A. fulvescens Rafinesque. Lake sturgeon (Fig. 14). Length 1,800
mm.; head 3.5; depth 5.75; average weight 50 lbs.; extreme weight
100 lbs.; color dark olive, often with large irregular blackish spots;
sides paler or reddish; dorsal plates 11 to 15; laterals 38; ventrals 10;
rays of dorsal fin 35; anal 26; plates large and rough in the young,
becoming smoother and often lost with age: basin of the Great Lakes
and the Mississippi Valley and northwards; abundant; the largest fish
in these regions.

A. transmontanus Richardson. White sturgeon. Length 1,500
mm.; head 4; depth 7; weight 125 lbs.; record length 4,000 mm.; record
weight 1,000 lbs.; color dark gray; dorsal plates 11; laterals 44; ventrals
10 to 12; rays of dorsal fin 45; anal 28: Pacific Ocean from Alaska to
Monterey, ascending the streams, in which it may remain throughout
the year.

A. acutirostris Ayres. Green sturgeon. Length 2,000 mm.; head
4.25; depth 7.5; weight 350 lbs.; color olive green, with a midventral
stripe and one on each side above the ventral plates; dorsal plates 10;

laterals 26 to 30; ventrals 7 to 10; rays of dorsal fin 35; anal 28: Pacific Ocean from San Francisco northwards, ascending the streams; not used for food.

2. Scaphirhynchus Heckel.   Snout broad and shovel-shaped; spiracles absent; caudal peduncle slender, long and flattened, and covered with bony plates; pseudobranchiæ absent; tail ending in a long filament; ribs 10 or 11: 1 species.

S. platorynchus (Rafinesque).   Shovel-nosed   sturgeon.   Length 1,200 mm.; head 4; depth 8; weight 9 lbs.; color pale olive; dorsal plates 17 or 18; laterals 41 to 46; ventrals 11 to 13; rays of dorsal fin 32; anal 20: upper and middle Mississippi Valley; common.

3. Parascaphirhynchus Forbes and Richardson.   Like *Scaphirhynchus* but with the belly naked; ribs 20 or 21: 1 species.

P. albus F. and R.   White sturgeon.   Length 1,000 mm.; weight 5 lbs.; color very light gray or white; dorsal plates 16 to 19; laterals 41 to 47; ventrals 10 to 13; rays of dorsal fin 35 to 43; anal 20 to 23: Mississippi and Missouri Rivers; rare.

Order 2.   Holostei.—The bony ganoids.   Skeleton bony; branchiostegals present; mouth terminal and with teeth; body covered with ganoid or cycloid scales; tail heterocercal; air bladder cellular and lung-like and connected by a sort of glottis with the œsophagus: 2 suborders, with 5 American species.

Key to These Suborders

a_1 Scales ganoid...1. *Ginglymodi* (p. 31).
a_2 Scales cycloid......................................2. *Halecomorphi* (p. 32)·

Suborder 1.   Ginglymodi.—Scales ganoid, rhombic in shape; vertebræ opisthocœlous: 1 family.

Family Lepisosteidæ.—The garpikes.   Body elongate and sub-cylindrical, with rhombic ganoid scales; jaws elongate, forming a long slender snout, the upper jaw of which is composed mostly of the premaxillaries; opercle supporting an acessory gill; branchiostegals 3; spiracles absent; spiral valve rudimentary; rays of both dorsal and anal fins 8: 3 genera.

Key to These Genera

a_1 Snout more than twice the length of the rest of the head......1. *Lepisosteus.*
a_2 Snout not longer than the rest of the head.
  b_1 Large teeth in upper jaw in a single row..................2. *Cylindrosteus.*
  b_2 Large teeth in upper jaw in 2 rows on each side...........3. *Atractosteus.*

1. **Lepisosteus** Lacépède (*Lepidosteus* Agassiz). Palatine teeth uniform; snout very long and narrow: about 1 species in the fresh waters of North America, and one (*L. tropicus* Gill) in Central America; flesh usually not used for food, except in the southern States.

L. osseus (L.). Common garpike. Length 1,300 mm.; head 3; depth 10 to 13; color olivaceous, silvery below; hinder parts with black spots; very young animals with a black lateral band; scales in lateral line about 62: Great Lakes and Mississippi Valley to the

FIG. 15.—*Atractosteus tristœchus* (*Jordan & Evermann*).

Rio Grande; Atlantic and Gulf slope from Vermont southwards; in rivers and lakes, sometimes entering the sea; common.

2. **Cylindrosteus** Rafinesque.   Palatine teeth uneven; snout short and broad: 5 species.

C. platostomus Rafinesque. Short-nosed gar. Length 900 mm.; head 3 to 3.9; depth 8 to 10; color olivaceous, but darker than *L. osseus;* scales in lateral line 56: Great Lakes and Mississippi Valley to Rio Grande; common; more so southwards.

3. **Atractosteus** Rafinesque. Snout broad; large teeth in upper jaw in 2 rows on each side: 3 species.

A. tristœchus (Block and Schneider). Alligator gar (Fig. 15). Length up to 6,000 mm.; head 3.7; depth 8; color greenish, paler below; scales in lateral line 60: southern States, north to the Ohio and Illinois Rivers.

Suborder 2.   Halecomorphi.—Scales cycloid in shape; vertebræ amphicœlous: 1 family.

Family Amiidæ.—The bowfins. Body fusiform, compressed, with cycloid, imbricated scales; head subconical, covered with a hard bony helmet; snout short; branchiostegals 10 or 12; no opercular gill or pseudobranchiæ; dorsal fin very long; tail convex behind, somewhat heterocercal; lateral line present: 1 genus.

Amia L. (*Amiatus* Rafinesque). With the characters of the family: 1 species.

A. calva L. Dogfish; bowfin (Fig. 16). Length 450 to 600 mm.; head 3.7; depth 4 to 4.5; color dark olive or blackish, with traces of dark reticulate markings on the sides; paler below; male with a round black spot edged with orange at the base of the tail; dorsal fin with 48 rays; anal 10 to 12; scales 67: eastern and central States, southward to Florida and Texas; northward to Vermont and Minnesota; common; in lakes and sluggish waters; not used for food. The eggs are deposited in a nest formed by the male in a gravelly or sandy bottom, who then guards them and also the young after they are hatched.

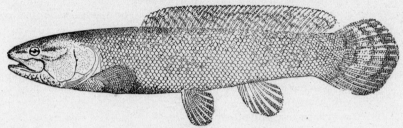

FIG. 16.—*Amia calva (Jordan & Evermann)*.

Series 2. Teleostei.—The bony fishes. Fishes with a bony skeleton and with usually a homocercal, never a heterocercal, tail; scales cycloid or ctenoid, or wanting; opercles present; air bladder usually present, but without cells and usually with a more or less rudimentary pneumatic duct, or none; without spiral valve; arterial bulb with a single pair of valves: many orders; 17 orders in the fresh waters of the United States.

Key to These Orders of Teleostei

a_1 Ventral fins, if present, abdominal (Fig. 3) in position; in eels absent.
  b_1 Head without scales.
    c_1 Fins without spines.
      d_1 Ventral fins present.
        e_1 Branchiostegals 4 or more; lake white-
fish and herring, salmon, trout...... 1. *Isospondyli* (p. 34).
        e_2 Branchiostegals 3.
          f_1 Pseudobranchiæ present (rarely ab-
sent); suckers, carp, dace, minnows 3. *Eventognathi* (p. 50).
          f_2 Pseudobranchiæ absent (but one
species in United States)......... 4. *Heterognathi* (p. 85).
      d_1 Ventral fins absent; eels................. 2. *Enchelycephali* (p. 50).
    c_1 Fins with spines.
      d_1 Barbels present; body scaleless; catfish... 5. *Nematognathi* (p. 85).
      d_2 No barbels present.
        e_1 Body covered with scales; trout-perch.. 8. *Salmopercæ* (p. 101).
        e_2 Body without scales, and either naked
or with bony plates; sticklebacks....11. *Thoracostei* (p. 102).

b_2 Head wholly or partly scaly.

 c_1 Lateral line wanting, or when present, imperfect and median in position.

  d_1 Lateral margin of upper jaw formed of the maxillaries, the premaxillary being short; pikes, pickerels...................... 6. *Haplomi* (p. 90).

  d_2 Upper jaw formed by the premaxilary; killifish, cavefish.................... 7. *Cyprinodontes* (p. 93)

 c_2 Lateral line ventral in position (but one species in the United States); garfish.............10. *Synentognathi* (p. 102)

a_2 Ventral fins thoracic or jugular (Fig. 3) in position, (except in the *Atherinidæ*).

 b_1 Fins without spines.

  c_1 Head symmetrical; burbots................12. *Anacanthini* (p. 104).

  c_2 Head asymmetrical; flatfish................13. *Heterosomata* (p. 105).

 b_2 Fins with spines.

  c_1 Anus jugular in position; pirate-perch....... 9. *Xenarchi* (p. 101).

  c_2 Anus normal in position.

   d_1 Body uniformly covered with scales.

    e_1 Spinous dorsal fin with less than 16 spines.

     f_1 Spinous dorsal with 6 to 15 spines; spiny-rayed fishes...............14. *Acanthopteri* (p. 105).

     f_2 Spinous dorsal with 2 to 8 spines; gobies........................17. *Gobioidea* (p. 133).

    e_2 Spinous dorsal fin with 16 or more spines; surffishes...................15. *Holconoti* (p. 130).

   d_2 Body without scales or irregularly scaled; sculpins.............................16. *Cataphracti* (p. 130).

Order 1. Isospondyli.—Herring; salmon; trout. Fishes with unmodified anterior vertebræ; lower pharyngeal arch simple, not falciform; head not scaly; maxillary distinct from the premaxillaries and forming part of the margin of the upper jaw; no barbels; air bladder, if present, with a pneumatic duct; fins without spines; ventral fins abdominal; scales usually cycloid, sometimes ctenoid, occasionally wanting: 20 to 25 families, mostly marine; 2 suborders and 7 families in fresh water.

Key to These Suborders

a_1 No adipose fin present............................1. *Clupeoidei* (p. 34).

a_2 Adipose fin present................................2. *Salmonoidei* (p. 37).

Suborder 1. Clupeoidei.—Herring-like fishes; no adipose fin: 3 fresh water families.

Key to These Families

a₁ Lateral line present..1. *Hiodontidæ*.
a₂ Lateral line absent.
   b₁ Last rays of dorsal fin much elongated....................2. *Dorosomidæ*.
   b₂ Dorsal fin normal...3. *Clupeidæ*.

Family 1. Hiodontidæ.—The mooneyes. Body oblong, compressed, covered with silvery cycloid scales, short; mouth terminal, oblique; tail forked; branchiostegals 8 to 10; lateral line present; teeth on jaws, margin of the tongue, vomer, sphenoid, hyoid, pterygoid and palatines; eyes very large; no pseudobranchiæ; 1 pyloric appendage: 2 genera.

   1. Hiodon LeSueur. Dorsal fin with 12 rays: 2 species, of little food value.

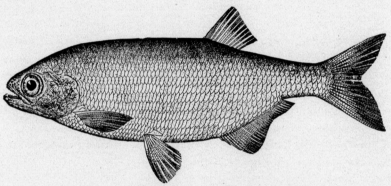

FIG. 17.—*Hiodon tergisus* (*Jordan & Evermann*).

   H. tergisus LeSueur (Fig. 17). Mooneye; silver bass. Length 300 mm.; head 4.3; depth 3; color olivaceous with silvery sides; rays of dorsal fin 12; anal 28; scales 5-55-7; belly behind ventrals somewhat carinated: basin of the Mississippi River; Great Lakes; common in large streams.

   H. selenops Jordan & Bean. Body elongate; length 300 mm.; head 4.1; depth 4; color clear silvery; rays of dorsal fin 12; anal 27; scales 50: Tennessee, Cumberland and Alabama Rivers; rare.

   2. Amphiodon Rafinesque. Dorsal fin with 9 rays: 1 species.

   A. alosoides. (Rafinesque). Mooneye. Length 300 mm.; head 4.5; depth 3.5; color bluish; sides silvery, with a golden lustre; rays of dorsal fin 9; anal 32; scales 6-56-9; belly in front of ventrals carinated: Ohio River basin and Great Lakes region to the Saskatchewan; common northwards.

   Family 2. Dorosomidæ.—Body short and deep, strongly compressed; scales cycloid; belly carinated; no lateral line; mouth toothless, small; branchiostegals 6; pseudobranchiæ large; eyelid adipose; anal fin very long and low; tail forked: 1 genus.

Dorosoma Rafinesque. With the characters of the family: 10 species of mud-feeding fishes, in warm seas and rivers; 1 in the United States.

D. cepedianum (LeSueur). Gizzard shad; mud shad. Length 375 mm.; head 4.3; depth 2.5; color silvery, being bluish above; rays of dorsal fin 12, its posterior ray very long and extending back half the distance to the tail; rays of anal fin 31; scales 56-23; stomach like a fowl's gizzard: Cape Cod to Mexico, in the sea and ascending the rivers; Mississippi Valley; introduced into Lakes Erie and Michigan and in ponds from New Jersey to Texas; common; of little food value.

Family 3. Clupeidæ.—Herring; shad. Body oblong or elongate, covered with cycloid scales; mouth large and terminal; teeth feeble or wanting; maxillaries formed of 2 or 3 pieces and forming side of upper jaw; pseudobranchiæ 6 to 15; no lateral line; branchiostegals 6 to 15; tail forked: about 30 genera and 150 species, mostly marine, inhabiting all seas; a few species live in fresh water and several marine ones enter streams to spawn. A number of marine species, such as the common herring, *Clupea harengus* L., the alewife, *Pomolobus pseudoharengus* (Wilson), the shad, *Alosa sapidissima* (Wil.), the European sardine *Clupanodon pilchardus* (Walbaum) and the menhaden, *Brevoortia tyrannus* (Latrobe), swim in large, often immense, schools, and are very important food fish.

Key to the Fresh Water Genera of Clupeidæ

a_1 Jaws with teeth...1. *Pomolobus*.
a_2 Jaws toothless...2. *Alosa*.

1. Pomolobus Rafinesque. Body eliptical, compressed; scales cycloid; teeth feeble: many species, mostly in northern seas.

P. chrysochloris Raf. Skipjack. Length 375 mm.; head 3.75; depth 3.75; color brilliant blue above; sides silvery, with golden reflections; rays of dorsal fin 16; anal 18; scales 52; lower jaw projecting: Mississippi Valley and Gulf of Mexico; common in the larger streams; introduced into Lake Erie and Michigan; of no food value.

P. pseudoharengus (Wilson). Alewife. Length 375 mm.; head 4.6; depth 3.3; color bluish above, with silvery sides; a small black spot behind the opercle; rays of dorsal fin 16; anal 19; scales 50: Atlantic Ocean, south to South Carolina, entering the streams to spawn; in Lake Ontario and the lakes of central New York; very common.

2. Alosa Cuvier. Body elliptical, compressed; jaws toothless; upper jaw with a deep notch at the tip: 3 American species.

A. sapidissima (Wilson). Shad. Length 750 mm.; head 4.25; depth 3; color bluish above; sides silvery; a dark spot, or a row of several, behind the opercle; gill-rakers 60, very long and slender; rays of dorsal fin 15; anal 21; scales 60: Atlantic Ocean, Newfoundland to the Carolinas, ascending the streams to spawn; common; introduced into the Pacific Ocean, and very common from San Diego to Fort Wrangel; the most valuable food fish in the eastern States.

A. alabamæ Jordan & Evermann. Length 375 mm.; head 4.6; depth 3; color like *A. sapidissima;* rays of dorsal fin 15; anal 20; scales 55: streams entering the Gulf of Mexico.

A. ohiensis Evermann. Length 375 mm.; head 4.5; depth 3.6; body very long and slender and compressed; rays of dorsal fin 18; anal 18: Ohio River at Louisville; rare.

Suborder 2. Salmonoidei.—Whitefish; salmon; trout. Body elongate, more or less elliptical, covered with cycloid scales; mouth terminal; maxillary, with supplementary maxillary, forming the side of the upper jaw; tail forked; pseudobranchiæ present; no barbels; lateral line present; air bladder large; pyloric cæca very numerous; posterior dorsal fin adipose: 4 families and numerous species in the fresh waters of the United States.

Key to the Families of Salmonoidei

a_1 Branchiostegals 10 to 20.
    b_1 Mouth small; upper jaw extending to the eye (Fig. 18)....1. *Coregonidæ.*
    b_2 Mouth large; upper jaw extending back of the eye (Fig. 21)...2. *Salmonidæ.*
a_2 Branchiostegals 6 to 10.
    b_1 Dorsal fin very long.....................................3. *Thymallidæ.*
    b_2 Dorsal fin short..4. *Osmeridæ.*

Family 1. Coregonidæ.—Mouth usually small; the maxillary extending to a point in front of or beneath the anterior border of the eye; dentition feeble; flesh white: 5 genera, 1 in Arctic America, in lakes and rivers.

Key to the Genera of Coregonidæ in the United States

a_1 Lower jaw shorter than the upper; premaxillaries broad, with the cutting edge vertical or directed backwards.
    b_1 Gill-rakers long and slender, with 17 to 20 on lower limb.......1. *Coregonus.*

b₂ Gill-rakers short, with 12 to 16 on lower limb..............2. *Prosopium.*

3. *Irillion.*

a₂ Lower jaw usually longer than the upper; premaxillaries with the
cutting edge horizontal or directed forwards................4. *Leucichthys.*

1. **Coregonus** L. Whitefish. Body elongate, compressed; head small; mouth small; teeth minute or wanting; pseudobranchiæ large; air bladder very large: 18 species, in clear lakes in the northern hemisphere, those in Arctic America descending to the sea; 1 species in the United States.

C. clupeaformis (Mitchill) (Fig. 18). Common whitefish. Length 600 mm. or more; greatest weight about 23 lbs.; head 4.5 to 5; depth 3.5

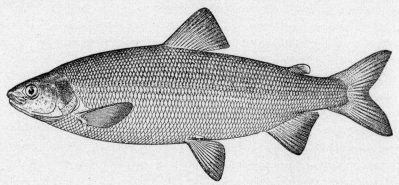

Fig. 18.—*Coregonus clupeaformis (from Jordan & Evermann).*

to 4; color olivaceous above; sides white; rays of dorsal fin 11; anal 11; scales 72 to 86, usually over 75; branchiostegals 9 to 10; gill-rakers long and slender: Great Lakes and neighboring waters, and northward to the Arctic Ocean; abundant; the most valuable food fish in the Great Lakes. The whitefish feeds on small crustaceans and mollusks and lives most of the year in deep water, but in the fall and early winter, at spawning time, it approaches the shores.

2. **Prosopium** Milner. River whitefish. Body slender; head short gill-rakers short and thick, 12 to 16 on the lower limb; no teeth on the jaws: 10 species; in northern America; 6 in the United States.

Key to the United States Species

a₁ Species in the eastern and central States.
  b₁ Upper jaw reaching beyond the front margin of eye.......*P. stanleyi.*
  b₂ Upper jaw not reaching the eye........................*P. quadrilateralis.*
a₂ Species in the far west.................................*P. williamsoni.*

P. coulteri.

P. spilonotus.

P. abyssicola.

P. stanleyi Kendall. Length 230 mm.; head 4.5; depth 4.3; color of back blue-black; sides and belly yellowish; body of male and of many females covered with white tubercles; rays of dorsal fin 10; anal 11; scales 10-82-7: lakes of Maine; abundant.

P. quadrilateralis Richardson. Menominee whitefish; frostfish. Length 300 mm.; head 5.5; depth 4.5; color dark bluish above; silvery beneath; rays of dorsal fin 11; anal 12; scales 8-90-7; branchiostegals 8; gill-rakers short and stout; body slender and elongate: the upper Great Lakes and northward; lakes of the Adirondack region and of New England; common.

P. williamsoni Girard. Rocky Mountain whitefish. Length 400 mm.; head 4.5 to 5; depth 4 to 5; color bluish above; sides silvery; fins tipped with black; rays of dorsal and anal fins 10 to 13; scales 8 to 10-78 to 88-7 or 8; body elliptical, but little compressed; head short, conic: from western Montana into Washington and Oregon; southward in Nevada to the Truckee; common in clear streams and lakes.

P. coulteri Eigenmann & Eigenmann. Length 200 mm.; color dull silvery; rays of dorsal and anal fins 10 to 11; scales 8-60 to 63-6; body heavy; snout blunt: head waters of the Columbia; rare.

P. spilonotus (Snyder). Length 200 mm.; color silvery, spotted with dusky spots, which disappear with age; dorsal and anal fins with 11 rays each; scales 11-80-8; maxillary reaches eye: Bear Lake, Idaho, in deep water.

P. abyssicola (Snyder). Length 225 mm.; color silvery; rays of dorsal fin 10, of ventral fin 11; scales 8-75-7; maxillary very short, not reaching the eye: Bear Lake, Idaho, in deep water.

3. Irillion Jordan. Similar to *Prosopium*, but with a very long sharp snout, and a large adipose fin: 1 species.

I. oregonius (Jordan & Snyder). Chisel-mouth jack. Length 425 mm.; head 4; depth 5; color silvery; rays of dorsal and anal fins 12; scales 9-86-6; body long and slender; snout very long, with a fleshy tip; adipose fin very large: basin of the Columbia; common.

4. Leucichthys Dybowski. Ciscoes; lake herrings. Similar to *Coregonus* but differing from it in having a larger mouth and longer jaws, the premaxillaries being horizontal in position and the lower jaw usually more or less projecting; gill-raker very long and slender; jaws toothless: numerous species, in the northern hemisphere, 19 in the United States, 8 in Arctic America; all valuable food fishes.

L. harengus (Richardson). Length 300 mm.; head 4.3; depth 4.5; body elongate; color dark bluish above; silvery on the sides; rays of dorsal fin 11; anal 12; scales 10-83-9; adipose fin very small: shallow waters of Lake Superior, Huron and Michigan; deep waters of New York lakes; variable; very abundant.

L. ontariensis J. & E.   Length 300 mm.; head 4.5; depth 4; color dark blue above, silvery on the sides; rays of dorsal fin 10; anal 11; scales 9-76-8; body elongate, elliptical, pale in color: Lakes Ontario and Cayuga; common.

L. artedi (LeSueur).   Common lake herring.   Length 300 mm.; head 4.5; depth 3 to 4; color gray or greenish; sides silvery; adipose fin large; rays of dorsal fin 10; anal 12; scales 8-69 to 75-7; body elliptical; head long, compressed and pointed: Great Lakes, and neighboring small lakes; very variable; very abundant, occurring along the shores in immense schools; the most important of the lake herrings commercially.

L. eriensis (J. & E.).   Jumbo herring.   Length 450 mm.; head 4.4; depth 3.4; color dark above, without blue shades; rays of dorsal fin 10; anal fins 11; scales 71; body very deep and robust: Lake Erie, especially in the northern portion, occasionally in Lake Huron; abundant; the best of the lake herrings as a food fish.

L. supernas J. & E.   Head 4.4; depth 4; color silvery; rays of dorsal fin 10; anal 12; scales 8-76-7; lower jaw projecting: Lake Superior, in deep water.

L. reighardi Koelz.   Length 225 mm.; body terete; head short; snout truncate; scales 75; fins edged with black: upper Great Lakes.

L. alpenæ Koelz.   Length 375 mm.; scales 80; body elongate: Lakes Michigan and Huron.

L. kiyi Koelz.   Body slender, small; head long and pointed; color silvery; the back densely pigmented; scales 84: Great Lakes, very abundant in deep water.

L. bergei (Wagner).   Body slender; scales 70; color pale; upper fins dark-edged: Green Lake, Wisconsin; in deep water.

L. prognathus (H. M. Smith).   Long-jaw.   Length 375 mm.; head 4.3; depth 3.5 to 4; color dusky above; sides silvery; rays of dorsal fin 9 or 10; anal 10 to 12; scales 9-75-8; body thick; back elevated; mouth large; mandible projecting and very long, reaching to the hinder margin of the eye or beyond: Lake Ontario and other Great Lakes, in deep water; spawning in the summer.

L. nigripinnis (Gill).   Bluefin; blackfin.   Length 450 mm.; head and depth 4; color dark bluish above; sides silvery, with dark dots; fins black; rays of dorsal fin 11; anal 12; scales 8-75-8; body elliptical; mouth large: Great Lakes, and small lakes of Wisconsin and Minnesota, in deep water; common.

L. cyanopterus J. & E. Length 320 mm.; head 4; depth 3.75; color silvery, bluish above; rays of dorsal fin 10 or 11; anal 11 or 12; scales 8-76 to 87-7: Lake Superior, in deep water.

L. hoyi (Gill). Cisco. Length 325 mm.; head and depth 4; color bluish above; sides silvery; rays of dorsal fin 10; anal 11 or 12; scales 7-73-7; body slender; pseudobranchiæ very large: Great Lakes; locally abundant.

L. zenithicus (J. & E.). Long-jaw. Length 250 mm.; head 3.8 to 4; depth 4 to 4.75; color blue above, silvery on the sides; rays of dorsal fin 10 or 11; anal 11 or 12; scales 8-77 to 83-7: Lake Superior, in deep water.

Fig. 19.—*Leucichthys tullibee (from Jordan & Evermann's Salmonoid Fishes of the Great Lakes).*

L. tullibee (Rich.). Tullibee (Fig. 19). Length 450 mm.; head 4; depth 3; color bluish above; sides white with fine dots; rays of dorsal and anal fins 12; scales 8 or 9-67 to 74-8; body short, very deep, compressed; adipose fin large: basin of Lake Winnipeg; small lakes of Minnesota and Wisconsin; Lakes of central New York; common.

Family 2. Salmonidæ.—Salmon and trout. Mouth large, the maxillary extending to a point behind the eye; dentition strong and complete, teeth occurring on the jaws, vomer, palatines and tongue; scales small; flesh usually pink or orange in color: 4 genera in the United States.

Key to Genera of Salmonidæ in the United States

a_1 Anal fin with 13 to 17 rays; Pacific salmon..................1. *Oncorhynchus.*
a_2 Anal fin with from 9 to 12 rays.
  b_1 Body not spotted with red.
    c_1 Body spotted with black.

d₁ Vomerine teeth not numerous and often deciduous;
   Atlantic salmon.................................2. *Salmo.*
d₂ Vomerine teeth numerous and persistent; western
   trout...3. *Trutta*
c₂ Body spotted with gray.............................4. *Cristivomer.*
b₂ Body spotted with red..................................5. *Salvelinus.*

1. **Oncorhynchus** Suckley. Pacific salmon. Body elongate, compressed, elliptical; mouth wide; during the breeding season, in the fall, the snout of the male becomes distorted, both upper and lower jaw being elongated, the former hooking over the latter, which is itself hooked at the tip, the teeth become enormously enlarged, a fleshy hump develops in front of the dorsal fin, and the flesh loses its pink color more or less completely: 6 species; north Pacific Ocean, ascending the rivers of both America and Asia to spawn; the most valuable commercial fishes in the country. The king salmon and blueback begin their run up the streams generally the last of March and continue it until the spawning season in the fall; the other species run only in the fall. The spring and summer are when the most valuable catches are made and when the fish are in the best condition. The fall catches are of far less commercial value as the flesh of the fishes is then poor, dry and colorless. The fish do not feed during the run, and most of them probably die after spawning. The young salmon descend the stream to the sea where they feed for a period of years, which for the king salmon is from 3 to 5 years, before arriving at maturity, when they migrate to the spawning grounds.

Key to the American Species of Oncorhynchus

a₁ Gill-rakers short and comparatively few (20 to 25 in number);
   b₁ Tail with large oblong spots; scales very small.............*O. gorbuscha.*
   b₂ Tail without large oblong spots.
      c₁ Rays of dorsal fin 9; branchiostegals 13 or 14..........*O. keta.*
      c₂ Rays of dorsal fin 11; branchiostegals 15 to 19..........*O. tschawytscha.*
      c₃ Rays of dorsal fin 10; branchiostegals 13 or 14..........*O. kisutch.*
a₂ Gill-rakers long and 30 to 40 in number.....................*O. nerka.*
                                                               O. kennerlyi.

O. gorbuscha (Walbaum). Humpback salmon. Weight up to 6 lbs.; color bluish, sides silvery; hinder part of back, adipose fin, and tail with numerous oblong spots; rays of dorsal fin 11; anal 15; scales very small, 200 in the lateral line; pyloric cæca 180: Pacific Ocean, from central California northwards; common in Alaska; introduced to the coast of Maine; of small food value.

O. keta (Walbaum). Dog salmon. Weight 12 lbs.; head 4; depth 4; color dusky above; sides paler; no spots, only fine dots, which may be absent; breeding male with brick-red sides, often barred or mottled; rays of dorsal fin 9; anal 13 or 14; scales 28-150-30; pyloric cæca 140 to 185: San Francisco to Bering Straits; of small food value.

O. tschawytscha (Walbaum). Chinook; king salmon; quinnat salmon. Length 600 to 1,500 mm.; usual weight 22 lbs.; extreme weight 100 lbs.; head 4; depth 4; color dusky above; sides silvery; back and tail spotted with small black spots; rays of dorsal fin 11; anal 16; scales 27-146-29; body robust; flesh red in the spring, becoming paler in the fall; pyloric cæca 145 to 185: Ventura river, California, to Alaska; the principal salmon in the Columbia and Sacramento Rivers; the most important food fish in the country; introduced into eastern America.

O. kisutch (Walbaum). Silver salmon. Length 375 mm.; weight 5 lbs.; color bluish green; sides silvery with dark punctulations; no spots except a few obscure ones; males mostly red in the fall; rays of the dorsal fin 10; anal 13 or 14; scales 25-127-29; pyloric cæca 45 to 80: San Francisco northwards; the principal salmon in Puget Sound and in the shorter rivers of Oregon and Washington; a very important food fish.

O. nerka (Walbaum). Blueback; redfish. Length 600 mm.; weight 6 lbs.; head 4; depth 4; color bright blue above and without spots; sides silvery; breeding male blood red above, white below; rays of dorsal fin 11; anal 14 to 16; scales 20-133-20; body rather slender; flesh deep red: California to Alaska; the principal salmon of the Fraser River and of Alaska; after the king salmon the most important member of the genus commercially.

O. kennerlyi (Suckley). Similar to *O. nerka* in structure, but about half its size when mature: Oregon and northwards into Alaska; in mountain lakes.

2. Salmo L. Salmon. Body elongate; mouth large; dorsal and anal fins usually with 10 to 12 rays each; body usually spotted with black: about 30 species in the United States, mostly in the west.

S. salar L. Atlantic salmon. Length to 1,500 mm.; average weight 15 lbs.; body slender, elliptical; head 4; depth 4; rays of dorsal fins 11; anal 9; scales 23-120-21; color brownish above; sides silvery, with numerous black spots all over; young with 11 dusky cross bars, and spots and red patches: north Atlantic Ocean, ascending the rivers north of Cape Cod, and occasionally as far south as the Delaware; sometimes landlocked in lakes; an important game fish: northern Europe, as far south as northern Spain. The salmon enters the rivers in the spring to feed, but probably returns to the sea before spawning, and again ascends late in the fall for that purpose.

Subspecies of S. salar

S. s. sebago Girard.   Smaller and non-migratory; average weight 2 lbs.: Sebago Pond, Maine, and other lakes to the northward.

S. s. ouananiche Jordan & Evermann.   Average weight 2 lbs.; teeth, fins and eyes very large: Lake St. John and other lakes in Quebec.

3. Trutta L.   Trout.   Similar to *Salmo;* vomerine teeth numerous; scales moderate or small, numbering 115 to 200: many species, all on the Pacific Slope and in the Rocky Mountain region, and allied to the European and Asiatic trout.

T. clarkii Richardson.   Cutthroat trout; black-spotted trout (Fig. 20).   Length up to 400 mm. or more; weight up to 20 lbs.; head 4;

Fig. 20.—*Trutta clarkii (from Jordan & Evermann).*

depth 4; rays of dorsal fin 10; anal 10; scales 39-160 to 170-30; body elongate; head short and blunt; pyloric cæca 43; color usually silver gray, profusely spotted with black, round spots which may extend on to the belly; lower jaw blotched with red (cutthroat); middle of side usually with a broad rosy wash: coastal streams and lakes from northern California to British Columbia and Alaska; up the Columbia River basin as far as Shoshone Falls; spawning in the spring and early summer.

T. lewisi (Girard).   Yellowstone trout.   Similar to *T. clarkii*, but more robust; spots not extending on the belly: Columbia River basin above Shoshone Falls; head waters of the Missouri; Yellowstone Park.

T. gibbsii (Suckley).   Silver trout.   Similar to *T. clarkii*, but with scarcely any red on the lower jaw; scales 140 to 145: Idaho, Oregon and Washington between Shoshone Falls and the Cascades.

T. henshawi Gill & Gordon.   Tahoe trout; redfish.   Similar to *T. clarkii;* body slender; head pointed; rays of dorsal fin 11; anal 12; color green above, sides silvery, with a copper shade; spotted all over: lakes and streams on the eastern slope of the Sierras.

T. tahoensis J. & E.   Silver trout.   Similar to *T. clarkii;* size very large; rays of dorsal fin 9; anal 12; scales 33-205-40: Lake Tahoe, in deep water.

T. virginalis Gir.   Similar to *T. clarkii;* scales 145; spots small and confined to the back; size very large: upper Rio Grande basin; southward into Mexico.

T. utah Suckley.   Similar to *T. virginalis;* color pale: Utah Lake and westward of the Wahsatch range.

T. pleuriticus Cope.   Similar to *T. clarkii;* scales 185 to 190; size large; lower fins red; spots numerous: head waters of the Colorado.

T. bouvieri Bendire.   Similar to *T. clarkii;* spots all behind the dorsal fin: Waha Lake, Idaho.

T. stomias Cope.   Green-back.   Similar to *T. clarkii;* body deep green above; spots mostly back of the anal fin: head waters of the Arkansas and South Platte.

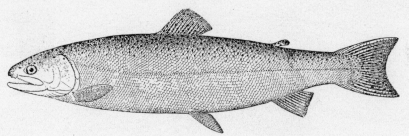

Fig. 21.—*Trutta gairdneri (from Jordan & Evermann).*

T. macdonaldi J. & E.   Yellow-fin.   Similar to *T. clarkii;* spots small and numerous on hinder part of body, few or none anteriorly; lower fins bright yellow; size large: headwaters of the Arkansas.

T. declivifrons Meek.   Similar to *T. clarkii;* color dark blue; fore part of the body with a sharp upward curve; scales 148; no spots except a few on the caudal fin: Lake Southerland, Washington.

T. jordani Meek.   Similar to *T. clarkii;* spots very numerous and very black; fins orange; scales 146: Lake Southerland, Washington.

T. gairdneri Richardson.   Steelhead trout (Fig. 21).   Length 750 mm.; weight about 4 lbs.; extreme weight 20 lbs.; color olive green above; sides silvery; back and sides more or less covered with small black spots; sides often with a broad pink stripe; rays of dorsal fin 11; anal 12; scales about 150: Pacific Ocean and coastwise streams from northern California to British Columbia and northwards; an important food and game fish.

T. beardslei Jordan & Seale.   Blue-back.   Similar to *T. gairdneri;* color very dark blue; no lateral rosy band; under parts white, not silvery; size large; scales 130: Crescent Lake, Washington.

T. crescentis Jordan & Beardslee. Similar to *T. gairdneri;* color very dark blue; spots not numerous; a large black blotch on the cheek: Crescent Lake, Washington.

T. bathœcetor Meek. Length 600 mm.; head 3.5; depth 5.5; scales 150; rays of dorsal fin 10; anal 11; color blue; spots numerous; form slender: Crescent Lake, Washington, in deep water.

T. irideus Gibbons. Rainbow trout (Fig. 22). Length 375 mm. or more; weight about 3 lbs.; head 4; depth 3.8; rays of dorsal fin 11; anal 10; scales 21-135-20; color bluish above; sides silvery, with a broad pink lateral band; back profusely spotted: in mountain brooks of the Coast Range of California.

FIG. 22.—*Trutta irideus (from Jordan & Evermann).*

T. shasta Jordan. Rainbow trout. Similar to *T. irideus;* coloration rather dark; spots extending at least to the lateral line; scales 145: streams of the Sierra Nevada from Mount Shasta southward; the usual rainbow trout of the fish culturists, which has been introduced extensively into the eastern States.

T. gilberti Jord. Similar to *T. irideus;* scales 165; back and sides profusely spotted: Kern River, California.

T. stonei Jord. Similar to *T. irideus;* size much larger; scales 155; spots few, mostly on the hinder part of the body: upper Sacramento basin.

T. agua-bonita Jord. Similar to *T. irideus;* size very small; scales 175; sides and belly golden; spots few: south Fork of the Kern River, California.

T. roosevelti Evermann. Golden trout. Length 30 mm.; head 3.5; depth 4; rays of dorsal fins 11; anal 11; scales 200; color olive above, golden yellow below the lateral line; a broad rosy lateral band crossed by 10 black blotches and a midventral red stripe present; lower fins red; dorsal and caudal fins and tail alone spotted: Volcano Creek, Kern River basin, California.

T. whitei Evermann. Golden trout. Similar to *T. roosevelti;* back and sides profusely spotted; scales larger; lower fins yellowish; no red on throat: in the western tributaries of the Kern River, California.

T. smaragda Snyder. Greenback. Form slender; scales 124; color green above: Pyramid Lake region, Nevada.

T. aquilarum Snyder. Length 480 mm.; head 4.2; depth 4.2; scales 136; color dark olive above; below the lateral line and on belly coppery red; a trace of red on the throat; profusely spotted above the lateral line: Eagle Lake, California.

4. Cristivomer Gill & Jordan. Great Lakes trout. Body of large size, spotted with gray; scales very small; vomer elongate, with a raised

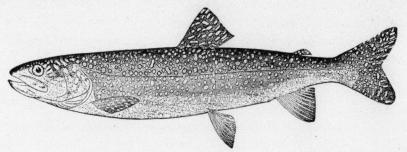

Fig. 23.—*Cristivomer namaycush (from Jordan & Evermann's Salmonoid Fishes of the Great Lakes).*

median crest armed with strong teeth; hyoid with a broad band of strong teeth: 2 species, which are the largest of the trouts.

C. namaycush (Walbaum). Mackinaw trout; lake trout (Fig. 23). Length 900 mm.; head 4.5; depth 4; average weight 16 lbs.; extreme weight 90 lbs.; color dark gray, often greenish on the sides, everywhere with rounded paler spots which are often tinged with reddish; rays of dorsal fin 11; anal 11; scales 185 to 205; body elongate; head very long; mouth large: northern North America from Maine to Vancouver and northward to the Arctic and Alaska; common in the Great Lakes, where after the sturgeon, it is the largest fish, and, after the whitefish, the most important fish commercially.

C. siscowet (Agassiz). Similar to *C. namaycush*, but with a deeper body and an excessive development of fatty tissue beneath the skin; color paler; scales 175: Lake Superior; abundant in deeper water; also in Lakes Huron and Erie.

5. Salvelinus Nilsson. Brook trout. Body moderately elongate, spotted with red; scales very small and imbedded and hidden; vomer elongate, with teeth on front end only, hinder portion depressed and without teeth; hyoid with weak teeth or none: many species, which live

in cold, clear streams in the northern hemisphere, sometimes descending
into the sea; 5 species in the United States.

S. fontinalis (Mitchill).   Brook trout; speckled trout.   Length 200
mm. or more; weight 1 lb. or more; extreme weight 8 lbs.; head and
depth 4.5; color of back and sides dark olive, marbled or barred on the
back and with numerous red spots on the sides, each spot margined with
brown; lower fins dusky, edged anteriorly with black and orange; rays
of dorsal fin 10; anal 9; scales 37-230-30: Maine to Montana and Saskatchewan; northward into Labrador; southward in the Appalachian
Mountains to Georgia; in none of the Great Lakes except Lake Superior;
introduced into other parts of the country; spawning occurs in the fall,
the eggs hatching the following spring.

S. spectabilis (Girard).   Dolly Varden trout.   Length 500 mm.;
weight up to 12 lbs.; head 3.6; depth 4; color olivaceous, the sides with
round red spots nearly the size of the eye, the back with smaller, paler
ones; rays of dorsal fin 11; anal 9; scales 39-240-36; body rather slender:
east and west slopes of the Cascade Range from the upper Sacramento
to Montana, and northward into Alaska; common.

S. alpinus (L.).   Saibling; European trout.   Length 225 mm.;
head 4.5; depth 5; color grayish or greenish above, red beneath; sides
silvery, with round red dots; rays of dorsal fin 13; anal 12; scales 195 to
200; body elongate, compressed; back not marbled: northern and
central Europe; introduced into Starling Lake, New York.

S. aureolus Bean.   American saibling.   Length 300 mm.; head and
depth 4.2; color dark green above, without mottling; sides silver gray,
with small yellow spots; belly orange; fins very large; rays of dorsal fin
9; anal 8; scales 35-210-40: Sunapee Lake, Maine and other lakes in
Maine and New Hampshire; probably introduced from Europe.

S. oquassa (Girard).   Blueblack trout.   Length 300 mm.; head and
depth 5; color dark blue above with round red spots on the sides; rays of
dorsal fin 10; anal 9; scales 230; body slender: Rangeley Lakes, Maine,
and northwards.

S. marstoni Garman.   Similar to *S. oquassa*, but with a larger
mouth and teeth and fewer red spots; rays of dorsal fin 13; anal 13;
Lac de Marbre, Quebec.

S. timagamiensis Henn and Rinkenbach.   Mouth very large;
maxillary extending beyond the eye; red spots very few: Timigami
region, Quebec.

Family 3.   Thymallidæ.—Graylings.   Body elongate, compressed,
slender; head short; mouth terminal; maxillary extending to a point
below the middle of the eye; tail forked; adipose fin present; dorsal fin

very long and high, with simple anterior and bifurcated posterior rays:
1 genus.

Thymallus Cuvier.   With the characters of the family: 5 species, all
in the cold waters of the northern hemisphere, 2 in the United States.

T. tricolor Cope (Fig. 24).   Michigan grayling.   Length 450;
head 5; depth 4.6; color purplish gray; sides with small scattered black
spots back of head; dorsal fin spotted and with rose colored and dark
stripes; rays of dorsal fin 21 or 22; anal 11; scales 93 to 98: northern
Michigan; scarce.

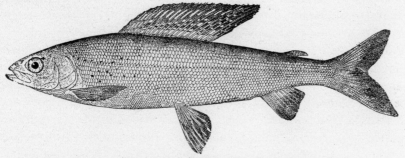

FIG. 24.—*Thymallus tricolor (from Jordan & Evermann).*

T. montanus Milner.   Montana grayling.   Similar to *T. tricolor*, but
with dorsal fins a little smaller and with smaller scales; sides with trans-
versely elongated spots: upper Missouri basin, above the Great Falls;
locally abundant.

Family 4.   Osmeridæ—Smelts.   Body elongate, slender, small,
covered with usually cycloid scales; head naked; mouth terminal;
stomach a blind sac, the cardiac and pyloric ends being close together;
pyloric cæca few or wanting; adipose fin present; tail forked: about
15 species, mostly marine, some of the species ascending the streams;
2 freshwater genera in the United States.

1. Thaleichthys Girard.   Body very slender; scales very small;
mouth small; teeth very feeble: 1 species in the United States.

T. pacificus (Richardson).   Candlefish.   Length 300 mm.; head
4.75; depth 6; color white, with numerous dark dots above; rays of
dorsal fin 11; anal 21; scales 75; lower jaw projecting: Oregon to
Alaska; marine; ascending the streams from the Columbia River northwards in enormous numbers in the spring; flesh very oily and of delicious
flavor; an important food fish; when dried used as candles.

2. Osmerus L.   Body very slender; teeth strong, those on the
tongue long and fang-like; scales large; 5 species in the United States
along the shores of both oceans, 1 ascending the streams.

O. mordax (Mitchill). American smelt. Length 300 mm.; head 4; depth 6.5; color greenish above, with dark dots; sides silvery; rays of dorsal fin 10; anal 15; scales 68; mouth large, lower jaw projecting: Atlantic Ocean from Virginia to Labrador, ascending the streams in the winter to spawn in immense numbers; common in Lake Champlain and other lakes; often landlocked; an important food fish.

O. thaleichthys Ayres. Length 200 mm.; head 4.5; depth 5.5; color olivaceous; rays of dorsal fin 9; anal 14; scales 55 to 58: Pacific Ocean from San Francisco to Alaska, ascending the streams in February.

Order 2. Enchelycephali.—Body very elongate, cylindrical, with minute imbedded scales or none; ventral fins wanting; anterior vertebræ distinct, without Weberian ossicles; premaxillaries atrophied or absent; maxillaries lateral; air bladder, if present, with pneumatic duct; opercular and pharyngeal bones more or less deficient; fins without spines; gill-openings small; pseudobranchiæ absent: 10 families, the species being mostly marine and tropical; 1 species in the United States.

Family Anguillidæ.—Eels. Body very elongate, compressed behind; head conical; mouth large, with projecting jaws; operculum present; dorsal and anal fins confluent with the caudal; scales minute, imbedded and hidden; lateral line present: 1 genus, with 4 or 5 species, which occur in fresh, salt and brackish water in all parts of the world except the Pacific coasts of North America and the islands of the Pacific. American eels breed in the ocean between the West Indies and Bermuda, and die soon after. Spawning may also occur in fresh water. The young eels are very different in appearance from their parents and are called *Leptocephali*. During the second spring the young eels ascend the streams to feed in fresh water, in which they live several years. When they are full grown they descend the streams to the sea; their reproductive glands, however, do not mature for several weeks. Eels eat fishes, crustaceans and carrion, and are voracious feeders. They often travel considerable distances on land, through wet grass.

Anguilla Shaw. With the characters of the family: several species, 1 in America.

A. rostrata (LeSueur). Common eel. Length 1,500 mm. or less; weight up to 7 lbs.; color brown, often yellowish, paler beneath; head 8.5; depth 12 to 17: Atlantic Ocean, from Greenland to Brazil; also in the West Indies; ascending all the rivers east of the Rockies; not found in the Great Lakes above Niagara Falls or the upper Mississippi Valley, unless introduced.

Order 3. Eventognathi.—The suckers and carps. Anterior vertebræ modified, with Weberian ossicles; fins soft-rayed, being without spines; ventral fins abdominal; no adipose fin; lower pharyngeals falciform, parallel with the gill-arches; maxillaries perfect; jaws toothless; no pyloric cæca; air bladder with pneumatic duct: 2 very large families of fresh water fishes.

Key to Families of Eventognathi

a₁ Lips usually thick and fleshy; dorsal fin with more
    than 10 rays...1. *Catostomidæ.*
a₂ Lips thin; dorsal fin with less than 10 rays...................2. *Cyprinidæ.*

Family 1. Catostomidæ.—Suckers; mullets. Fishes of medium size, with an elongate, more or less compressed body covered with cycloid scales; head naked, without barbels; jaws toothless; mouth usually with thick, fleshy, protractile lips; sides of the upper jaw formed by the maxillaries; lower pharyngeal bones with a single row of teeth; branchiostegals 3; gill membranes united to the isthmus; pseudobranchiæ present; fins not scaled; dorsal fin often long; anal fin short; tail forked; air bladder large, divided into 2 or 3 compartments: about 15 genera and 70 species, of which 2 occur in eastern Asia and the others in the fresh waters of North America. They live near the bottom and feed on vegetation and small, inactive animals. In the spring they usually ascend the streams to spawn, often in swarms. The flesh of most species is not highly valued for food.

Key to the Genera of Catostomidæ

a₁ Dorsal fin long, with 24 to 30 rays; air bladder in 2 parts.
    b₁ Scales large, 35 to 41 being in the lateral line.
                                                    1. *Ictiobus.*
                                                    2. *Megastomatobus.*
                                                    3. *Carpiodes.*
    b₂ Scales smaller, about 56 in the lateral line.............4. *Cycleptus.*
a₂ Dorsal fin with 9 to 18 rays.
    b₁ Scales small, 50 or more in the lateral line; air bladder in
        2 parts.
        c₁ Small species in the Rocky Mountain region; hinder
            division of air bladder slender...................5. *Pantosteus.*
        c₂ Hinder division of air bladder broad.
            d₁ No hump back of head.
                e₁ Mouth inferior, with thick papillose lips.
                    f₁ Scales small (over 55)...................6. *Catostomus.*
                    f₂ Scales larger (under 50).
                        g₁ Head concave above.................7. *Hypentelium.*
                        g₂ Head not concave above..............9. *Thoburnia.*
                e₂ Mouth large, terminal, with thin lips.........8. *Chasmistes.*
            d₂ A high hump back of the head..................10. *Xyrauchen.*

b₂ Scales larger, 36 to 50 in the lateral line.
   c₁ Lateral line wanting or incomplete; air bladder in 2
      parts.
      d₁ Lateral line entirely wanting.................11. *Erimyzon.*
      d₂ Lateral line interrupted......................12. *Minytrema.*
   c₂ Lateral line complete; air bladder in 3 parts.
      d₁ Lower lip entire or merely lobed.
         e₁ Teeth compressed; mouth small.............13. *Moxostoma.*
                                  14. *Scartomyzon*
         e₂ Lower teeth enlarged and cylindrical; mouth
           large....................................15. *Placopharynx.*
      d₂ Lower lip split, forming two separate lobes......16. *Logochila.*

1. Ictiobus Rafinesque. Buffalo fish. Large, rather stout fishes
with large head, furrowed opercles and broad subopercles; fontanelle
present; mouth inferior; lips thin, somewhat plicate; scales large; lateral

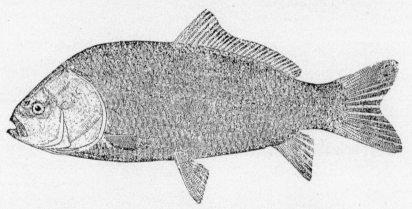

FIG. 25.—*Megastomatobus cyprinella (from Jordan & Evermann).*

line prominent; dorsal fin long, the anterior rays being longer than
the others: 2 species in the United States, 1 in Mexico, all rather
important food fish.

I. urus (Agassiz). Black buffalo. Similar to *M. cyprinella*, but
with a smaller mouth and a much darker color; head 4; lips thick,
plicate; dorsal fin with 30 rays; anal 10; scales 8-41-7: Mississippi
Valley; less common than *M. cyprinella*.

I. bubalus (Raf.). Small-mouthed buffalo. Extreme length 900
mm.; extreme weight 35 lbs.; head 4; depth 2.5; mouth small, inferior;
lips thick, plicate; color pale; dorsal fin with 29 rays; anal 10; scales
8-39-6: Mississippi Valley; common; in the larger rivers.

2. Megastomatobus Fowler. Similar to *Ictiobus;* dorsal fin
elongate; mouth terminal, oblique; lips smooth and thin: 1 species.

M. cyprinella (Cuvier and Valenciennes) (Fig. 25). Common buffalo. Length 900 mm.; extreme weight 50 lbs.; head 3.5; depth 3; color brownish olive; rays of dorsal fin 27 to 29; anal 9; scales 7-37 to 41-6: Mississippi Valley; common in large streams.

3. Carpiodes Rafinesque. Carp suckers. Similar to *Ictiobus*, but smaller, pale and silvery in color and with a weak dentition: 12 species; 5 in Mexico.

Key to the Species of Carpiodes

a_1 In the Mississippi and Great Lakes basins.
  b_1 Body subfusiform and robust; depth about 3................*C. carpio.*
  b_2 Body thin and compressed; depth about 2.5; opercle striate.
    c_1 Lips thin and white.
      d_1 Snout very blunt, the nostrils being near the tip........*C. difformis.*
      d_2 Head small and pointed.............................*C. thompsoni.*
    c_2 Lips thick and reddish in color.........................*C. velifer.*
a_2 On the Atlantic slope.......................................*C. cyprinus.*

C. carpio (Raf.). Carp sucker. Extreme length 900 mm.; extreme weight 10 lbs.; head 4 to 5; depth 3; color silvery gray; rays of dorsal

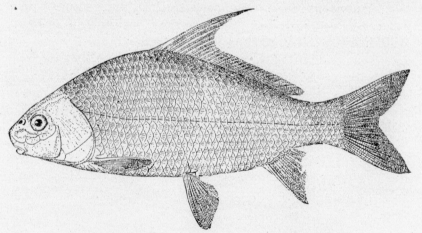

Fig. 26.—*Carpiodes cyprinus (from Jordan & Evermann).*

fin 27; anal 7; scales 36; lips thin: Ohio Valley, southwestward to central Texas; abundant.

C. difformis Cope. Length 300 mm.; head 4.5; depth 2.5; color silvery; snout very blunt; rays of dorsal fin 24, the anterior rays greatly elongated; anal 8; scales 6-35-6; dorsal fin very high: Ohio Valley and westwards; common.

C. thompsoni Agassiz. Length 500 mm.; head 4.25; depth 2.5; color silvery; rays of dorsal fin 27; anal 7; scales 7-39 to 41-6; head small and pointed: basins of the Great Lakes and the St. Lawrence; common.

C. velifer (Raf.). Quillback. Length 300 mm.; head 4; depth 2.5 to 3; color pale; rays of dorsal fin 26 or 27, the anterior rays twice as long as the others; scales 7-37 to 40-6; opercle striate; lips thick and flesh-colored in life, the two halves of lower lip meeting at an acute angle: Mississippi Valley and southwestward to the Rio Grande; common.

C. cyprinus (LeSueur). Carp sucker (Fig. 26). Similar to *C. velifer*, but with a smooth opercle; body elongate: streams entering Chesapeake Bay; common.

4. Cycleptus Rafinesque. Body elongate and similar to the two previous genera, but with a closed fontanelle; head very small: 1 species.

C. elongatus (LeSueur). Blackhorse; Missouri sucker. Length 750 mm.; head 6 to 8; depth 4 to 5; color blackish; dorsal fin with 30 rays, the anterior 2 or 3 being much prolonged; anal fin with 7 to 8 rays; scales 9-56-8; mouth small; upper lip thick and pendant: Mississippi Valley, often common in large streams; a good food fish.

5. Pantosteus Cope. Mountain suckers. Body small, elongate, similar to *Catostomus;* lips thick, papillose; mouth ventral, with a cartilaginous sheath on each jaw: several species, in the Rocky Mountain region, all of little food value.

P. generosus (Girard). Length 200 mm.; head 5; depth 5.5; color light brown, with dusky spots; chin, fins and lateral band red in male; rays of dorsal fin 9; scales 15-81-14: Great Basin of Utah; very common.

P. plebeius (Baird & Girard). Length 300 mm.; head 4.6; depth 4.75; color dark brown with orange lateral markings in male; scales 80; body stout: basin of the Rio Grande; very common.

P. delphinus (Cope). Length 300 mm.; head 4.75; color bluish above, yellowish below; sides of male rosy; rays of dorsal fin 10; scales 16–96 to 105-14; tail very slender: basin of the Colorado; very common.

P. jordani Evermann. Length 300 mm.; head and depth 5; color dark greenish, speckled; males with orange lateral band; dorsal fin with 10 or 11 rays; anal with 7 rays; scales 16-90 to 100-14, 48 before the dorsal: basin of the upper Missouri and Columbia; generally distributed.

6. Catostomus LeSueur. Fine-scaled suckers. Body elongate; mouth rather large, ventral; upper lip thick, papillose and protractile; lower lip very large with a broad free margin usually in two more or less distinct lobes; scales small; dorsal and anal fins high and rather short:

many species, all North American except *C. rostratus* Tilesius, which occurs in Siberia.

Key to the Species of Catostomus here described

a_1 More than 80 scales in the lateral line.
  b_1 Upper lip broad, with 5 or 6 rows of papillæ.
    c_1 Upper lip not projecting; in the Colorado River basin.
      d_1 In the lower Colorado basin.......................*C. latipinnis.*
      d_2 In the upper Colorado basin.......................*C. discobolus.*
    c_2 Upper lip very long and pendant; in the upper Missouri..*C. griseus.*
  b_2 Upper lip narrow, with about 3 rows of papillæ.
    c_1 In the northern United States.......................*C. catostomus.*
    c_2 In Lake Tahoe.....................................*C. tahoensis.*
a_2 Less than 75 scales in the lateral line.
  b_1 In the western States.
    c_1 On the Pacific slope.
      d_1 In California.....................................*C. occidentalis.*
                                      C. mniotiltus.
      d_2 In Oregon.......................................*C. tsiltcoosensis.*
      d_3 In Oregon and California.........................*C. snyderi.*
                                       C. microps.
    c_2 In the Great Basin and the Rocky Mountains.
      d_1 From Oregon to Montana.........................*C. macrocheilus.*
      d_2 In Utah...*C. ardens.*
  b_2 In the eastern and central States........................*C. commersonii.*

C. latipinnis Baird & Girard. Length 600 mm.; head 4; depth 5.5; color dark olive; sides and fins orange; rays of dorsal fin 14 or 15; anal 7; scales 19-89 to 102-18, 46 to 50 before the dorsal fin; lips very thick, the lower extending backward to beneath the eye; fins very large: basins of the lower Colorado; common.

C. discobolus Cope. Length 300 mm. or more; head 3.8 to 4.5; depth 5.25; rays of dorsal fin 12 or 13; anal 7; scales 19 to 21-101 to 109-17 to 21, 52 to 63 before the dorsal fin; mouth as in *C. latipinnis;* muzzle extending to slightly beyond upper lip: upper Colorado basin; Montana.

C. griseus (Girard). Length 500 mm.; head 4; depth 5.5; color brown; rays of dorsal fin 10 to 12; scales 16-90 to 110-14; upper lip very long and pendant; lower lip deeply incised: upper Missouri basin; abundant in the Yellowstone.

C. catostomus (Forster). Long-nose sucker. Length 750 mm.; head 4.5; depth 4.5; rays of dorsal fin 10 to 11; anal 7; scales 14 to 17-95 to 117-13; upper lip with 2 to 4 rows of tubercles; lower lip deeply incised; mouth inferior; head very long and slender, the snout overhanging the mouth: from Maine and the basin of the St. Lawrence and the Great Lakes to southeastern Oregon and the upper Columbia, and northward to Alaska; abundant northward; spawning in spring; of some food value.

C. tahoensis Jordan. Red sucker. Similar to *C. catostomus*, but with 83 to 92 scales in the lateral line and a stouter body: region of Lake Tahoe; very abundant.

C. occidentalis Ayres. Length 250 mm.; head 4.5; depth 5; body slender; color dark above; dorsal fin with 12 to 14 rays; scales 13-75-10, 40 before the dorsal fin; middle California; common.

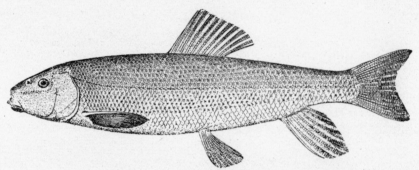

FIG. 27.—*Catastomus commersoni (from Jordan & Evermann).*

C. mniotiltus Snyder. Length 200 mm.; head and depth 4.8; rays of dorsal fin 12; anal 7; scales 57: Monterey County, California.

C. macrocheilus Girard. Length 150 mm.; head 4; depth 5; color dark, with a darker lateral stripe; rays of dorsal fin 12 to 14; anal 7; scales 12-72-10; head large; upper lip with 6 to 8 rows of papillæ: Oregon and Washington, into Montana; common.

C. commersonii (Lacépède). Common sucker (Fig. 27). Length 450 mm.; head and depth 4 to 5; color olivaceous; rays of dorsal fin 12; anal 7; scales 10-55 to 70-9; mouth large; upper lip narrow, with 3 to 5 rows of papillæ: Maine, Valley of the St. Lawrence and Great Lakes to Montana; northward to New Brunswick, Labrador and Hudson Bay; southward into Georgia and Missouri; very common in small streams and ponds; a good food fish.

C. ardens Jordan & Gilbert. Similar to *C. commersonii*, but with a larger mouth and lips; scales 12-70 to 72-12: Great Basin of Utah; very common.

C. snyderi Gilbert. Length 500 mm.; head 4.5; depth 4; color dusky; belly white; rays of dorsal fin 11; anal 7; scales 13-70-11: Klamath Lakes region.

C. microps Rutter. Length 130 mm.; head 4.5; depth 4.7; rays of dorsal fin 11; anal 7; scales 17-81 to 87-14; eye very small: Modoc County, California.

C. tsiltcoosensis Evermann & Meek. Length 300 mm.; head 4.5; depth 5; rays of dorsal fin 13; anal 7; scales 13-65-8, 34 before the dorsal; fins small: coastal streams of middle Oregon.

7. Hypentelium Rafinesque. Similar to *Catostomus* but with larger scales (about 50 in lateral line); head large, concave above: 1 species.

H. nigricans (LeSueur.). Hog sucker. Length 600 mm.; head 4.5; depth 5; color olivaceous, sides brassy; lower fins red; back and sides with black blotches; rays of dorsal fin 10 or 11; scales 7-46 to 51-6; head large; upper lip very thick, with 8 to 10 series of papillæ: New York to Minnesota; southward to the Carolinas and Arkansas; abundant in clear streams.

8. Chasmistes Jordan. Head large; snout elevated; mouth terminal and very large, with a long, very oblique lower jaw; upper lip thin and smooth; lower lip with a broad flap on each side and narrow in front: 6 species, all in the far-west.

C. liorus Jord. Length 450 mm.; head 3.5; depth 5; end of snout elevated; color dusky; back and sides covered with dark punctulations; rays of dorsal fin 11; anal 7; scales 9-63-8: Utah Lake; very common.

C. cujus Cope. Rays of dorsal fin 11; anal 7; scales 13-65-11: Pyramid Lake, Nevada, in deep water.

C. brevirostris Cope. Rays of dorsal fin 11; anal 9; scales 12-75-11: Klamath Lakes, Oregon.

C. (Deltistes Seale) *luxatus* Cope. Length 900 mm.; head 4; depth 4.8; color dusky, with black punctulations; rays of dorsal fin 12; anal 7; scales 12-76 to 81-9; body elongate; head very long and slender: Klamath Lakes region, where it is abundant and the most important food fish.

C. stomias Gilbert. Length 450 mm.; color dark above; rays of dorsal fin 10; anal 7; scales 14 or 15-76 to 82-11: Upper Klamath Lake; common.

C. copei Evermann & Meek. Similar to *C. stomias;* scales 13-80-12; mouth very oblique: Klamath Lakes.

9. Thoburnia Jordan and Snyder. Similar to *Catostomus*, but with larger scales (about 50 in lateral line); head very small, flat above: 1 species.

T. rhothœca (Thoburn).   Length 125 mm.; color olive, with a black lateral stripe and black crossbars; scales 7-48-5; rays of dorsal fin 11; of ventral 8: Atlantic slope of Virginia.

10. Xyrauchen Eigenmann & Kirsch.   Like *Catostomus*, except that immediately behind the head is a very prominent, sharp-edged hump; snout blunt: 1 species.

X. texanus (Abbott).   Razor-back.   Head and depth 4; rays of dorsal fin 13 or 14; anal 7; scales 13 to 15-72 to 77-13; color olivaceous: Colorado basin; abundant.

11. Erimyzon Jordan.   Body fusiform, compressed; scales large; lateral line wanting: 1 species.

FIG. 28.—*Erimyzon sucetta (from Jordan & Evermann).*

E. sucetta (Lacépède).   Chub sucker (Fig. 28).   Length 250 mm.; head 4.25; depth 3; color dusky, with a coppery lustre; young with a broad black lateral band or series of blotches; rays of dorsal fin 11 to 12; anal 7; scales 36-15, in southern specimens, but 43-15 north of Virginia: Great Lakes region; Mississippi Valley; coastwise from Virginia to Texas; very common.

12. Minytrema Jordan.   Body elongate, little compressed, with an interrupted lateral line in the adult, and a small black spot at the base of each scale on the side: 1 species.

M. melanops (Rafinesque).   Spotted sucker.   Length 600 mm.; head 4.3; depth 3 to 4; color dusky above, with usually a black blotch behind the dorsal fin; rays of dorsal fin 12 to 14; anal 7; scales 44 to 47: Great Lakes to Florida; upper Mississippi Valley to Texas; common.

13. Moxostoma Rafinesque.   Redhorse.   Body elongate; mouth inferior; lips well developed, with transverse folds (Fig. 29); jaws without cartilaginous sheath; upper lip protractile; scales large; anal fin high, with 7 rays; fontanelle present: about 20 species, all in the eastern and central States; in rivers and lakes.

M. papillosum (Cope). White mullet. Length 600 mm.; head and depth 4; color silvery; lower fins usually reddish; lips full, the folds broken into papillæ; rays of dorsal fin 12 to 14; scales 6-42-5: Atlantic slope, from Dismal Swamp to central Georgia; common.

M. anisurum (Raf.). Whitenose. Length 450 mm.; head 4; depth 3 to 4; color silvery; fins large; lower fins reddish; rays of dorsal fin 15; scales 6-42 to 45-6; lips plicate; mouth large: Great Lakes region and Ohio River basin; common.

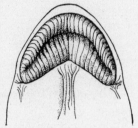

M. aureolum (LeSueur). Common redhorse (Fig. 29). Length 600 mm.; head 4 or 5; depth 3.5; color olivaceous; sides silvery; lower fins red in adult; rays of dorsal fin 12 to 14; scales 5-41 to 45-5 to 7; head small; lips thick: Lake

FIG. 29.—Lips of *Moxostoma aureolum* (*from Fishes of Illinois*).

Ontario to upper Mississippi Valley; southwestward to Missouri and Arkansas; southeastward to North Carolina and Georgia; common; the most important food fish of the genus.

M. crassilabre (Cope). Length 600 mm.; head 5; depth 3.5; color pale yellowish or reddish; dorsal fin falcate, rays 12 or 13; scales 5-44-5; lips full: eastern North Carolina; abundant.

M. collapsum (Cope). Small mouth. Similar to *M. anisurum*, but with a smaller mouth; lips plicate: lowland streams of North Carolina.

M. macrolepidotum (LeSueur). Red mullet. Length 600 mm.; color silvery, lower fins orange-red; head broad; mouth large, with thick lips; scales 5-45-4: coastal streams Delaware Bay to North Carolina.

M. duquesnii LeSueur. Similar to *M. aureolum;* scales 47: mountain streams of North Carolina and westwards.

M. lesueurii (Richardson). Body compressed; mouth very small; dorsal fin falcate, rays 13; scales 6-45-5: Ohio Valley and Great Lakes and northwards.

14. Scartomyzon Fowler. Similar to *Moxostoma*, but of much smaller size and living in mountain brooks: 2 species.

S. rupiscartes Jordan & Jenkins. Length 300 mm.; head 5; depth 5.5 to 6; color olive brown; rays of dorsal fin 11; anal 8; scales 6-50-6, 18 before the dorsal fin: south Atlantic States, from the Catawba to the Chattahoochee Rivers; often abundant.

S. cervinum (Cope).   Length 250 mm.; head 5; body elongate; color greenish brown, with a pale blotch on each scale, these forming continuous lines along the sides; rays of the dorsal fin 10 to 12; scales 6-43-5, 13 before the dorsal: from the James River to the Neuse; abundant in rapid water.

15. Placopharynx Cope.   Large suckers, like *Moxostoma*, except that the pharyngeal bones are stronger and the lower teeth very large, nearly cylindrical in form, and 6 to 10 in number; upper teeth small and compressed: 1 species.

P. carinatus Cope.   Big-jawed sucker.   Length 750 mm.; head 4; depth 3.8; color dark olive green; caudal and lower fins bright red; rays of dorsal fin 12 or 13; anal 9; scales 6-45-6; head and mouth large; lips very thick: Michigan to Georgia and Arkansas; abundant in large streams.

16. Logochila Jordan & Brayton.   Like *Moxostoma*, except that the upper lip is not protractile and the lower lip is split, consisting of two lobes: 1 species.

L. lacera J. & B.   Harelip sucker.   Head short; depth 4.6; color pale olive; sides and belly silvery; rays of dorsal fin 12; anal 7; scales 5-45-5; mouth large, inferior, the upper lip being prolonged: middle Mississippi Valley; locally common.

Family 2.   Cyprinidæ.—Minnows; carp; dace.   Small or medium sized fishes with an elongate body, usually covered with cycloid scales and with a naked head; margin of the upper jaw formed by the premaxillaries alone; jaws toothless; the two paired lower pharyngeal bones parallel with the gill arches, each being falciform in shape and bearing 1 or 2 (in some European species 3) rows of teeth on each side, there being 4, 5 or 6 teeth in the main or hindermost row in the American species, and 1 or 2 teeth in the other row, if present at all; pseudobranchiæ usually present; branchiostegal rays 3; gills 4; fins typically spineless; ventral fins abdominal in position; air bladder large, with usually 2 compartments: over 200 genera and 1,000 species, in North America and the Old World, all in fresh water; most of which have no food value.

The American species are mostly small, often very small, fishes which abound in every brook and small stream.   Many are very brightly colored, especially in the springtime when the males have their nuptial coloration of reds and yellows.   Numerous conspicuous tubercles may also cover the top of the head and other portions of the body of the male at this time.   Two important members of this family have been introduced from Europe, the carp and the goldfish, both however natives of China, where they have been domesticated from time immemorial.

In the classification of these small fishes the lower pharyngeal teeth (Fig. 30) are of great importance, and their number and form are usually given in the descriptions. Thus "teeth 4-4" means that there is a single row of 4 pharyngeal teeth on each side of the mouth; "teeth

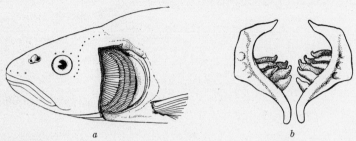

a   *b*

FIG. 30.—Lower pharyngeal teeth of the chub (*Semotilus atromaculatus*): *a*, head of fish with left opercle removed showing the left pharyngeal arch back of the gill-arches; *b*, the two pharyngeal arches, the formula of the teeth being, 2, 4-5, 2 (*from Fishes of Illinois*).

4-5" means there is a row of 4 teeth on one side and 5 on the other; "teeth 1, 4-5, 2" means there are 4 teeth in the main or hindermost row and 1 tooth in the second or foremost row on one side, and on the other side 5 and 2 teeth, respectively, in the two rows. In the herbivorous species the teeth are nearly straight, and either without a hook at the tip or with a slight hook. Near the base of the tooth is often a masticatory surface in the form of a groove.

Key to the Genera of United States Cyprinidæ (not including the European Carp and the Goldfish)

a_1 Digestive canal very long, being more than twice the length
of the body; peritoneum usually black.
  b_1 Digestive canal wound around air bladder.............. 3. *Campostoma*.
  b_2 Digestive canal not wound around air bladder.
    c_1 Pseudobranchiæ absent; on the Pacific slope.......... 4. *Orthodon*.
    c_2 Pseudobranchiæ present.
      d_1 Each jaw with a conspicuous horny plate; in the
Columbia basin............................. 5. *Acrocheilus*.
      d_2 Jaw without horny plate.
        e_1 Teeth in main row usually 5-5.
          f_1 Lateral line complete; in California.......... 6. *Lavinia*.
          f_2 Lateral line incomplete; eastern and central
States................................ 7. *Chrosomus*.
        e_2 Teeth in main row 4-4.
          f_1 First ray of dorsal fin not peculiar.
            g_1 Teeth long and scarcely hooked.......... 8. *Hybognathus*.
            g_2 Teeth short and distinctly hooked........ 9. *Dionda*.

   f_2 First ray of dorsal fin separate and joined with
    the other rays by a membrane.
    g_1 Lateral line incomplete..................10. *Pimephales.*
    g_2 Lateral line complete....................11. *Hyborhynchus.*
a_2 Digestive canal short, less than twice the length of the body;
 peritoneum usually pale.
 b_1 Teeth mostly blunt and enlarged, but slightly hooked;
  large fishes on the Pacific Slope.
  c_1 No barbels present...............................12. *Mylopharodon.*
  c_2 Barbels present.....................................13. *Mylocheilus.*
 b_2 Teeth slender, hooked; species mostly not on the Pacific
  Slope.
  c_1 Teeth in main row 5-5 or 4-5.
   d_1 Barbels present, often very small.
    e_1 Tail symmetrical; in the eastern and central
     States.
     f_1 Dorsal fin without a black spot.............14. *Leucosomus.*
     f_2 Dorsal fin with a black spot...............15. *Semotilus.*
    e_2 The upper lobe of tail longer than the lower; in
     California................................16. *Pogonichthys.*
   d_2 Barbels absent (except in *Margariscus*).
    e_1 Abdomen behind ventral fins rounded and scaled.
     f_1 Teeth 2-rowed, usually with 2 teeth in the
      lesser row.
      g_1 Size very large, the length being up to 1,000
       mm...................................17. *Ptychocheilus.*
      g_2 Length not over 400 mm.
       h_1 Caudal peduncle very long and slender..18. *Gila.*
       h_2 Caudal peduncle stout.
        i_1 Lateral line complete.
         j_1 Mouth moderate in size; the Pacific
          Slope and Rocky Mountain
          region.
          k_1 Anal fin with 7 or 8 rays; fins
           low.
          l_1 Caudal peduncle very deep..19. *Siboma.*
          l_2 Caudal peduncle not very
           deep.....................20. *Tigoma.*
          k_2 Anal fin with 9 to 22 rays; fins
           high.....................21. *Cheonda.*
            22. *Richardsonius.*
         j_2 Mouth very wide; lower jaw much
          projecting; Atlantic Slope......23. *Clinostomus.*
        i_2 Lateral line incomplete or wanting;
         eastern and central States.
         j_1 Lateral line very short...........24. *Pfrille.*
         j_2 Lateral line more or less incom-
          plete.

k₁ Minute barbel present........25. *Margariscus.*
k₂ No barbel present; lateral line
short....................26. *Hemitremia.*
j₃ Lateral line wanting............27. *Iotichthus.*
f₂ Teeth 1-rowed, being either 4-5 or 5-5.
g₁ In the extreme western States...........28. *Siphateles.*
29. *Hesperoleucus.*
g₂ In the central and southeastern States.
h₁ Mouth vertical....................30. *Opsopœodus.*
h₂ Mouth horizontal...................31. *Opsopœa.*
e₂ Abdomen behind ventral fins compressed to an
acute edge which is scaleless; central States....32. *Notemigonus.*
c₂ Teeth in main row 4-4, the lesser row being often absent.
d₁ Lower jaw normally formed.
e₁ Barbles absent; eastern and central States.
f₁ Mouth not like that of a sucker.
g₁ First (rudimentary) ray of dorsal fin separated from next ray, to which it is joined
by a membrane.....................33. *Ceratichthys.*
g₂ First ray of dorsal fin closely joined to next.
h₁ No cavernous channels in mandible and
opercle.
i₁ Teeth in 1 or 2 rows, 4 being in the
main row and 1 or none in the
short row on each side or both.
j₁ Dorsal fin nearly above the
ventrals.....................34. *Hybopsis.*
j₂ Dorsal fin mostly behind the
ventrals.....................35. *Cyprinella.*
i₂ Teeth in 2 rows, being 2, 4-4, 2, or
rarely 1.
j₁ Size moderate; length mostly
125 mm. to 200 mm...........36. *Luxilus.*
37. *Hydrophlox.*
j₂ Size very small; length 50 mm. to
100 mm.....................38. *Notropis.*
39. *Lythrurus.*
h₂ Conspicuous cavernous channels in
mandible and opercle..............40. *Ericymba.*
f₂ Mouth and lower lips fleshy like a suckers....41. *Phenacobius*
e₂ Barbels present.
f₁ Scales very small, 60 to 90 in the lateral line.
g₁ Premaxillaries not protractile...........42. *Rhinichythys*
g₂ Premaxillaries protractile.
h₁ Barbels minute; Rocky Mountain region 43. *Apocope.*
h₂ Barbels well developed..............49. *Couesius.*
f₂ Scales large, 35 to 50 in the lateral line.
g₁ Size small or moderate.

h₁ Teeth 1-rowed, being 4-4.
 i₁ Scales about 38 in the lateral line.
  j₁ Scales without a keel............44. *Extrarius.*
  j₂ Scales with a keel..............45. *Macrhybopsis.*
 i₂ Scales 44 to 50 in the lateral line....46. *Erimystax.*
 h₂ Teeth 2-rowed, being 2, 4-4, 2 or 1.....47. *Erinemus.*
g₂ Size large, being 250 mm. or more in length.
 h₁ Head large and broad...............48. *Nocomis.*
 h₂ Head small, very broad, depressed.....50. *Platygobio.*
d₂ Lower jaw 3-lobed; eastern States................51. *Exoglossum.*

1. Cyprinus L. Body robust, compressed; mouth with 4 long barbels; snout rounded; pharyngeal teeth 1, 1, 3-3, 1, 1; scales large; dorsal fin very long; anal short: 1 species.

C. carpio. L. European carp (Fig. 31). Length 450 mm. or more; head 3 to 4; depth 2.75 to 3.4; color blackish gray above, yellowish on the sides and belly; 3 spinous and 17 to 21 soft rays in dorsal fin and 3

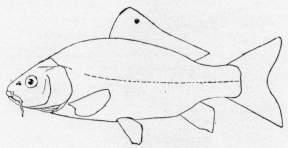

FIG. 31.—*Cyprinus carpio (from Süssw. Fauna Deut.).*

spinous and 5 soft rays in the anal fin; scales 5 or 6-35 to 37-5 or 6: fresh waters of eastern Asia and introduced into Europe and America; abundant and an important food fish in the eastern and central parts of the country.

2. Carassius Nilsson. Body oblong; mouth without barbels; scales large; pharyngeal teeth 4-4; dorsal fin very long: 1 species.

C. auratus (L.) Goldfish. Length up to 400 mm.; color olivaceous, becoming reddish or golden in domestication, but often reverting to the natural color, when wild; 2 spinous and 18 soft rays in the dorsal and 2 spinous and 7 soft rays in the anal fin: Asia and Europe, first domesticated in China; in many ponds and streams in the eastern States.

3. Campostoma Agassiz. Body elongate; teeth with an oblique grinding surface and a slight hook; air bladder surrounded by numerous convolutions of the very long alimentary canal, an anatomical feature found only in this genus of fishes: 4 species, 1 in Mexico.

C. anomalum (Rafinesque). Stone roller. Length 200 mm. or less; head 4.2; depth 4.4; color brownish, with a brassy lustre and a dusky vertical bar behind the opercle; dorsal and anal fin each with a dark cross bar; male with many tubercles in spring; rays of dorsal fin 8; anal 7; scales 7-53-8: New York to Michigan, southward to Georgia and Texas; westward to Wyoming; abundant in small streams; herbivorous.

C. formulosum Girard. Head short, with a projecting snout; head 4; depth 4.5; color grayish, with a black spot at the base of the tail and one on the dorsal fin; scales 46: Texas, from the San Antonio to the Rio Grande.

4. Orthodon Girard. Body elongate; teeth 6-6 or 6-5, compressed and nearly straight; scales very small; pseudobranchiæ absent: 1 species.

O. microlepidotus (Ayres). Length 375 mm.; head 4; depth 4.5; color olivaceous; rays of dorsal fin 9; anal 8; scales 21-105-12; teeth very long: basin of lower Sacramento and San Joaquin; abundant.

5. Acrocheilus Agassiz. Body elongate; teeth 4-5, hooked; jaws each with a conspicuous, broad, straight, horny plate; size rather large: 1 species.

A. alutaceus Agassiz & Pickering. Chisel-mouth. Length 300 mm.; head 4.5; depth 4; color very dark, body studded with minute dark points; rays of dorsal fin 10; anal 9; scales 20-85-16: basin of the lower Columbia, as far up as Spokane and Shoshone Falls; southeastern Oregon; abundant.

6. Lavinia Girard. Body elliptical, compressed, with a slender caudal peduncle; teeth 4-5 or 5-5, slightly hooked; size large: 1 species.

L. exilicauda Baird & Girard. Hitch. Length 300 mm.; head 4.6; depth 3.3; color dark, speckled, with silvery sides; rays of dorsal fin 10; anal 12; scales 13-64-18: Coast Range, from Monterey to Clear Lake; common.

7. Chrosomus Rafinesque. Body moderately elongate; size small; teeth 5-5 or 4-4, moderately hooked; scales minute; lateral line short or wanting: 4 species.

C. erythrogaster Raf. Red-bellied dace (Fig. 32). Length 75 mm.; head 4; depth 4; color brownish olive above, often with black spots; sides and belly silvery, with 2 black lateral bands, one running from the snout through the eye and curving down along the belly to a black spot in the tail; male in spring with yellow fins and bright scarlet belly; teeth 5-5; rays of dorsal fin 8; anal 9; scales 16-85-10: central New York and Pennsylvania to Dakota; southward to Alabama; common in clear, small streams; one of the brightest of the minnows.

C. eos Cope. Similar to *C. erythrogaster*, but with a slenderer body, the lateral line often wanting and the two lateral black bands uniting in the caudal peduncle: east of Alleghenies.

C. dakotensis Evermann & Cox. Similar to *C. erythrogaster*, but smaller and stouter and without the black spot on the tail; rays of dorsal fin 8; anal 8; scales about 80, 24 in a cross series; teeth 4-4: Missouri River basin in Nebraska and South Dakota.

C. oreas Cope. Similar to *C. erythrogaster*, but with a somewhat different color pattern, the upper band ending in the caudal black spot, the lower band ending at the anal fin; scales 67: head waters of the Roanoke River and the Tennessee; abundant.

Fig. 32.—*Chrosomus erythrogaster* (*from Fishes of Illinois*).

8. Hybognathus Agassiz. Body elongate; teeth 4-4, with little or no hook; scales large; rays of both dorsal and anal fins usually 8; lateral line complete: 4 species.

H. nuchalis Ag. Silver minnow. Length 150 mm.; head 4.5; depth 5; color olivaceous green; sides silvery; rays of anal fin 7; scales 5-38-4, 12 to 14 scales before the dorsal fin: New York to the upper Missouri; southward to Georgia and Texas; common in large rivers.

H. hayi Jordan. Like *H. nuchalis*, but with a slenderer body; scales 5-36-3: lower Mississippi region, northward at least to Memphis.

H. regia Girard. Similar to *H. nuchalis*, but with a shorter and deeper head: Lake Ontario and New Jersey to James and Neuse Rivers.

H. hankinsoni Hubbs. Similar to *H. nuchalis*, but with a shorter head and darker color: Great Lakes basin; west to Colorado.

9. Dionda Girard. Teeth short, hooked; body elongate; scales large: 6 species, 2 in Mexico.

D. serena (Girard). Length 60 mm.; color dusky with a black lateral band; scales 5-32 to 34-3; teeth hooked: western Texas.

D. episcopa (Girard). Length 75 mm.; color dusky, with a black lateral band; scales 9-37 to 41-4; teeth hooked: western Texas.

D. nubila (Forbes). Length 60; head 4.5; depth 4; color very dark with a dark lateral band; rays of anal fin 9; scales 5-37-3; teeth hooked: western Illinois to Wyoming; southward to the Ozarks; common.

D. plumbea (Girard). Color uniform; rays of anal fin 7; scales 53 to 58; teeth hooked: Oklahoma, Arkansas River basin.

10. Pimephales Rafinesque. Teeth 4-4, one or more hooked; upper jaw protractile; dorsal fin over the ventrals, its first ray separated from the rest by a membrane; size small: 2 species.

P. promelas Raf. Fathead. Body stout; length 60 mm.; head and depth 4; color olivaceous; belly yellow; a dark lateral band; dorsal fin with a large black cross bar; male with a black head and with several large tubercles in the spring; lateral line variable, being nearly wanting or complete; rays of dorsal fin I,7; anal 7; scales 7-47-4; body short and deep: Maine to Montana, southward to Tennessee and the

FIG. 33.—*Hyborhynchus notatus (from Fishes of Illinois)*.

Rio Grande; common in sluggish brooks, especially in the Missouri basin.

11. Hyborhynchus Agassiz. Similar to *Pimephales;* body elongate; lateral line complete: 1 species.

H. notatus (Raf.). Blunt nose (Fig. 33). Length 100 mm.; head 4.5; depth 5; color olivaceous; sides bluish, with a dark stripe; a dark spot towards the base of the dorsal fin; rays of the dorsal fin I, 8; anal 7; scales 6-45-4: Quebec to Dakota, southward to Alabama and Arkansas; very common in small streams west of the Alleghanies.

12. Mylopharodon Ayres. Body elongate; head large; teeth 2, 4-5, 2; mouth terminal, large; lips thickened; lateral line continuous; dorsal fin behind the ventrals; size very large: 1 species.

M. conocephalus (Baird & Girard). Length 900 mm.; head 3.5; depth 4.6; color dark, without red; rays of dorsal fin 8; anal 8; scales 17-74-7; body elongate, fusiform, compressed; caudal peduncle very long: Sacramento and San Joaquin Rivers; southeastern Oregon; not common.

13. Mylocheilus Agassiz.   Body elongate; upper jaw protractile with a small barbel on the maxillary; size large: 1 species.

M. lateralis Agassiz & Pickering.   Whitefish; chub.   Length 300 mm.; head 4.2; depth 4.5; color dark above and pale beneath; sides silvery, with two dark lateral bands enclosing a silvery band; teeth 1 or 2, 5-5, 2 or 1; rays of dorsal fin 8; scales 12-77-7: Oregon into British Columbia to the Fraser River; eastward to Flathead Lake; often enters the sea; abundant; a good food fish.

14. Leucosomus Heckel.   Similar to *Semotilus;* size large; scales not crowded anteriorly: 1 species.

L. corporalis (Mitchill).   Fallfish; chub.   Length 450 mm.; head and depth 4; color steel blue above; sides and belly silvery; males in spring with belly and fins red; rays of dorsal fin 8; anal 8; dorsal fin half way between nostril and tail fin; scales 8-45-4, about 22 before the dorsal fin: from Maine and the St. Lawrence to the James, east of the Alleghanies; common in swift streams and clear lakes; a game and food fish.

15. Semotilus Rafinesque.   Body stout; head large; upper jaw protractile; a minute barbel on the maxillary just above its extremity; teeth 2, 5-4, 2, hooked; size large: 2 species.

S. atromaculatus (Mitch.) (Fig. 30)   Horned dace; common chub Length 250 mm.; head 3.75; depth 4; color dusky bluish; dorsal fin with a conspicuous black spot at its base and bordered by red in front in the male; teeth variable; rays of dorsal fin 7; anal 8; scales 9 to 11-55 to 69-5 to 7; dorsal fin midway between pupil and tail fin: from Maine to Wyoming; southward to Alabama; common, chiefly in small streams.

16. Pogonichthys Girard.   Body elongate; maxillary with a barbel; caudal fin asymmetrical, the upper lobe being much the longer; size large: 1 species.

P. macrolepidotus (Ayres).   Split-tail.   Length 300 mm.; head 4.2; depth 3.75; teeth 2, 5-5, 2, hooked; color uniform, sides silvery; rays of dorsal fin 9; anal 8; scales 10-66-6: central California; common.

17. Ptychocheilus Agassiz.   Body elongate; caudal peduncle stout; no barbels; teeth 2, 5-4, 2; scales small; lateral line decurved; size very large: 4 species.

P. oregonensis (Richardson).   Squawfish.   Length up to 1,200 mm.; head 3.75; depth 5; color greenish; belly silvery; rays of dorsal fin 10; anal 8; scales 20-70: extreme northwest, ascending the Columbia and tributaries into Montana; common; a food and game fish.

P. umpquæ Snyder.   Similar to *P. oregonensis;* scales 75 to 80: coastal streams of central Oregon.

P. grandis (Ayres). Similar to *P. oregonensis;* rays of dorsal fin 8; anal 8; scales 70 to 80: central and northern California; Oregon; common.

P. lucius Girard. White salmon. Length up to 1,500 mm.; weight up to 80 lbs.; head 3.5; depth 5.5; color uniform; rays of dorsal fin 9; anal 9; scales 83 to 90: Colorado basin; very common; the largest species in the family.

18. Gila Baird & Girard. Body elongate; caudal peduncle long and slender; tail widely forked; teeth 2, 5-4, 2, hooked; scales very small; dorsal fin behind the middle of the body; size large: 3 species.

G. elegans B. & G. Bony-tail. Length 300 mm.; head and depth 5; color bluish above; rays of dorsal fin 9; anal 10; scales 23-85-10; back arched; head short and broad: Colorado and Gila Rivers; abundant.

G. robusta B. & G. Roundtail. Length 400 mm.; head 4; depth 5; color plain; rays of dorsal fin 9; anal 9; scales 17-80-10: Colorado and Gila Rivers; very common.

19. Siboma Girard. Lateral line complete in adult; caudal peduncle very stout; dorsal above ventrals; scales comparatively large and well imbricated: 2 species.

S. crassicauda (Baird & Girard). Length 300 mm.; head 4; depth 3; color brownish; scales 9-56-7; body short, compressed, deep: California, common in the Sacramento and San Joaquin.

20. Tigoma Girard. Lateral line complete in adult; caudal peduncle not stout; scales small and not closely imbricated; dorsal behind ventrals: 7 species.

T. bicolor (Girard). Length 300 mm.; head and depth 3.75; color dusky above, silvery below; scales 13-60-7; teeth 2, 5-5, 2; dorsal fin over ventrals: Klamath Lakes, Oregon.

T. atraria (Gir.). Chub. Length 350 mm.; head and depth 3.5; color blackish, the scales dotted and with dark edges which form lines; rays of dorsal fin 9; scales 10-55 to 63-5; mouth very oblique: Great Basin of Utah; Yellowstone Park; Snake River basin; common.

21. Cheonda Girard. Lateral line complete in adult; anal fin long; scales not closely imbricated: 8 species.

C. copei Jordan and Gilbert. Length 150 mm.; head 4.25; depth 3.75; color bluish olive above; sides silvery; scales very small, 19-80-12: Great Basin of Utah; very common.

C. egregia (Gir.). Length 85; head 3.6; depth 4.25; color blackish with 2 parallel, lateral dark bands separated by a light one which meet on the caudal peduncle, and a broad red band; belly golden, reddish in male; rays of anal fin 9; scales 12 or 13-52 to 56-6 to 8: northern Nevada; very common in Lake Tahoe.

C. hydrophlox (Cope). Length 125; head 4.3; depth 4; color dusky, with a dark lateral band between 2 silvery ones; in males the dark band and belly being red; rays of dorsal fin 9; anal 10 to 13; scales 12-58-5: Salt Lake basin; Snake River; very common.

22. Richardsonius Girard. Similar to *Cheonda;* anal fin very long: 4 species.

R. balteatus (Richardson). Length 150 mm.; head 4.5; depth 3.25; color plain, usually with a dark lateral band; rays of dorsal fin 10; anal 11 to 22; scales 13-55 to 63-6; body compressed: Columbia basin and streams entering Puget Sound; southeastern Oregon; eastward to Montana; common.

23. Clinostomus Girard. Lateral line complete; mouth very wide, the lower jaw much projecting; dorsal behind ventrals: 2 species.

C. elongatus (Kirtland). Shiner. Length 125 mm.; head 4; depth 5; color dark bluish, mottled with paler; a broad black lateral band, the anterior half of which is crimson in the spring in males; rays of anal fin 9; scales 10-70-5; head long; mouth large: region of the Great Lakes and upper Mississippi Valley; common in clear streams northwards.

C. vandoisulus Cuvier & Valenciennes. Length 125 mm.; head 3.6; depth 4.75; color bluish green, mottled; a dark lateral band; males in spring bright red anteriorly; rays of dorsal fin 9; scales 48 to 53: streams about Chesapeake Bay to Georgia; common in clear, swift streams.

24. Pfrille Jordan. Lateral line incomplete; scales minute; body plump: 1 species.

P. neogæus (Cope). Length 75 mm.; head 4; depth 4.25; color dusky above, with a dark lateral band; in spring belly and lower fins crimson in males; lateral line incomplete; teeth 2, 4-5, 2; scales 18-80-10; head very large: region of the Great Lakes and upper Mississippi Valley; rare.

25. Margariscus Cockerell. Lateral line incomplete; maxillary mostly with a small barbel; dorsal behind ventrals: 2 species.

M. margarita (Cope). Length 75 mm.; head 4; depth 4.25; color dusky olive above; sides silvery; belly white, males crimson in spring; rays of anal fin 9; scales punctate, 11-52 to 58-8; lateral line more or less incomplete; snout very blunt: Susquehanna to the James; not common.

26. Hemitremia Cope. Lateral line incomplete; no barbel present: 2 species.

H. vittata Cope. Length 60 mm.; head and depth 4; color dark above; a black lateral band; males scarlet in spring; a small black spot at base of tail; scales 7-43-5; lateral line very short: basin of the Tennessee; common in northern Alabama.

27. Iotichthys Jordan and Evermann.   Size minute; no lateral line: 1 species.

I. phlegethontis (Cope).   Length 35 mm.; head 3.75; depth 3.3; color olivaceous, with a dark lateral band; belly golden; rays of dorsal fin 7; scales 6-36-4, 17 before the dorsal fin; teeth 1, 5-4, 2; lateral line absent: basin of Great Salt and Sevier Lakes; very common; the smallest of the family.

28. Siphateles Cope. Roaches. Body stout, somewhat compressed, mouth oblique; no barbels; size moderate; teeth 4-5, 5-5 or 6-5; rays of dorsal and anal fins usually 8: numerous species in America, Europe and Asia; 7 species in the United States, all in the extreme west.

S. olivaceus (Cope).   Length 300 mm.; head 4; depth 4.3; teeth 5-5; body slender, compressed; color dusky olive above; body and fins dotted with black; scales 11-56-6: Lake Tahoe and Pyramid Lake; very common.

S. bicolor (Girard).   Length 200 mm.; head 4; depth 4.5; color olivaceous with a bluish lateral band; body with some brown spots; rays of anal fin 7; scales 9-48-6; teeth 4-5: Lakes of southeastern Oregon; Sacramento-San Joaquin Basin common.

S. oregonensis Snyder.   Length 200 mm.; head and depth 3.6; color dark; scales 13-52-8: southeastern Oregon.

S. columbianus Snyder.   Length 136 mm.; head and depth 3.7; color silvery, dark above; scales 12-49-7: southeastern Oregon.

29. Hesperoleucus Snyder. Similar to *Siphateles*, but with a shorter head and a slenderer body: several species, all near San Francisco Bay.

H. symmetricus (Baird & Girard).   Length 125 mm.; head 3.75; depth 4.2; color dusky above; sides pale, more or less dotted with black and sometimes with a dark lateral band; rays of dorsal and anal fins 8; teeth 5-4; scales 14-52 to 67-5; body rather elongate: central and northern California, Oregon, Nevada and Utah.

H. venustus Snyder. Length 100 mm.; head and depth about 4; color silvery, with a narrow lateral stripe; rays of dorsal fin 9; anal 8; scales 53: in streams entering San Francisco and San Pablo Bays.

H. navarroensis Snyder. Length 90 mm.; head and depth 3.6; color dark above, silvery below, with a narrow lateral stripe; rays of dorsal and anal fins 8; scales 56: Navarro basin, northern California.

H. parvipinnis Snyder.   Length 80 mm.; head and depth 3.9; scales 59; rays of dorsal fin 8; anal 7: Gualala River basin, California.

30. Opsopœodus Hay.   Mouth very small, terminal; teeth 5-5 or 4-5, strongly hooked; upper jaw protractile; size small: 2 species.

O. emiliæ Hay.   Length 55 mm.; head 4.5; depth 4.4; color yellowish; sides silvery, with usually a dark lateral band; a black spot on dorsal fin; rays of dorsal fin 9; anal 8; scales 6-40-4; mouth very oblique; body elongate, compressed: Lake Erie to Georgia and Texas; common towards the south in sandy lowland streams.

31. Opsopœa Jordan and Evermann.   Similar to *Opsopœodus*, but with mouth subinferior and nearly horizontal: 1 species.

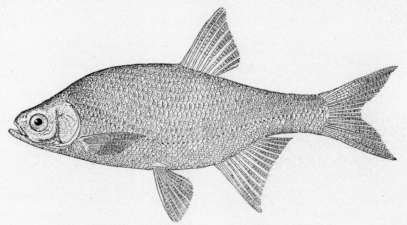

Fig. 34.—*Notemigonus crysoleucas* (*from Jordan & Evermann*).

O. bollmani (Gilbert).   Length 50 mm.; head 4.4; depth 4.6; color dark olive, with a black lateral band and a large spot at the base of the tail; rays of the dorsal and anal fins 8; scales 5-37-4; mouth slightly oblique; lateral line on but 7 or 8 scales: Georgia and Tennessee to Kansas; scarce.

32. Notemigonus Rafinesque.   Breams.   Body elliptical, strongly compressed, the belly forming a keel behind the ventral fins which is naked; teeth 5-5, hooked; no barbels; dorsal fin behind the ventrals: Europe and America; 2 species in the United States.

N. crysoleucas (Mitchill).   Golden shiner (Fig. 34).   Length 300 mm.; head 4.5; depth 3; color clear greenish above; sides silvery, with golden reflections; fins yellowish; rays of dorsal fin 8; anal 11 to 14; scales 10-46 to 55-3; mouth small, oblique; lateral line decurved: Nova Scotia to Dakota, southward to Tennessee and Texas; very common in weedly ponds and streams.

N. bosci (Cuvier & Valenciennes). Rays of anal fin 16; scales 8-43-2; lower fins scarlet in males: south Atlantic States.

33. Ceratichthys Baird and Girard. Body stout; teeth 4-4; dorsal fin over ventrals and with its first ray separated from the rest by a membrane: 2 species.

C. vigilax Baird & Girard. Bullhead minnow. Length 75 mm.; head 4.25; depth 4.5; color dusky olive or yellowish with a dark lateral band which terminates with a black spot; dorsal fin with 8 rays, on each of which is a black spot; anal rays 7; scales 8-42-6, 28 before the dorsal: Ohio to Iowa, southward to Georgia and Texas; very common.

34. Hybopsis Agassiz. Minnows. Small fishes with teeth 4-4 or 1, 4-4, 1 or 0; scales rather large, not closely imbricated, 32 to 39 in

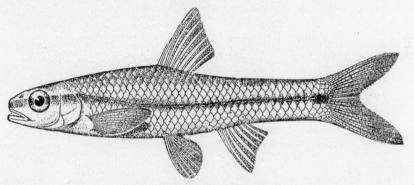

FIG. 35.—*Hybopsis atrocaudalis (from Jordan & Evermann).*

the lateral line; first ray of dorsal fin rudimentary; dorsal fin without black spot and nearly over the ventrals; anal fin with 7 or 8 rays: about 35 species, many in the west and southwest.

H. bifrenatus (Cope). Length 50 mm.; head and depth 4.2; straw-color, with a black lateral band bordered by orange on the snout; scales 5-36-3, 13 before the dorsal fin; body slender, lateral line very short; snout very obtuse: Massachusetts to Maryland, in coastal streams; not common.

H. anogenus Forbes. Length 35 mm.; head 4.25; depth 4; color dusky with a dark lateral band through the eye ending in a black spot at the base of the tail fin; mouth very small and oblique; chin black; snout obtuse; scales 34 to 37: western New York to northern Illinois; scarce.

H. atrocaudalis (Evermann) (Fig. 35). Length 60 mm.; head 4.5; depth 4.5; color olivaceous, with a black stripe through the snout and eye, a dusky lateral shade and a small caudal spot; belly yellow; scales

36, 14 before the dorsal fin; mouth very small: northern New York to South Dakota; southward to Texas; not rare.

H. heterodon (Cope).   Length 60 mm.; head 4; depth 4; color olivaceous; chin black; sides with a dusky band; scales 5-36-3, 13 before the dorsal fin; snout pointed; body stout: western New York to Kansas and Minnesota; common.

H. blennius (Girard).   Length 60 mm.; head 4; depth 5; color pale olivaceous, with sometimes a darker lateral stripe; scales 5-32 to 38-3, 15 before the dorsal fin; mouth small, horizontal; snout obtuse: Great Lakes region to Dakota; southward to Tennessee and Texas; abundant in small streams.

H. deliciosus (Girard).   Length 60 mm.; head 4; depth 5; teeth 4-4; rays of anal 7; lateral line complete; color pale olivaceous: basin of the Great Lakes and the Mississippi; very common.

H. procne (Cope).   Length 60 mm.; head 4.75; depth 5.25; color olivaceous, with a dark lateral band; scales 5-32 to 34-3, 13 before the dorsal fin; rays of anal fin 7; body slender: Delaware River to the Neuse, in coastal streams; very common.

H. kanawha Jordan & Jenkins.   Length 85 mm.; head 4.4; depth 4.6; color translucent green; sides silvery; rays of anal fin 9; scales 4-37-2, 16 before the dorsal: tributaries of the Kanawha River, Virginia.

H. spectrunculus (Cope).   Length 75 mm.; head 4; depth 5.5; color pale olive; silvery white below; a dark band along the sides and a conspicuous black spot at the base of the tail fin; rays of anal fin 9; scales 37, 15 before the dorsal fin: head waters of the Tennessee River; very common.

H. topeka Gilbert.   Length 90 mm.; head 4; depth 3.6; color olivaceous, with a dusky lateral band ending in a small caudal spot; males in spring and summer with sides and lower fins bright red; scales 5-35-4, 14 before the dorsal fin: western Iowa and eastern South Dakota to Kansas; common.

H. dorsalis Agassiz.   Length 60 mm.; head 4; depth 5; color light olive with dusky streaks and specks; rays of anal fin 8; scales 5-35-4, 17 before the dorsal fin; body slender: Missouri and Nebraska to Minnesota and New York; common in muddy streams.

H. nocomis Evermann.   Length 60 mm.; head 4.3; depth 5; color yellowish, with dark specks and a dark lateral band; scales 6-36-3; teeth 1, 4-4, 1; eyes large: Trinity, San Marco and Comal Rivers, Texas; common.

H. shumardi (Gir.).   Length 75 mm.; head 3.75; depth 4.2; color olivaceous with dusky streaks and dark specks; eyes very large; scales

5-36-2, 12 before the dorsal fin; rays of anal fin 7: Ohio and Tennessee basins to Iowa and the Ozark region; common towards the south in cold streams.

H. hudsonius (DeWitt Clinton). Spot-tail; shiner. Length 150 mm.; head 4.75; depth 4; color very pale; sides with a broad silvery band; usually a black spot at the base of tail fin; teeth 1 or 2, 4-4, 0, 1 or 2; scales 5-39-4, 18 before the dorsal fin; body elongate; head short; muzzle blunt: Dakota to New England; southward in coastwise streams to Georgia; in large rivers and lakes; abundant in the Great Lakes; very variable.

35. Cyprinella Girard. Teeth similar to *Hybopsis*; scales closely imbricated, 31 to 44 in the lateral line; dorsal fin usually behind the ventrals; anal fin with 8 or 9 rays: 15 species.

C. lutrensis (Baird & Girard). Redfin. Length 75 mm.; teeth one-rowed, 4-4; head 3.6; depth 3 to 4; color of male steel blue; male tuberculate in spring with belly and fins red; a conspicuous violet crescent behind the shoulder; females plain greenish; scales 6-35-2; back arched; body compressed: southern Illinois to Dakota; southward to the Rio Grande; very common in clear brooks southward.

C. macrostoma (Gir.). Head 4; depth 4.1; color brownish; sides silvery; teeth 1, 4-4, 1; rays of anal fin 9; scales 36: Kansas to the Rio Grande.

C. stigmatura (Jord.). Spotted tail. Length 110 mm.; head 4.5; depth 4.75; color pale olive with a large black spot at the base of the tail fin; scales 7-42 to 44-3, 20 before the dorsal fin; body elongate; a large blotch on the dorsal fin: Alabama basin; very common.

C. cercostigma Cope. Like *C. stigmatura* except that there are 37 to 39 scales in the lateral line: sandy streams tributary to the Gulf, from the Pearl to the Nueces Rivers; abundant.

C. trichroistia (Jordan & Gilbert). Length 85 mm.; head 4.1; depth 4.25; color steel blue above; sides white, with a large black spot at the base of the tail fin; dorsal fin red with white tips and a broad dusky band at its base; belly and lower fins white; scales 6-42-3: Alabama basin; common.

C. callistia (Jord.). Length 100 mm.; head 4.2; depth 4.6; color very dark blue; sides silvery violet, with a reddish lateral band; belly and lower fins white; dorsal and caudal fins red, with a white tip; caudal spot present; scales 5-40-3: Alabama basin.

C. eurystoma (Jord.). Length 100 mm.; head 4.25; depth 4.3, color olivaceous; sides silvery, with a black caudal spot; belly and lower fins white; scales 6-39-3: basin of the Chattahoochee River.

C. cœrulea (Jord.). Length 75 mm.; head 4.3; depth 4.6; color steel blue; sides and belly white, with a lateral blue-green band and a spot at the base of the tail fin; fins bright yellow with white tips; scales 6-38-3: Alabama basin; common.

C. whipplii (Gir.). Silver-fin. Length 100 mm.; head 4.3; depth 4.6; color silvery, being bluish in the male; edges of scales dusky; a large black spot on the upper posterior part of the dorsal fin; paired fins white; scales 5-35 to 40-3: western New York to Minnesota; southward to Alabama and Arkansas; abundant in clear streams.

Fig. 36.—*Luxilus cornutus (from Fishes of Illinois).*

C. galactura (Cope). Length 150 mm.; head and depth 4.3; color steel blue above; a black blotch on the hinder rays of the dorsal fin; caudal fin yellow at base; scales 6-41-3: Ozark region to Georgia and South Carolina; abundant in mountain streams.

C. camura (Jordan and Meek). Length 100 mm.; head 4.3; depth 3.5; color as in *C. whipplii;* rays of anal fin 9; scales 6-38-4: Arkansas, Kansas and southwestern Missouri; not rare.

C. pyrrhomelas (Cope). Length 80 mm.; head 4; depth 3.75; color dark steel blue, abruptly white below; head reddish; dorsal fin very high, dusky at base, with a black blotch above and red in front; anal fin large and with 10 rays; tail fin very broad, pale at base and tip and with dark and scarlet cross bands; scales 6-35-3: Santee basin, Carolina; very common.

36. Luxilus Rafinesque. Shiners. Teeth 2, 4-4, 2 or rarely 2, 4-4, 1; scales large, about 40 in the lateral line; size relatively large; anal fin with 9 rays; usually with no black spot on dorsal fin: 6 species.

L. cornutus (Mitchill). Common shiner; redfin; dace (Fig. 36). Length 125 to 200 mm.; head 4; depth 3.3 to 4.4; teeth 2, 4-4, 2; color dark steel blue above, silvery on the sides and belly; forward part of body tuberculate and lower fins and belly of males salmon pink in spring; a dark shade behind the shoulder; rays of anal fin 9; scales 6-37 to 40-3; body short, compressed; lateral line decurved: entire region east of the Rockies except the Atlantic coast region south of the Neuse River and Texas; very common in small streams; very variable.

L. cerasinus (Cope). Shiner. Length 100 mm.; scales 6-37-3; sides marked with irregular cross bars, otherwise like *L. cornutus;* colors very brilliant; basin of the Roanoke, in mountain brooks.

L. albeolus Jord. Length 175 mm.; like *L. cornutus,* but with paler colors; scales 38: Roanoke, Tar and Neuse Rivers; not in mountain streams.

37. Hydrophlox Jordan & Brayton. Similar to *Luxilus;* size rather small; anal fin mostly with 8 rays: 8 species.

H. macdonaldi Jord. & Jen. Length 125 mm.; head 3.75; depth 4.75; teeth 2, 4-4, 2; color greenish; rays of anal fin 9 or 10; scales 7-42-2; mouth large, the lower jaw projecting: basin of the James and Shenandoah Rivers; in mountain streams; common.

H. coccogenis (Cope). Length 125 mm.; head 4; depth 4.25; color olivaceous, males rosy in spring; a vertical scarlet bar on the preopercle; lower jaw projecting; upper half of dorsal and caudal fins dark; scales 7-42-3: mountain streams from Kentucky to Georgia; common.

H. zonatus (Agassiz). Length 125 mm.; head 4.25; depth 4.6; color olivaceous, with a dark lateral line; male in spring with red belly and sides; rays of anal fin 9; scales 6-39-4: mountain streams in Tennessee and the Ozarks; common.

H. rubricroceus (Cope). Red fallfish. Length 100 mm.; head 4; depth 4.5; color steel blue, with a dark lateral band; fin all red; head pale red; in high coloration the whole body more or less red; rays of anal fin 9; scales 7-38-3: head waters of the Tennessee and Savannah Rivers.

H. chlorocephalus (Cope). Length 60 mm.; head 4; depth 5; color olivaceous, with black specks which form a lateral band ending in a dusky spot at the base of the tail fin; upper part of the head metallic green; belly in males red; scales 6-39-3: Santee basin; common in mountain streams.

H. chiliticus (Cope). Length 50 mm.; head 4; depth 5.5; color olivaceous, with a silvery lateral band; dorsal and anal fins each with a vermilion band; a dark caudal spot; scales 7-36-2: basin of the Great Pedee River; common in upland streams.

H. altipinnis (Cope). Length 60 mm.; head 4.3; depth 3.5; color greenish, with a silvery lateral band and a black band across the eye and snout; lower jaw blackish; rays of anal fin 9; scales 5-36-2: basin of the Great Pedee and Cape Fear Rivers; in pine woods; common.

H. roseus (Jord.). Length 60 mm.; head 4.3; depth 4.5; color ŏlivaceous, with a dark lateral line; fins red in male; top head red; rays of anal fin always 7; scales 5-38-5; body short and stout; a dark caudal spot: lowland streams of the Gulf States from the Ogeechee to the Mississippi; common.

H. chalybæus (Cope). Length 50 mm.; head 3.8; depth 5; color dark, with a black lateral band; belly straw color, orange in spring males; a small dark caudal spot; scales 6-35-3; body slender; mouth very oblique: Ogeechee River to the Delaware, in coastal streams and swamps; scarce.

H. chrosomus (Jord.). Length 60 mm.; head 4.3; depth 5; color greenish; belly silvery; a scarlet bar across the dorsal, anal and the base of the caudal fins; a narrow scarlet lateral band; a small black spot at base of tail fin; scales 5-37-3: Alabama basin; very common.

H. xænocephalus (Jord.). Length 70 mm.; head 4.2; depth 5; color dark olivaceous, with a dark band along the sides of the caudal peduncle and the head and a dusky blotch at the base of the tail fin; males without red; rays of anal fin 7; scales 5-38-3: Georgia to Mississippi; common in pine woods; descending to the sea.

38. Notropis Rafinesque. Shiners. Body elongate, with little pigment; teeth 2, 4-4, 2; anal fin long, with 9 to 12 rays; scales not closely imbricated, with 45 to 50 in the lateral line; first ray of dorsal fin rudimentary; dorsal behind or over the ventrals: 10 species.

N. ariommus (Cope). Length 125 mm.; head 3.75; depth 4.25; color olivaceous; rays of anal fin 9; scales 6-39-2; eyes very large: basin of the Ohio and Tennessee Rivers; common about Indianapolis.

N. jejunus (Forbes). Length 75 mm.; head 4; depth 4.6; color pale, with a broad silvery lateral band; rays of anal fin 7; scales 5-37-3; teeth 2, 4-4, 1: western Pennsylvania to Kansas; southward to Tennessee northward to Winnipeg; not rare.

N. leuciodus (Cope). Length 75 mm.; head 4.5; depth 5; color olivaceous; sides silvery, with a purplish lateral band; a black spot at base of tail fin; scales 5-39-3: basin of the upper Tennessee; very common; not in mountain streams.

N. telescopus (Cope). Length 100 mm.; head 4.25; depth 4.75; color pale greenish, the scales dark edged; rays of anal fin 10; scales 5-35 to 38-3; mouth very oblique; eyes very large: basin of the upper Tennessee, in cold streams; very common; also in Arkansas.

N. stilbius Jord. Length 75 mm.; head 4.2; depth 5; color pale green; sides with a broad silvery band and numerous dark dots which form a blotch at the base of the tail fin; rays of anal fin 10; scales 5-37-2; teeth 2, 4-4, 1; eyes very large: Tennessee and Alabama; common.

N. atherinoides Raf. Length 150 mm.; head 4.6; depth 5.5; color translucent green; sides silvery; rays of anal fin 11; scales 5-38-3; body long and slender; mouth very oblique; eyes very large: Great Lakes region and Ohio and Mississippi Valleys; northward to Winnipeg; common in lakes and river channels.

N. dilectus (Gir.). Length 85 mm.; head 4.6; depth 4.5; color very pale; snout and base of fins rosy; rays of anal fin 11; scales 7-38-3; body elongate; mouth oblique: basin of the Ohio to the Rio Grande; common.

N. rubrifrons (Cope). Length 70 mm.; head 4; depth 5; color olivaceous; sides silvery; rays of anal fin 10; scales 5-39-3; mouth very oblique: New York and western Pennsylvania to southern Michigan; southward to Mississippi and Kansas; very common in clear streams, especially in the Ohio Valley.

N. photogenis (Cope). Length 75 mm.; head 4.25; depth 5.5; color olivaceous; sides and belly silvery, with dark specks along the lateral line rays; rays of anal fin 10; scales 6-40-3, 25 before the dorsal fin: western Pennsylvania to Michigan and southward; common in clear streams.

N. scepticus (J. & G.). Length 75 mm.; head 3.75; depth 4.5; color pale green; sides with a silvery band; rays of anal fin 10; scales 6-38-3, 14 before the dorsal fin; eyes very large: the Cape Fear to the Santee Rivers; common.

N. micropteryx (Cope). Length 70 mm.; head 4.5; depth 5.5; color olivaceous; sides silvery, with a dusky blotch at the base of the tail fin; rays of anal fin 10; scales 6-39-2; body very slender, compressed; mouth large, oblique: head waters of the Cumberland and Tennessee Rivers; also in the Ozark region; common.

N. metallicus J. & M. Length 45 mm.; head 4; depth 5; color dark brown, with a rosy band from the eye to the upper lobe of the tail, below which is a metallic dusky band ending in a broad black spot at the base of the tail fin; rays of anal fin 11; scales 5-35-3: swamps and streams in southern Georgia and northern Florida.

39. Lythrurus Jordan. Similar to *Notropis;* body elongate, compressed; scales closely impricated; dorsal fin with a black spot and behind the ventrals; anal fin with 10 to 12 rays: 4 species.

L. lirus Jord.   Length 60 mm.; head 4.3; depth 5.25; color pale green; sides with a metallic blue band formed of dark dots; fins red in males; rays of anal fin 10; scales 8-45-4: basin of the Tennessee and Alabama Rivers; common in sandy streams.

L. roseipinnis (Hay).   Length 85 mm.; head 4.5; depth 4; color dark, the scales above having dark dots; a dark lateral band; vertical fins red; rays of anal fin 11; scales 8-45-3; body slender, compressed; a black spot on the dorsal and anal fins: tributaries of the Gulf from Mississippi to Florida.

L. umbratilis (Gir.).   Redfin.   Length 75 mm.; head 4.25; depth 4 to 4.5; color steel blue above; pale beneath; a dark spot at the base of the dorsal fin; male in the spring with belly and lower fins brick red and with white tubercles covering the anterior portion of the body; rays of dorsal fin 7; anal fin 11; scales 9-40, 3; body stout, compressed; caudal peduncle long: western New York to Minnesota; southward to Alabama and Kansas; common in small clear streams.

L. atripes (Jord.).   Blackfin.   Dorsal and anal fins each with a black bar across its upper part: southern Illinois and Iowa.

L. cyanocephalus (Copeland).   Dorsal fin with 8 rays; anal 11 to 13; scales 9-50-3; top of head blue: Minnesota to Ohio river basin; common.

L. matutinus (Cope).   Rays of dorsal fin 8; scales 7-44-3; colors pale; body slender; males with snout, chin and upper half of dorsal fin red; a dark caudal spot: Neuse and Pimlico Rivers; common.

40. Ericymba Cope.   Body elongate; teeth 1, 4-4, 0, hooked; scales large; dorsal fin above ventrals; eyes very large; dentaries, interopercles and suborbitals broad and with conspicuous mucous channels: 1 species.

E. buccata Cope.   Length 100 mm.; head 4; depth 5; color olivaceous, with silvery sides; rays of dorsal and anal fins 8; scales 5-33-3; breast naked: western Pennsylvania and Michigan to western Florida and Kansas; locally very common.

41. Phenacobius Cope.   Sucker-mouths.   Body elongate; teeth 4-4; hooked; mouth small, ventral, each side of the lower lip enlarged into a fleshy lobe; rays of dorsal fin 8; anal 7; isthmus very broad; size small: 4 species, which look like young suckers.

P. teretulus Cope.   Length 85 mm.; head 4.6; depth 4.5; color pale yellowish, the scales above dark-edged; snout blackish; a plumbeous lateral band; scales 6-43-5: Kanawha River, West Virginia; not common.

P. mirabilis (Girard).   (Fig. 37).   Length 85 mm.; head 4.3; depth 4.6; color olivaceous, with a silvery lateral band and a conspicuous black spot at the base of the tail fin; scales 6-43 to 51-5: Illinois River to

Arkansas; basin of the Tennessee River; rather common in sandy streams.

P. uranops Cope. Length 100 mm.; head 4.75; depth 6; color pale olivaceous, with a dark spot at the base of the tail fin; scales 7-60-6: upper Tennessee basin; common in the river channels.

P. catostomus Jordan. Length 100 mm.; head 4.5; depth 5.6; color olivaceous, with a silvery lateral band, dark at the base of the tail fin; scales 7-60-5: Alabama River basin; common.

42. Rhinichthys Agassiz. Body elongate; head long and slender; a minute barbel on the maxillary; teeth mostly 2, 4-4, 1 or 2, hooked; scales small; dorsal fin behind the ventrals; coloration dark; males rosy in the spring: 3 species, 1 in Mexico.

a   *b*

Fig. 37.—Head of *Phenacobius mirabilis: a,* side view; *b,* ventral view (*from Fishes of Illinois*).

R. cataractæ (Cuvier & Valenciennes). Long nosed dace. Length 125 mm.; head 4; depth 5 to 5.5; color dark olive, paler below; back almost black; a dark spot on the opercle; body elongate; head long; mouth inferior; rays of dorsal fin 8; anal 7; scales 65: New England to the Columbia; southward to North Carolina and the Great Salt Lake basin; in swift streams; common and variable.

R. atronasus (Mitchill). Black nosed dace. Length 75 mm.; head 4; depth 4.5; color blackish, with a black lateral band; males in spring with the lateral band, lower fins and sometimes the whole body crimson, the lateral band in late summer becoming orange and later getting dark; rays of dorsal fin 7; anal 7; scales 64; teeth 2, 4-4, 2: New England to Minnesota; southward to Alabama; very common in clear brooks; very variable.

43. Apocope Cope. Similar to *Rhinichthys* except that the premaxillaries are protractile; rays of dorsal fin mostly 8; anal 7: 10 species, all in the Rocky Mountain region.

Key to the Species of Apocope

a_1 Teeth, 1, 4-4, 1.
    b_1 Dorsal fin with 8 rays.
        c_1 Scales small, more than 70 in the lateral line.
            d_1 Scales about 89..................................*A. oscula.*

d_2 Scales about 78...................................*A. yarrowi.*

d_3 Scales about 74...................................*A. couesii.*

c_2 Scales less than 70 in the lateral line..................*A. adobe.*

A. nevadensis.

A. nubila.

b_2 Dorsal fin with 10 or 11 rays, the anterior one spinelike.

c_1 Scales 63 to 70.......................................*A. umatilla.*

c_2 Scales 52 to 57.......................................*A. falcata.*

a_2 Teeth 4-4...*A. chrysogaster.*

A. oscula (Gir.). Length 60 mm.; head 4; depth 4.75; color dusky olive; a scarlet patch above the gill opening and one on the side of the muzzle; scales 18-89-15: lower Colorado and Gila Rivers; not rare.

A. yarrowi Jordan & Evermann. Length 125 mm.; head 4.1; depth 5 to 5.5; color dark olive, with 2 ill-defined dark lateral bands; scales 16-78-13: Colorado River basin; very common.

A. couesii (Yarrow). Length 110 mm.; head 4; depth 4.25; color dark gray; scales 12-74-11: Colorado River basin.

A. adobe J. & E. Length 100 mm.; head 3.6; depth 4.5; clay colored, with a dark lateral band; scales 12-63 to 70-10: Sevier River, Utah; locally abundant.

A. nevadensis (Gilbert). Head 3.5; depth 4; color brown, much speckled above, and with a dark lateral stripe; scales 65: warm springs in the deserts of southwestern Nevada.

A. nubila (Gir.). Length 85 mm.; head 3.75 to 4.6; depth 3.75 to 5; color dark gray, with a faint lateral band; scales 47 to 70, usually 52 to 65: coastwise streams of Washington, Oregon and basin of the Columbia to Idaho; Yellowstone Park; southeastern Oregon.

A. umatilla Gilbert & Evermann. Color dark, mottled; anterior ray of median fins spine-like; scales 13 or 14-63 to 70-7 or 8: Payette and Umatilla Rivers, Idaho.

A. falcata Eigenmann & Eigenmann. Color dark, mottled; fins falcate; ventral fins with inner rays united with the body; scales 52 to 57; Columbia River basin; locally abundant.

A. chrysogaster Gir. Color dark iron gray, with a darker lateral band; scales 88; teeth 4-4; males with a yellowish belly: Gila River basin.

44. Extrarius Jordan. Teeth one-rowed, 4-4; 1 or 2 pairs of barbels on the maxillary; 36 to 38 scales in the lateral line; snout projecting: 3 species.

E. tetranemus (Gilbert). Length 50 mm.; head 4; depth 5.3; color silvery, spotted with black; lateral line with 36 to 38 scales; 2 long barbels on each side; head very slender; dorsal fin over the ventrals: basin of the Arkansas; not rare.

E. æstivalis (Girard). Length 60 mm.; head 3.75; depth 5.3; color silvery, spotted with black; scales 6-36-4; head very slender; snout projecting beyond the mouth: Platte River to the Rio Grande; common in sandy river channels; not in small brooks.

E. hyostomus (Gilb.). Length 60 mm.; head 4; depth 5.5; color silvery speckled with black; scales 37; snout long, acute, projecting beyond the mouth half its length: Indiana to Iowa; southward to the Alabama River; northward to Minnesota; common in sandy river channels.

45. Macrhybopsis Cockerell & Alliston. Similar to *Extrarius:* 1 pair of barbels; scales each with a longitudinal keel: 1 species.

M. gelidus (Girard). Length 50 mm.; head 4; depth 5; color silvery, speckled with black above; scales 6-44-4; snout very long, projecting in front of the mouth; rays of anal fin 9; caudal peduncle very long and slender; tail deeply forked; eastern Nebraska to Wyoming and Montana; locally common.

46. Erimystax Jordan. Teeth one-rowed, 4-4; 1 pair of barbels; scales 44 to 50 in lateral line: 2 species.

E. dissimilis (Kirtland). Length 100 mm.; head 4.5; depth 5; color olivaceous, mottled; sides with a bluish lateral band, in which is a series of dusky spots; eyes very large; scales 6-40 to 47-5; body long and slender: Lake Erie to the head waters of the Tennessee; common in the river channels.

E. watauga J. & E. Similar to *H. dissimilis;* scales 5-48 to 52-4: Virginia to Arkansas; northward to Indiana.

47. Erinemus Jordan. Teeth two-rowed, 1, 4-4, 1 or 0; scales large, 34 to 40 in lateral line; 1 pair of barbels: 1 species.

E. labrosus (Cope). Length 75 mm.; head 4.25; depth 4.2; color in males dark steel blue with black markings, in females silvery with a blue lateral streak; a large dark spot on the hinder rays of the dorsal fin; a small spot at the base of the tail fin; scales 5-34 to 40-3: basin of the Santee; common.

E. hypsinotus (Cope). Length 75 mm.; head 3.75; depth 4; color silvery, with a double series of black specks along the lateral line and a black lateral band; males with red fins; scales 5-40-3: Santee basin; rare.

E. rubrifrons (Jordan). Length 75 mm.; head 4; depth 5; color olivaceous, with a plumbeous silvery lateral band; snout in males red with numerous dust-like tubercles and in the spring with red fins; scales 5-36-3: basin of the Altamaha, Georgia; common.

E. *hyalinus* (Cope). Silver chub. Length 75 mm.; head 4; depth 5; color greenish, with a silvery lateral band; scales 5-38-4; rays of anal fin 7: New York to Iowa; southwards to Alabama; very common in the Ohio Valley.

E. *storerianus* (Kirtland). Length 250 mm.; head 4.3; depth 4; color greenish, sides silvery; no red present; scales 6-40-4; body compressed, the back elevated; eyes very large: Lake Erie to eastern Wyoming; southwards to Tennessee and Nebraska.

FIG. 38.—*Nocomis biguttatus (from Fishes of Illinois)*.

48. Nocomis Girard. Size large; mouth large, nearly terminal; dorsal fin slightly behind the ventrals; eye small: 1 species.

N. *biguttatus* (Kirtland). Horny-head; river chub; jerker (Fig. 38). Length 250 mm.; head 4; depth 4.25; color bluish olive; sides with greenish reflection; fins pale orange; a dusky bar behind the opercle; males in the spring with a crimson spot on the side of the head; scales 6-41-5; adults with a swollen crest on the head: Pennsylvania to Wyoming; southward to Alabama; very common in larger streams.

49. Couesius Jordan. Body elongate; mouth terminal; a barbel on each maxillary; teeth 2, 4-4, 2, hooked; scales small; rays of both dorsal and anal fins 8: 4 species in the United States, 1 in Mexico.

C. *plumbeus* (Agassiz). Length 150 mm.; head 4.5; depth 4.5; color dusky; sides silvery, with a dark lateral band; free margin of the dorsal fin concave; scales 11-60 to 70-7: Lake Superior to northern New York and New Brunswick; very common northwards.

C. *dissimilis* (Girard). Like C. *plumbeus*, but more robust; free margin of dorsal fin nearly straight: upper Missouri and Black Hills region.

C. *greeni* Jord. Length 150 mm.; head 4; depth 4; color dark olive; sides reddish silvery; a dark streak under the eyes; scales 10-57-7; body robust; back convex: head waters of the Fraser River; Idaho.

50. Platygobio Gill. Body elongate, somewhat compressed; teeth 2, 4-4, 2; head broad and flat; a barbel on each maxillary; rays of both dorsal and anal fins 8; scales large: 2 species.

P. physignathus (Cope). Length 150 mm.; head and depth 4.6; color olivaceous, with a plumbeous lateral band; belly white; scales 6-48-5, 20 before the dorsal fin; body slender: upper waters of the Arkansas; very common in the river channels.

P. gracilis (Richardson). Flatheaded chub. Length 300 mm.; head 4.25; depth 4.75; color pale olive; head white; scales 6-50-5, 23 before the dorsal fin: head waters of the Missouri and Yellowstone to the Saskatchewan; eastward to Kansas City; common in river channels.

51. Exoglossum Rafinesque. Body moderately elongate; the two sides of the lower jaw united its whole length, instead of forming a broad arch, and looking like a projecting tongue; teeth 1, 4-4, 1: 1 species.

E. maxillingua (LeSueur). Cut-lip; nigger chub. Length 150 mm.; head 4; depth 4.5; color olivaceous; a black bar behind the opercle; rays of dorsal fin 8; anal 7; scales 8-53-5: St. Lawrence River and Lake Ontario to Virginia; locally abundant.

Order 4. Heterognathi.—The four anterior vertebræ modified and coössified, and Weberian ossicles present; fins soft-rayed; lower pharyngeals not falciform; ventral fins abdominal; no pseudobranchiæ: 2 families of tropical fishes, represented by a single species in Texas.

Family Characinidæ.—Adipose fin present; head naked; scales cycloid: 300 species.

Astyanax Baird and Girard. Body oblong, compressed; lateral line complete; premaxillary teeth in a double row: 40 species.

A. mexicanus (Filippi). Head 4; depth 3; color olivaceous, with a lateral silvery band and a black caudal spot; rays of dorsal fin 10; anal 21; scales 6-38-6: southern Texas and Mexico; abundant.

Order 5. Nematognathi.—Catfish. The four anterior vertebræ modified and with Weberian ossicles; no subopercle; ventral fins abdominal; fins soft rayed, except the dorsal and pectoral fins, each of which has a single spine; scales wanting, the skin being naked or with bony plates; the border of the mouth formed by the premaxillaries, the maxillary being often rudimentary; barbels present on the maxillaries: several families, 1 in the fresh waters of America.

Family Ameiuridæ.—Body elongate, naked; upper jaw formed of premaxillaries alone; maxillaries rudimentary; barbels 8, on anterior part of head; adipose fin present; a stout spine forms the anterior ray of dorsal and pectoral fins; lower pharyngeals separate; air bladder large: over 900 species and 100 genera, most of which are fresh water fish living in the warmer regions of Africa and South America, especially the Amazon region; a few species marine, mostly in tropical waters; about 30 species in the United States, none of which are on the Pacific slope except a few which have been introduced.

Key to the Genera of Ameiuridæ in the United States

a_1 Posterior margin of adipose fin not adnate to back.
  b_1 Rays of anal fin 17 to 35.
    c_1 Complete bony ridge extending from the head to the dorsal
      fin...1. *Ictalurus.*
    c_2 Bony ridge from head to dorsal fin interrupted.
      d_1 Tail fin forked.......................................2. *Villarius.*
      d_2 Tail fin truncate or lunate.
        e_1 Eyes normal.....................................3. *Ameiurus.*
        e_2 Eyes under the skin; cave fishes..................4. *Gronias.*
  b_2 Rays of anal fin 12 to 15................................5. *Opladelus.*
a_2 Posterior margin of adipose fin adnate to back; size small or very
  small.
  b_1 Adipose fin separated from caudal fin by a distinct notch......6. *Noturus.*
  b_2 Adipose fin not separated from caudal fin.
    c_1 Pectoral spines not serrate...........................7. *Schilbeodes.*
    c_2 Pectoral spines more or less serrate....................8. *Rabida.*

1. Ictalurus Rafinesque. Channel cats. Body slender; head conical; mouth small; supraoccipital process prolonged posteriorly, its emarginate end receiving the anterior tip of the second interspinal, thus forming a continuous bony ridge between the head and the dorsal fin; rays of dorsal fin usually I, 6; caudal fin deeply forked; 8 barbels present: 4 species, 1 in Guatemala, all important food fishes.

Key to the United States Species of Ictalurus

a_1 Body not spotted.
  b_1 Anal fin with 32 to 35 rays.................................*I. furcatus.*
  b_2 Anal fin with 24 to 26 rays.................................*I. anguilla.*
a_2 Body spotted..*I. punctatus.*

I. furcatus (Cuvier and Valenciennes). Great forked-tail cat (Fig. 39). Extreme length 1,500 mm.; extreme weight 150 lbs.; average weight 10 lbs.; head 4.5; depth 5; color silvery; anal fin almost one third the length of the body: Mississippi Valley and Gulf States; northward to Iowa and Ohio; abundant in the south.

I. punctatus (Raf.). Channel cat; spotted cat (Fig. 40). Extreme length 900 mm.; extreme weight 25 lbs.; head 4; depth 5; color oli-vaceous, with small irregular round black spots; anal fin with 25 to

29 rays: Great Lakes region, Gulf slope and Mississippi Valley regions; generally abundant in the channels of large streams.

I. anguilla Evermann & Kendall. Eel cat. Length 450 mm.; color pale bluish or yellowish: Mississippi Valley from northern Illinois to Louisiana.

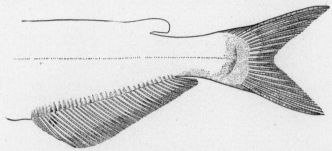

FIG. 39.—Anal and caudal fins of *Ictalurus furcatus* (*from Fishes of Illinois*).

2. Villarius Rutter. Caudal fin lunate or forked; body similar to *Ameiurus;* size large; supraoccipital process prolonged posteriorly, but not reaching the dorsal fin: several species.

V. lacustris (Walbaum). Great Lakes catfish. Length up to 1,500 mm.; average weight 8 lbs.; extreme weight 40 lbs.; head 4; depth 5; color slaty; sides paler; rays of dorsal fin I, 5; anal 25 to 32; tail deeply forked: Great Lakes basin and large lakes and rivers northwards.

V. catus (L.). White cat. Length 600 mm.; head 3.8; color pale bluish, without spots, but sometimes mottled; anal fin with about 19 rays; tail deeply forked; head very broad and mouth very large:

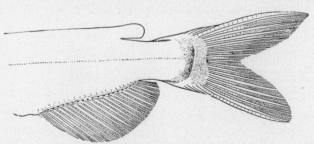

FIG. 40.—Anal and caudal fins of *Ictalurus punctatus* (*from Fishes of Illinois*).

eastern States from New York to Texas; introduced into California; very common in coastwise streams and swamps.

3. Ameiurus Rafinesque. Small catfish and bullheads. Body rather stout; head broad; mouth large; rays of dorsal fin about I, 6; anal 24 to 27; tail usually convex or truncate; barbels 8: premaxillary teeth a transverse band (Fig. 41): numerous species, all in America except *A. cantonensis*, in China.

A. erebennus Jordan. Body elongate; length 300 mm.; head and depth 4; color black above, pale below; fins and barbels black; tail truncated: coastwise waters from New Jersey to Florida; rare.

A. natalis (LeSueur). Yellow cat. Length 450 mm.; head 3.5; color yellowish, clouded with darker; caudal fin truncated; body stout; mouth wide: from Great Lakes region southwards into Virginia and Texas; very common.

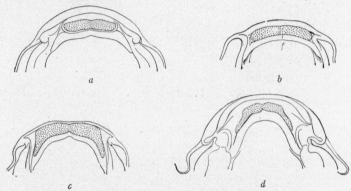

FIG. 41.—Premaxillary teeth of: *a, Ameiurus melas; b, Schilbeodes gyrinus; c, Opladelus olivaris*, and *d, Noturus flavus (from Fishes of Illinois).*

A. nebulosus (LeSueur). Common bullhead; horned pout. Length up to 450 mm.; head 3.8; depth 4 to 4.5; color dark yellowish brown, mottled with darker; anal fin with 21 or 22 rays and extending about a quarter the length of the body; upper jaw longer than the lower: Maine to North Dakota; southward to Virginia and Texas; introduced into California; very common.

Subspecies of A. nebulosus

A. n. catulus (Girard). Color nearly black: Texas; common.

A. n. marmoratus (Holbrook). Color strongly marked: Indiana to Florida.

A. melas (Raf.) (Fig. 41, a). Black bullhead. Length 250 mm.; depth 3.5 to 4.5; color blackish; body stout; anal fin very deep, with 17 to 19 white rays: northern New York to Nebraska; southward to Kentucky and Texas; common, especially westward of the Mississippi.

A. platycephalus (Gir.). Brown cat. Length 450 mm.; head 3.5; color olive brown; body very slender; head flat and broad; upper jaw projecting; anal fin with 16 to 20 rays: Carolina and Georgia; common.

4. Gronias Cope. Blind catfish. Eyes covered by the skin: 1 species.

G. nigrilabris (Cope). Length 250 mm.; color black above; anal fin with 18 rays; eyes rudimentary, beneath the skin; barbels short: in cave streams tributary to the Conestoga River in eastern Pennsylvania.

5. Opladelus Rafinesque. Body large, elongate; head very wide and flat; mouth very large, with a projecting lower jaw; skin thick and villose; premaxillary teeth form a broad villiform band, convex anteriorly, with a backward prolongation on each side (Fig. 41); anal fin slightly concave: 1 species.

L. olivaris (Raf.). Mud cat; goujon. Extreme length 1,500 mm.; extreme weight 100 lbs.; average weight 35 lbs.; color yellowish, mottled with brown or greenish; body slender; anal fin with 12 to 15 rays; dorsal spine short: Mississippi Valley and Gulf States; common in deep, sluggish waters.

6. Noturus Rafinesque. Body elongate and similar to *Opladelus;* dentition also similar (Fig. 41); adipose fin long, low and keel-like and adnate posteriorly and separated from the tail by a notch; a poison gland at the base of the pectoral spine; skin tough and villose: 1 species.

N. flavus Raf. Stone cat. Length 300 mm.; head 4.25; depth 5.6; color yellowish brown; dorsal spines very short; anal fin with about 16 rays; barbels short: Great Lakes region and westward into Montana; southward to Texas; often common in small sluggish streams.

7. Schilbeodes Bleeker. Mad-toms. Body small, elongate; head flattened; mouth large, with a somewhat projecting upper jaw; teeth in a broad convex band in each jaw (Fig. 41); adipose fin as in *Noturus;* anal fin with 12 to 23 rays; a poison gland as in *Noturus:* several species, some very rare, in southern and western States, in small streams; the sting of the sharp pectoral spines may be very painful.

S. gyrinus (Mitchill). Mad-tom (Fig. 42). Length 125 mm.; head 3.5 to 4; depth 4 to 5.5; color uniform yellowish brown, with a narrow lateral black streak; pectoral spine smooth; adipose fin continuous with the tail fin; anal fin with 13 to 15 rays: Hudson River and westward throughout the Great Lakes region and Mississippi Valley; common towards the north.

S. nocturnus (Jordan and Gilbert). Length 75 mm.; head 3.6; color dark brown, dotted with black; rays of anal fin 15 or 16: adipose fin high, joined to the caudal: Mississippi Valley from Indiana to Arkansas.

8. Rabida Jordan. Mad Toms. Body similar to *Schilbeodes;* pectoral spines serrate behind: several species; pectoral spines able to give a painful wound.

R. exilis (Nelson). Length 100 mm.; head 4; depth 5 to 6.5; color yellowish, mottled; anal fin with 14 to 17 rays: Wisconsin to Kansas; common.

R. insignis (Richardson). Mad-tom. Length 250 mm.; head 4.25; depth 6; color dark brown, somewhat mottled; fins dark edged; anal fin with 14 to 16 rays; upper jaw projecting: New York to South Carolina; very common in coastal streams.

FIG. 42.—*Schilbeodes gyrinus (from Fishes of Illinois).*

R. miura (Jordan). Length 100 mm.; head 4; depth 5; color mottled black and gray, with 4 black blotches; top of head, tip of dorsal, middle of adipose and edge of caudal fins black; adipose fin with a deep notch, but connected with the tail fin; anal fin with 13 to 15 rays: Mississippi Valley and tributaries of Lake Michigan; common.

R. leptacantha (Jordan). Length 75 mm.; body slender; color yellowish, mottled; spines short; rays of anal fin 14: Gulf States, in sandy streams; rare.

R. gilberti (Jordan & Evermann). Length 100 mm.; body slender; color yellowish; base of tail fin and most of its lower lobe black; rays of anal fin 15; dorsal fin black at base: Roanoke River; common.

R. eleuthera (Jordan). Length 100 mm.; head 3.8; color plain brownish, with faint saddle-like blotches on the back; rays of anal fin 13: Mississippi Valley; often common.

Order 6. Haplomi.—Pike and pickerel. Soft rayed fish with anterior vertebræ distinct and without Weberian ossicles; no adipose fin; pseudobranchiæ wanting or glandular; body covered with cycloid scales; ventral fins abdominal; head usually more or less scaly; air bladder with pneumatic duct: 2 families of mainly fresh water fishes.

Key to the Families of Haplomi

a_1 No lateral line present; fishes of small size.....................1. *Umbridæ.*
a_2 Lateral line present; fishes of large size.........................2. *Esocidæ.*

Family 1. Umbridæ.—Mud minnows. Body elliptical, broad anteriorly, compressed posteriorly; teeth well developed and on the premaxillaries, mandibles, vomer and palatines; maxillaries toothless; no lateral line; no pyloric cæca; dorsal fin more or less posterior in position; scales large; branchiostegals 6 or 8; tail fin rounded: 1 genus and 3 species of small fishes living near the bottom of ponds and sluggish streams.

Umbra Muller. With the characters of the family: 3 species, 2 in the United States.

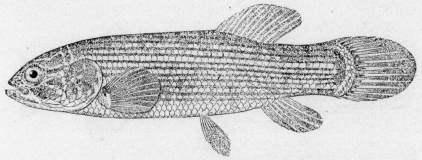

FIG. 43.—*Umbra pygmæa (from Jordan & Evermann).*

U. limi (Kirtland). Length 100 mm.; head 3.75; depth 4.25; color olive green, with 14 narrow irregular pale transverse dark bars; rays of dorsal fin 14; anal 8; scales 35: Quebec to Minnesota and southward to the Ohio river and Iowa; common in the basin of the Great Lakes.

U. pygmæa (Dekay) (Fig. 43). Length 100 mm.; head 4; depth 4-5; color dark greenish, with about 12 narrow longitudinal pale stripes and a dark transverse bar at the base of the tail fin; rays of the dorsal fin 13; anal 7; scales 35: coastwise streams and swamps from Long Island to the Neuse River; locally common.

Family 2. Esocidæ.—Body elongate, slender, compressed posteriorly; head long and flat; mouth very large, with a projecting lower jaw; maxillaries with a supplementary bone; teeth strong and on the premaxillaries, vomer, palatines, mandibles and tongue; head naked above and more or less scaled on the sides; scales small; lateral line weak, wanting in the young; tail forked; dorsal fin opposite the anal and near the tail; branchiostegals 12 to 20; no pyloric cæca: 1 genus; fresh water fish of moderate or large size noted for their fierceness and voracity.

Esox L. Pike: pickerel. With the characters of the family: 5 species; all important food and game fishes.

Key to the Species of Esox

a_1 Opercle not scaly on the lower half.
  b_1 Cheeks entirely scaly...................................*E. lucius.*
  b_2 Cheeks not scaly on the lower half......................*E. masquinongy.*
a_2 Opercle and cheek entirely scaly.
  b_1 Rays of dorsal fin 14.....................................*E. reticulatus.*
  b_2 Rays of dorsal fin 11 or 12.
    c_1 In the Mississippi Valley and Great Lakes basin........*E. vermiculatus.*
    c_2 In Atlantic coastwise streams........................*E. americanus.*

E. lucius L. Common Pike (Fig. 44). Length up to 1,200 mm.; weight up to 40 lbs.; head 3.4; depth 5; color bluish or greenish gray,

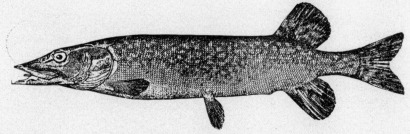

Fig. 44.—*Esox lucius (from Jordan & Evermann).*

with many irregular whitish or yellowish spots arranged in more or less longitudinal lines; median fins with irregular black spots; rays of dorsal fin 16 or 17; anal 13 or 14; scales 123; branchiostegals 14 to 16: northern America, Europe and Asia; southward to New York and the Ohio River; northward to Alaska; very common.

E. masquinongy Mitchill. Muscalonge; muskallunge. Length 900 mm.; extreme length 2,500 mm.; extreme weight 100 lbs.; head 3.6; depth 6; color dark gray; sides with numerous black spots; lower portion of cheek and opercle without scales; rays of dorsal fin 17; anal 15; scales 150; branchiostegals 17 to 19: Great Lakes region and upper Mississippi Valley, and northwards; not common; occasionally in the Ohio Valley as far south as North Carolina.

Subspecies of E. masquinongy

E. m. ohiensis (Kirtland). Sides with narrow dark cross bars which split up into diffuse spots: Ohio River basin; Lake Chautauqua.

E. m. immaculatus Jordan & Evermann. Body unspotted: northern Wisconsin; common.

E. niger LeSueur. Common pickerel; chain pickerel. Length 600 mm.; head 3.5; depth 6; color green; sides marked with numerous irregular dark lines forming a network; a dark band below the eye; fins plain; rays of dorsal fin 14; anal 13; scales 125; branchiostegals 14 to 16: Atlantic and Gulf slope, Maine to Florida and Louisiana; very numerous in the New York lakes and east and south of the Alleghenies.

E. vermiculatus LeSueur. Grass pike; little pickerel. Length 300 mm.; head 3.25; depth 5 to 6; color green or grayish, sometimes plain but usually with an irregular network of dark streaks on the sides; a dark bar downward from the eye; rays of dorsal and anal fins 11 or 12; body rather stout; scales 105; branchiostegals 11 to 13: Mississippi Valley and the southern tributaries of Lakes Michigan, Erie and Ontario; common.

E. americanus Gmelin. Banded pickerel. Length 300 mm.; head 3.6; depth 5.5; color dark green; sides with about 20 blackish curved bars; rays of dorsal and anal fins 11 or 12; scales 105; opercle fully scaled: coastwise streams and ponds from Maine to Florida; common.

Order 7. Cyprinodontes.—The killifishes. Dorsal fin single, posteriorly inserted; ventrals abdominal, when present; head usually scaled; upper jaw formed by the premaxillaries; size small: 3 families.

Key to These Families

a_1 Eyes normal.
   b_1 Anal fin of male normal...............................1. *Cyprinodontidæ*.
   b_2 Anal fin of male very long and inserted forwards.........2. *Pœciliidæ*.
a_2 Eyes very small or hidden in the skin....................3. *Amblyopsidæ*.

Family 1. Cyprinodontidæ.—Killifish. Small fish with moderately elongate body, flattened head and rather large cycloid scales; head more or less scaly; mouth small, terminal, with a projecting lower jaw; upper jaw very protractile, its margin formed by the premaxillaries; branchiostegals 4 to 6; tail not forked; no pyloric cæca; no lateral line; many species ovoviviparous: about 30 genera and 180 species, occurring in fresh and brackish water in all the warmer waters of Europe, Asia, Africa and America; about 30 fresh water species in the United States, largely in coastwise inlets and swamps of the southern States.

Key to the Fresh Water Genera of Cyprinodontidæ and Pœcillidæ in the United States

a_1 Lower jaw usually projecting beyond the upper; teeth little movable; species mostly carnivorous.
   b_1 Anal fin of male of normal shape; species oviparous (*Cyprinodontidæ*).
      c_1 Teeth pointed, and neither bicuspid nor tricuspid.

d₁ Teeth in more than one series.
   e₁ Dorsal fin relatively large, with 12 to 18 rays;
      bottom fishes.
      f₁ Scales relatively large, with 31 to 50 in the lateral
         line.
         g₁ Dorsal fin inserted before the anterior border
           of the anal........:........................ 1. *Fundulus.*
         g₂ Dorsal fin inserted over the anterior border
           of the anal............................ 3. *Xenisma.*
      f₂ Scales small, with about 60 in the lateral line.... 2. *Plancterus.*
   e₂ Dorsal fin small, with 7 to 10 rays; surface swimmers 4. *Zygonectes.*
   d₂ Teeth in a single series; dorsal fin in front of the anal.. 5. *Lucania.*
  c₂ Teeth not pointed but notched and tricuspid.
   d₁ Dorsal fin with 10 to 12 rays..................... 6. *Cyprinodon.*
   d₂ Dorsal fin with 15 to 18 rays..................... 7. *Jordanella.*
 b₂ Anal fin of male a long sword-shaped organ; species viviparous (*Pœciliidæ*)..................................... 1. *Gambusia.*
a₂ Lower jaw short; teeth movable; species mostly mud-eating.
 b₁ Teeth in a single series................................ 2. *Heterandria.*
 b₂ Teeth in more than one series.......................... 3. *Mollienisia.*

1. Fundulus Lacépède. Killifish. Body rather elongate, sometimes chubby; compressed behind; eyes large; teeth in 2 or more series

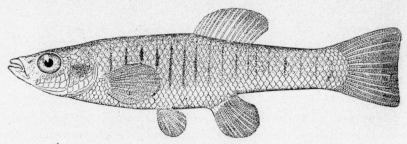

FIG. 45.—*Fundulus diaphanus (from Jordan & Evermann).*

in each jaw, and pointed; air bladder present: many species, mostly
American, living in fresh and brackish water and arms of the sea;
about 8 species in the United States.

F. heteroclitus (L.). Common killifish; mummichog. Length 75 to
150 mm.; head 3.5; depth 3.6; color of male greenish, sometimes orange
below; sides with many narrow, silvery bars made up of spots, besides
many scattered spots; median fins dark with pale spots; females plain;
dorsal fin 11; anal 10 or 11; scales 35 to 38-13: Gulf of St. Lawrence to
Mexico; very common in shallow water along the sea shore and in the
mouths of streams.

F. parvipinnis Girard. Length 100 mm.; head 3.5; depth 3.7;
dorsal fin with 13, anal with 11 rays; color light green, with about 20

short dark cross bars: coast of California from Point Conception to Lower California; often very common.

F. similis (Baird and Girard). Length 150 mm.; rays of dorsal fin 11 to 13, of anal 13; scales 33-11; color olivaceous, with 10 to 15 dark side bars; body slender; snout very long: coastal waters of the Gulf States, in brackish water; very common.

F. diaphanus (LeSueur) (Fig. 45). Length 100 mm.; head 4; depth 4.8; color olivaceous; sides silvery, with about 20 dark vertical bars; rays of dorsal fin 13; anal 11; scales 45-15; body rather slender: eastern and central States from Maine to Cape Hatteras; westward to Colorado; Great Lakes and tributaries; common in streams and ponds; also in the mouths of rivers.

Subspecies of F. diaphanus

F. d. menona Jordan & Copeland. Rays of dorsal fin 12; anal 10; scales 48-12; bars very distinct; back spotted: Ohio River to the Mississippi.

F. rathbuni Jordan & Meek. Length 65 mm.; head 3.8; depth 4.5; color pale green, with small irregular oblong dark brown spots scattered over head and body; rays of dorsal and anal fins 11; scales 38-12: eastern North Carolina; common; not in salt water.

F. albolineatus Gilbert. Length 85 mm.; head 3.3; depth 3.6; color dark brown; sides plumbeous, with whitish streaks in males and narrow black lines in females; rays of dorsal and anal fins 10 or 11; scales 42: Tennessee basin in Alabama.

F. majalis (Walbaum). Mayfish; killifish. Length 150 mm., being the largest of the genus; head long; color olivaceous, with about 12 dark bars; a black spot on the dorsal fin; dorsal with 12, anal 10 rays; scales 36 in the lateral line: Cape Cod to Florida; common in shallow bays.

2. **Plancterus** Garman. Intestine long and convoluted; pharyngeals very small: 2 species.

P. kansæ Gar. Length 75; head 3.5; depth 4.5; color greenish above; sides silvery, tinged with yellow and with 14 to 18 dark vertical bars; rays of dorsal fin 14 to 15; anal 13 or 14; scales 60-21: South Dakota to western Iowa, Texas and New Mexico; common in tributaries of the upper Arkansas.

3. **Xenisma** Jordan. Dorsal fin inserted over anterior part of anal; scales small, 50 in the lateral line; colors brilliant: 2 species.

X. catenatus (Storer). Length 150 mm.; head 4; depth 4.5; color bluish or greenish, with an orange spot on each scale forming thus regular lines; rays of dorsal fin 14; anal 15; scales 50: Tennessee and Cumberland Rivers and in the Ozark region, in mountain streams; abundant.

X. *stellifer* Jordan. Length 100 mm.; head 3.75; depth 5; color blue above, silvery below, with large orange spots irregularily placed; rays of dorsal and anal fins 13; scales 53: Alabama River basin.

4. Zygonectes Agassiz. Dorsal fin small, with 7 to 11 rays, inserted behind the anterior border of the anal fin; scales large, 29 to 40 in the lateral line; size small: about 10 species.

Z. *cingulatus* (Cuvier and Valenciennes). Length 75 mm.; head 3.25; depth 3.75; color dark olivaceous, with a dark orange spot on each scale posteriorly; faint narrow orange bars along the lower and hinder part of the body; rays of dorsal fin 7 or 8; anal 8 or 9; scales 32-11 or 12: streams and swamps of eastern Florida.

Z. *sciadicus* (Cope). Length 65 mm.; head 3.5; depth 3.2; color uniform olivaceous; rays of dorsal fin 10; anal 12; scales 39-13: eastern Nebraska and South Dakota to Colorado; common in grassy streams.

Z. *chrysotus* (Holbrook). Length 50 mm.; head 3.5; depth 3.8; color light olive brown; sides with about 14 indefinite half-bars; rays of dorsal fin 9; anal 11; scales 32 or 33-12: coastwise swamps from South Carolina to Florida.

Z. *cingulatus* (Cuvier & Valenciennes). Head 3.5; depth 3.75; color olivaceous, with fine dots; scales edged with dusky, forming a few faint longitudinal stripes; about 15 dark vertical bars; fins red; rays of dorsal fin 7; anal 8; scales 34-10: South Carolina to Florida, in coastwise swamps.

Z. *nottii* Agassiz. Length 35 mm.; head 3.6; depth 4.5; color silvery, with 6 narrow jet-black lines from head to tail, these being crossed by about 12 cross bars; cheeks orange; rays of dorsal fin 7 or 8; anal 9 or 10; scales 36-10: Florida to South Carolina.

Z. *guttatus* Ag. Head 3.75; depth 5; color orange brown; each scale with a black edge, these forming longitudinal stripes, but not confluent; cheeks orange; rays of dorsal fin 6 or 7; anal 8 or 9; scales 36-12: Florida to Texas.

Z. *dispar* Ag. (Fig. 46). Length 65 mm.; head 3.75; depth 3.5; color bluish or greenish in life, with a blue patch under the eye, female with 10 distinct longitudinal brownish lines; males with about 7 longitudinal rows of small brown spots and 9 dark cross bars; rays of dorsal fin 7; anal 9; scales 35-10: Michigan to Arkansas; southward to Mississippi; common in sluggish streams.

Z. notatus (Rafinesque). Top minnow. Length 75 mm.; head 4; depth 4.5; color brownish olive, with a broad dark band running from the tip of the snout to the tail; back dotted; rays of dorsal fin 9; anal 11; scales 34-11: Michigan to Alabama and Texas; common.

5. Lucania Girard. Body elliptical, compressed; lower jaw projecting and prominent, the mouth being short and oblique; each jaw with a single series of teeth; scales very large; dorsal fin above or in advance of the anal: 4 species of very small fishes in the coastwise swamps of the southern States.

FIG. 46.—*Zygonectes dispar: a*, male; *b*, female (*from Fishes of Illinois*).

L. ommata (Jordan). Length 20 mm.; head 3.3; depth 5; straw-color, the male with 5 or 6 dark bars, the female with a jet-black spot just in front of the anal fin and a larger spot at the upper part of the base of the tail; rays of the dorsal fin 6 or 7; anal 9 or 10; scales 26 to 28-9; body slender; eyes large: swamps of Florida; scarce; one of the smallest known fishes.

L. goodei Jord. Length 40 mm.; head 4; depth 4.25; color olivaceous, with a distinct black band running from the snout to the tail where it ends in a round spot; rays of dorsal and anal fins 9; scales 29 to 32-7: Everglades region; common.

L. parva (Baird & Girard). Rain-water fish. Length 45 mm.; head 3.25; depth 3.25; color olive; fins in male orange tipped with black; dorsal fin with a large black spot at its base and with 10 to 12 rays;

anal with 10 or 11; scales 26-8: Atlantic coast from Connecticut to Key West and Texas, near the shore and in brackish pools; very common towards the south.

6. Cyprinodon Lacépède. Body short, deep, elliptical, the back elevated; mouth small; teeth tricuspid, in a single series; scales very large; dorsal fin high and in advance of the anal: 9 species, in brackish waters of the southern States and Mexico.

C. variegatus Lac. Length 75 mm.; head 3.25; depth 2; color of male olivaceous, blue above; color of anterior portion of the sides and of belly salmon; tail with a black bar at base and tip; female light olive, with about 14 cross streaks; rays of dorsal fin 11; anal 10; scales 25-12. Cape Cod to the Rio Grande, in brackish waters and the mouth of streams; very common.

7. Jordanella Goode & Bean. Body short, deep, compressed; back elevated; mouth small; teeth in a single series; dorsal fin long; scales large; tail rounded; viviparous: 1 species.

J. floridæ G. & B. Length 65 mm.; head 3.5; depth 2 to 2.5; color olivaceous, with a blue stripe along each series of scales, and 4 or 5 vague vertical bars; rays of dorsal fin I, 14 to 16; anal I, 11 to 13; scales 25 to 27-11 or 12: streams and swamps of Florida; common.

Family 2.   Poecilliidæ.—Top minnows; mosquito fish. Anal fin of male modified to form an intromittant organ; all species viviparous: many species, all in tropical and subtropical America.

1. Gambusia Poey. Top minnow. Body elongate; mouth small; scales large, anal fin in male very long and slender and modified to form a long intromittant organ; ventral fins near the pectorals; dorsal fin behind the anal; viviparous: about 12 species of small fish in fresh waters of the southern States, West Indies, Central America, and Mexico; 2 species in the United States.

G. patruellis (Baird & Girard) (Fig. 47). Length 50 mm. (female); male much smaller; head 3.6; depth 4; color light olive, each scale edged with darker; a very narrow, often indefinite, lateral stripe; rays of dorsal fin 7; anal 10; scales 30-9: marshes of the South Atlantic and Gulf coasts from Delaware to Mexico and northward to Kentucky, Tennessee and southern Illinois in the Mississippi Valley; in brackish and fresh water; very common in the south; celebrated as mosquito-larvæ devourers.

G. holbrooki Girard. Similar to *G. patruellis*. Length 60 mm.; head 4; depth 3.8; rays of dorsal fin 8, of anal 10 or 11; scales 30-9: swamps and ditches, New Jersey to Florida; useful as a destroyer of mosquitoes; introduced for this purpose into many European countries.

2. Heterandria Agassiz. Top minnow. Body rather stout; mouth very small; both jaws with a single series of teeth; scales large; anal fin in advance of the dorsal, and in the male modified to form an intromittant organ; viviparous: 6 species of very small fish in swamps in the southern States, West Indies and Mexico; 2 species in the United States.

H. formosa Ag. Length 20 to 25 mm.; head 3.5; depth 3.75; color brownish olive, with a wide black lateral band crossed by 6 to 9 vertical bars; a black spot on the dorsal and anal fins; rays of dorsal fin 7; anal 6 to 9; scales 24 to 28: South Carolina to Florida; very common in swamps and ditches, often in company with *Gambusia patruellis;* one of the smallest of known fishes.

FIG. 47.—*Gambusia patruellis: a*, male; *b*, female (*from Fishes of Illinois*).

H. occidentalis Baird & Girard. Length 65 mm.; head 3.5; depth 4; color brownish, dotted with black, with a black lateral stripe; rays of dorsal fin 7 or 8; anal 9 or 10; scales 29-8: southern Arizona; common in springs and ditches.

3. Mollienisia LeSueur. Body rather stout; mouth small; both jaws with a narrow band of small teeth; scales large; anal fin behind the dorsal and modified in the male to form an intromittant organ: 4 species in the southern States and Mexico; 1 species in the United States.

M. latipinna LeS. Length 75 mm.; head 3.5 to 4; depth 2.5 to 3; color light green, in the male marbled with darker and spotted, with longitudinal lateral series of blackish spots; dorsal fin very long and in the male very elevated, exceeding the height of the body, translucent and with a series of spots; tail fin with round spots; rays of dorsal fin 15 to 16; anal 8; scales 26-9 or 10: South Carolina to Mexico, in swamps and streams; very common.

Family 3. Amblyopsidæ.—The blind fishes. Body elongate, compressed behind; head long, depressed; mouth large; premaxillaries forming the entire margin of the upper jaw; head naked; tail fin pointed or rounded behind; scales small, cycloid, more or less imbedded so that the body appears naked; no lateral line; anus close behind the gills; fins spineless; ovary single; viviparous: 3 genera and 5 species; in small streams along our southern coast, and also in subterranean streams, these being blind and colorless.

Key to the Genera of Amblyopsidæ

a_1 Eyes present and functional; ventral fin wanting.
    b_1 No tactile papillæ present..............................1. *Chologaster.*
    b_2 Tactile papillæ present...............................2. *Forbesella.*
a_2 Eyes concealed; colorless, subterraneous species.
    b_1 Ventral fins present...................................3. *Amblyopsis.*
    b_2 Ventral fins wanting..................................4. *Troglichthys.*
                                         5. *Typhlichthys.*

    1. Chologaster Agassiz.   Body very slender; eyes present; no ventral fins; pyloric cæca 2: 1 species, in swamps and caves.

Key to the Species of Chologaster and Forbesella

a_1 Lateral papillary ridges absent.
    b_1 Three narrow lateral stripes.............................*C. cornutus.*
    b_2 Body without stripes...................................*F. agassizii.*
a_2 Papillary ridges present...................................*F. papilliferus.*

    C. cornutus Ag.   Length 60 mm.; head 3.4; depth 4.5; color dark brown above; lower half abruptly white; whole body sprinkled with black dots; 3 narrow lateral stripes present; rays of dorsal and anal fins 8 or 9; scales 68: lowland swamps from Dismal to Okefinokee Swamps; locally very common.

    2. Forbesella Jordan and Evermann.   Tactile papillary ridges on sides of body; eyes imperfectly developed; pyloric cæca 2: 2 species; cave fishes.

    F. agassizii (Putnam).   Length 30 mm.; head 4; color light brown: Mammoth Cave and other subterranean streams in Tennessee and Kentucky.

    F. papillifera (Forbes).   Length 30 mm.; head 4; depth 5 or 6; color as in *Chologaster cornutus;* pectoral reaching half way to the dorsal fin; head with rows of tactile papillæ: caves in Union and Pope Counties, Illinois.

    3. Amblyopsis DeKay.   Eyes rudimentary and not functional; body and head with many vertical tactile ridges; 1 pyloric cæcum: 1 species.

A. speleus DeK. Length 125 mm.; head 3; depth 4.5; body color-less, translucent; rays of dorsal fin 9; anal 8: Mammoth Cave, and other subterranean streams in Kentucky and Indiana; common.

4. Troglichthys Eigenmann. Eyes very rudimentary, concealed beneath the skin; sides with tactile papillæ; scleral cartilages present; 1 pyloric cæcum; body colorless: 1 species.

T. rosæ Eig. Scleral cartilage large, forming a hook over the eye: caves of Missouri.

5. Typhlichthys Girard. Similar to *Amblyopsis*, except that it has no ventral fins: 1 species.

T. subterraneus Gir. Length 50 mm.; colorless and translucent; rays of dorsal and anal fins 7 or 8: subterranean streams and wells from Indiana to Alabama; common.

Order 8. Salmopercæ.—The trout perch. Adipose fin pres-ent; ventral fins abdominal; dorsal, anal and ventral fins each with 1 or 2 spines; maxillary toothless and not forming the margin of the mouth; scales ctenoid; head scaleless; pseudobranchiæ present: 1 family.

Family Percopsidæ.—Body elongate; caudal peduncle long and slender; mouth small, horizontal; branchiostegals 6; tail forked; stomach siphonal with 10 pyloric cæca: 2 genera.

1. Percopsis Agassiz. Body slender, pellucid; dorsal fin with 2 feeble spines; anal with 1: 1 species.

P. omiscomaycus (Walbaum). Trout perch. Length 150 mm.; head 3.75; depth 4.3; color pale olivaceous, with a silvery stripe along the lateral line; upper half of body with dark round spots; rays of dorsal fin II, 9; anal I, 7; scales 6-50-7: Delaware and Potomac Rivers to Kansas, and northward to Hudson Bay; common in the Great Lakes.

2. Columbia Eigenmann. Body rather robust; dorsal and anal fins with 2 strong spines each; posterior margin of preopercle with a few short spines; lateral line imperfect: 1 species.

C. transmontana Eig. Length 100 mm.; head 3; depth 3.5; color greenish, upper half of body with large dark spots; rays of dorsal fin II, 9; anal II, 6; scales 7 to 9-44 to 46-7: lagoons along the Columbia River; locally common.

Order 9. Xenarchi.—Pirate perch. Dorsal fin single, with few spines; ventrals thoracic and with 7 rays and without spines; no adipose fin: 1 family.

Family Aphredoderidæ.—Body elliptical; caudal peduncle thick; scales ctenoid; sides of head scaly; lateral line imperfect or wanting; pyloric cæca about 12; anus below the preopercle in the adult but behind the ventral fins in the young; tail fin rounded: 1 genus.

Aphredoderus LeSueur. With the characters of the family: 7 species.

A. sayanus (Gilliams). Pirate perch (Fig. 48). Length 190 mm.; head 3; depth 3.3; color dark olive, speckled with dark dots; 2 dark bars at the base of the tail fin; rays of dorsal fin III to IV, 10 to 11; anal II, 6; scales 9 to 13-45 to 60-12 to 14: Long Island to Texas; up the Mississippi Valley to Minnesota and eastward to Lake Erie; common.

Order 10. Synentognathi.—Garpike. Soft-rayed fishes with unmodified anterior vertebræ; air bladder without pneumatic duct in the adult; no pyloric cæca; fins without spines; ventral fins abdominal; no adipose fin; lower pharyngeal bones fully united: 4 families of marine fishes, one species of which enters the rivers along the Atlantic coast.

FIG. 48.—*Aphredoderus sayanus (from Fishes of Illinois).*

Family Belonidæ.—Body very elongate and slender, covered with small scales; lateral line very low, running along the side of the belly; jaws elongated to form a beak, each jaw with a band of sharp teeth; about 50 species of voracious, carnivorous fishes.

Strongylura Van Hasselt. With the characters of the family; no vomerine teeth; tail fin unequally forked: many species, mostly American.

S. marina (Walbaum). Garfish; billfish. Length 1,200 mm.; head 2.8; depth 5.5; color greenish; sides silvery, with a narrow silvery lateral stripe; a dark bar on the front of the opercle; rays of dorsal fin 15; anal 17; scales 300, 240 before the dorsal fin; body slender, cylindrical: marine, along the Atlantic coast from Cape Cod to Texas, ascending the rivers and often breeding in fresh water; very common.

Order 11. Thoracostei.—Gills normal (in *Gasterosteidæ*), but with the pharyngeals reduced in number; dorsal spines few or wanting; ventrals reduced or wanting; body more or less protected by bony plates; upper jaw formed by the premaxillaries: 5 families of mostly marine fishes, 1 family with fresh water representatives.

Family Gasterosteidæ.—Sticklebacks. Body elliptical, rather slender, compressed; caudal peduncle slender; tail fin small; no true scales present, but body either naked or protected laterally by vertically elongate bony plates; 2 to 15 free spines in front of the dorsal fin; a patch of naked skin between the pectoral fin and the opercle on each side; ventral fins consist of 1 spine and 1 or 2 rays and subabdominal in position; middle and sides of belly protected by the pubic bones: 5 genera and about 12 species in America and Europe, 6 in the United States; small fishes living in fresh waters and arms of the sea, most of which build elaborate nests in which the eggs are deposited and where they and the young are protected by the male; they are savage little fish and very destructive to the eggs and young of larger fishes.

Key to the Fresh Water Genera of Gasterosteidæ in the United States

a_1 Free dorsal spines 3 to 5.
  b_1 Sides protected by bony plates.
    c_1 Ventral spine serrate.............................1. *Gasterosteus.*
    c_2 Vertral spine not serrate.........................2. *Glandiunculus.*
  b_2 Sides naked.
    c_1 Free dorsal spines 5...............................3. *Eucalia.*
    c_2 Free dorsal spines 3...............................5. *Apeltes.*
a_2 Free dorsal spines 7 to 11.............................4. *Pungitius.*

1. Gasterosteus L. Sides of body usually protected by vertically elongated plates; 3 or 4 free dorsal spines; pubic bones broad and little divergent, joined on the belly, forming a median ventral plate behind and between the ventral fins; gill membranes not joined across the isthmus: several species in America and Europe, 1 in fresh water in America.

G. aculeatus L. Common stickleback. Length 60 mm. to 100 mm.; head 3.5; depth 4.5 to 5; dorsal fin II-I, 13; anal fin I, 9; ventral fin I, 1; color olivaceous, more or less mottled above; lateral plates and also the dorsal spines variable, depending in some degree on the salinity of the water: arctic and subarctic, on both coasts, in shallow bays and ascending the rivers; southwards to New Jersey and Lower California.

2. Glandiunculus Jordan and Evermann. Similar to *Gasterosteus;* ventral fin rays I, 2; ventral spine not serrate: 1 species.

G. wheatlandi (Putnam). Length 100 mm.; head 3.5; depth 4.5; color dark greenish above; sides silvery or yellow; ventral membrane often red; dorsal spines long and slender; rays of dorsal fin II, 10 or 11; anal I, 8; ventral fin I, 2; caudal peduncle very slender: Atlantic coast from New Jersey to Labrador, ascending the streams.

3. Eucalia Jordan.   Body naked; dorsal spines 5; gill membranes connected, forming a fold across the isthmus; pubic bones joined, forming a median ventral plate: 2 species.

E. inconstans (Kirtland).   Brook stickleback (Fig. 49).   Length 65 mm.; head 3.5; depth 4; color of males in spring jet black, tinged with red anteriorly; females olivaceous, mottled and dotted with black; rays of dorsal fins IV-I, 10; anal I, 10: Maine to Kansas and northward to Saskatchewan; in small streams; common.

E. pygmæa (Agassiz).   Size small; rays of dorsal fins IV-I, 6; anal I, 6: Lake Superior.

Fig. 49.—*Eucalia inconstans (from Fishes of Illinois)*.

4. Pungitius Coste.   Body naked except for small bony plates along the base of the median fins; free dorsal spines 9 to 11, diverging right and left; pubic bones weak; gill membranes as in *Eucalia:* 2 species, 1 of which, *P. sinensis*, is in China.

P. pungitius (L.).   Ten-spined stickleback.   Length 75 mm.; head 4; depth 5 or 6; color olivaceous, punctulate, irregularly barred with darker; rays of dorsal fin IX-I, 9; anal I, 8: Atlantic coast of America and Europe, from Long Island to the Arctic, ascending the rivers; also in tributaries of the Great Lakes and northward to Alaska; often very common.

5. Apeltes Dekay.   Body naked; back rather elevated; 3 strong free dorsal spines; tail very slender; pubic bones weak, not joined in the median line; gill membranes joined to isthmus: 1 species.

A. quadracus (Mitchill).   Four-spined stickleback.   Length 50 mm.; head 4; depth 4; rays of dorsal fin III-I, 11; anal I, 8; color brownish olive above; silvery below; male almost black; body stout: Labrador to New Jersey, in salt water, often ascending the streams; very common northward.

Order 12.   Anacanthini.—Dorsal and anal fins very long and without spines; ventral fins jugular, without spines; no pseudobranchiæ: 3 families, all marine, with 1 species in fresh water.

Family Gadidæ.—The codfishes. Body elongate; scales cycloid; mouth large, terminal; pyloric cæca numerous: 140 species, in northern seas; 1 species in fresh water.

Lota Cuvier. Body long and low, depressed in front, compressed behind; anterior nostrils each with a short barbel; chin with a long barbel; 2 dorsal fins, the first short, the second very long; caudal fin rounded: 1 species.

L. maculosa (LeSueur). Burbot; lawyer; ling. Length 250 mm.; head 4.5; depth 6; color dark olive marbled with blackish; rays of dorsal fins 13-76; anal 68: lakes and sluggish streams, from New England to the upper Missouri; northward to the Arctic and Bering Strait; southward to the Ohio; common towards the north.

Order 13. Heterostomata.—The flat-fish. Bones of the head unsymmetrical, both eyes being on the same side; anus near the head; pseudobranchiæ present; dorsal fin extending the length of the body; anal fin similar but shorter; body much compressed, the side without an eye being usually colorless and kept lowermost; young individuals symmetrical: 2 families, all marine, one species in fresh water.

Family Soleidæ.—The soles. Body oval in outline; cranium much twisted, the mouth very small; teeth rudimentary or wanting: 150 species.

Achirus Lacépède. Eyes and color on right side; scales well developed, ctenoid; eyes separated by a bony ridge; pectoral fins minute or wanting: numerous species.

A. fasciatus Lac. Length 200 mm.; head 4; depth 1.8; color dusky olive, mottled with 8 dark, narrow, vertical stripes; rays of dorsal fin 50 to 55; anal 37 to 46; scales 66 to 75; origin of dorsal fin at tip of snout: Cape Ann to Texas, ascending rivers; common.

Order 14. Acanthopteri.—The spiny-rayed fishes. Anterior vertebræ unmodified and without Weberian ossicles; ventral fins usually more or less anterior in position. being either thoracic or jugular, and possessing normally 1 spine and 5 soft rays; anterior rays of dorsal and also of anal fins spinous; scales typically ctenoid; margin of mouth formed by the premaxillaries alone; air bladder typically without pneumatic duct in the adult: over 40 families, mostly of marine fishes; about 7 families (in the United States) include fresh water fishes.

Key to the Fresh Water Families

a_1 Ventral fins abdominal in position.........................1. *Atherinidæ*.
a_2 Ventral fins thoracic or jugular in position.
  b_1 Lateral line wanting......................................2. *Elassomidæ*.

b₂ Lateral line present (except in *Microperca*), more or
    less complete.
  c₁ Lateral line not extending on to the tail fin.
    d₁ But one dorsal fin present (the spinous and
        soft-rayed portions being joined); sunfish
        and black bass...........................3. *Centrarchidæ.*
    d₂ Two dorsal fins present (the spinous and soft-
        rayed portions not being joined).
      e₁ Anal spines 1 or 2.
        f₁ Pseudobranchiæ well developed; pre-
            opercle serrate; branchiostegals 7;
            perch and pike....................4. *Percidæ.*
        f₂ Pseudobranchiæ imperfect or wanting;
            preopercle not serrate; branchio-
            stegals 6; darters..................5. *Etheostomidæ.*
      e₂ Anal spines 3..........................6. *Moronidæ*
  c₂ Lateral line extending on to the tail fin............7. *Sciænidæ.*

Family 1.   Atherinidæ.—Silversides. Body elongate, somewhat
compressed; pseudobranchiæ present; 2 dorsal fins, the anterior with
spinous rays; anal fin long; ventral fins abdominal, with rays I, 5; no
lateral line; no pyloric cæca; branchiostegals 5 or 6: 15 genera and
about 60 species, which live along the sea coasts of the warmer continents; a few species are found in rivers.

FIG. 50.—*Labidesthes sicculus (from Fishes of Illinois).*

  1. Menidia Bonaparte. Body elongate; mouth small, very
oblique; premaxillaries protractile; teeth in bands, none on the palatines
or vomer; a silvery band along the sides; tail fin deeply forked: 10
species, all American, mostly marine, some entering rivers.

  M. beryllina (Cope). Length 65; head 4.3; depth 5 to 5.5; color
pale olive with a well defined lateral silvery band; rays of dorsal fins
V-I, 9 to 11; anal I, 15 to 18; scales 38 to 40-8; eyes very large: Massachusetts to Florida; lower Mississippi; Tennessee, in fresh and brackish
water; common locally.

  2. Labidesthes Cope. Similar to *Menidia* but with the jaws produced to form a short beak: 1 species.

L. sicculus (Cope). Brook silversides (Fig. 50). Length 85 mm.; head 4.5; depth 6 to 8; color pale olive green with a distinct lateral silvery band; back dotted with black; rays of dorsal fins IV-I, 9 to 11; anal I, 23; scales 14-75; body very slender: western New York and the Great Lakes to Iowa; southward to Florida and Texas; locally common in ponds and sluggish streams.

Family 2. Elassomidæ.—Pigmy sunfish. Body elliptical, compressed, very small in size, with rather large cycloid scales; mouth small, with strong teeth; upper jaw protractile; eyes large; checks and opercles scaly; no lateral line; 1 dorsal fin: 1 genus.

Elassoma Jordan. With the characters of the family: 2 species.

E. zonatum Jord. Length 35 mm.; head 3; depth 3.5; color olive green, with fine dots; sides with 11 vertical dark bands; rays of dorsal fin IV to V, 9 or 10; anal III, 5; scales 18-38 to 42-19: southern Illinois to Texas and Louisiana; in sluggish streams; not common.

E. evergladei Jord. Scales very large, 27 to 30: swamps from Carolinas to Georgia and Florida; common in the Everglades.

Family 3. Centrarchidæ.—The sunfish and black bass. Body compressed and more or less shortened; mouth terminal; teeth in villiform bands on the jaws, vomer, and often on the palatines, tongue and hyoids; premaxillaries protractile; maxillaries usually with supplementary bone; pseudobranchiæ imperfect; lateral line present; but 1 dorsal fin, with 6 to 13 spines, the spinous and soft-rayed portions being confluent; 6 to 10 pyloric cæca: about 16 genera and about 38 species of fresh water fishes, all but one in the eastern States and all among the most familiar food and game fishes.

Key to the Genera of Centrarchidæ

a_1 Anal fin relatively long, almost as long as the dorsal.
    b_1 Spines of dorsal fin 11 to 13............................ 1. *Centrarchus.*
    b_2 Spines of dorsal fin 5 to 8............................ 2. *Pomoxis.*
a_2 Anal fin relatively short, much shorter than the dorsal.
    b_1 Spinous and soft-rayed portions of dorsal fin not separated
        by a deep notch; depth of body usually more than two-
        thirds the length; sunfish.
        c_1 Hinder margin of tail convex.
            d_1 Spines of anal fin 5............................ 3. *Acantharchus.*
            d_2 Spines of anal fin 3.
                e_1 Spines of dorsal fin 9........................ 7. *Enneacanthus.*
                e_2 Spines of dorsal fin 10........................ 8. *Mesogonistius.*
        c_2 Hinder margin of tail mostly concave or forked.
            d_1 Spines of anal fin 5 to 8.
                e_1 In the region east of the Rockies.............. 4. *Ambloplites.*
                e_2 In the region west of the Rockies.............. 5. *Archoplites.*

  d_2 Spines of anal fin 3.
    e_1 Teeth present on the tongue................. 6. *Chænobryttus.*
    e_2 No teeth on the tongue.
      f_1 Lower pharyngeals narrow with sharp teeth.
        g_1 Supplementary maxillary well developed..10. *Apomotis.*
        g_2 Supplementary maxillary rudimentary or
          wanting.
          h_1 Lateral incomplete..................11. *Lethogrammus.*
          h_2 Lateral line complete.
            i_1 Palatines with teeth.
              j_1 Opercle extended behind as a long
                flap......................... 9. *Lepomis.*
              j_2 Opercular flap short and stiff.....12. *Sclerotis.*
            i_2 Palestines without teeth............13. *Xenotes.*
                       14. *Allotis.*
                       15. *Helioperca.*
      f_2 Lower pharyngeals broad and with blunt teeth 16. *Eupomotis.*
  b_2 Spinous and soft-rayed portions of dorsal fin separated by
  a deep notch; depth of body about one-third the length;
  black bass.
    c_1 Maxillary not extending back of the eye (Fig. 54)......17. *Micropterus.*
    c_2 Maxillary extending back of the eye (Fig. 54)........18. *Huro.*

1. Centrarchus Cuvier & Valenciennes. Body short, deep and strongly compressed; mouth large, with a projecting lower jaw; gill rakers very long; fins very large; hinder margin of tail concave: 1 species.

C. macropterus (Lacépède). Round sunfish. Length 150 mm.; head 3.25; depth 2; color yellowish green, with rows of dark spots along the sides; rays of dorsal fin XI to XIII, 12 to 14; anal VII or VIII, 15; scales 5-44-14: Virginia to Louisiana; northward in the Mississippi Valley to southern Illinois, in clear water; locally common.

2. Pomoxis Rafinesque. Body strongly compressed, elliptical; mouth large, oblique; lower jaw projecting; supplementary maxillary well developed; scales large, feebly ctenoid; fins large; gill-rakers very long; hinder margin of tail concave: 2 species.

P. annularis Raf. Crappie. Length 300 mm.; head 3; depth 2.3; color silvery olive, mottled with dark green and with indistinct vertical bars; fins very high; rays of dorsal fin VI, 18; anal VI, 18; scales 36 to 48; body rather elongate: Great Lakes to Kansas and Texas; introduced on Pacific Coast; very common in sluggish streams and ponds.

P. sparoides (Lacépède). Calico bass. Length 300 mm.; head 3; depth 2.2; color silvery olive, mottled with green or black spots; median fins with dark and pale spots in rows; rays of dorsal fin VII or VIII, 15; anal VI, 17 or 18; scales 40 to 45; body elevated; fins very high: New

York to Texas, in coastwise streams; the basins of the Great Lakes and the Mississippi; common in sluggish streams and ponds.

3. Acantharchus Gill. Body rather elongate, not much compressed or elevated; mouth rather large, oblique; scales large, cycloid; tail fin rounded; supplementary maxillary present: 1 species.

A. pomotis (Baird). Mud sunfish. Length 150 mm.; head 2.6; depth 2; color very dark greenish with several indistinct wide dark lateral bands; fins dusky; a black spot on the opercle; rays of dorsal fin XI or XII, 10 or 11; anal V, 10; scales 6-43-12: New York to South Carolina, in sluggish coastwise streams; common.

4. Ambloplites Rafinesque. Body elliptical, compressed, moderately elevated; mouth large, the lower jaw projecting; supplementary maxillary large; opercle ending in 2 flat points; scales large, somewhat ctenoid, lingual teeth in one patch; gill-rakers less than 10; lateral line complete; dorsal fin much longer than anal; caudal margin concave: 1 species.

A. rupestris (Raf.). Rock bass (Fig. 9). Length 300 mm.; head 2.75; depth 2 to 2.5; color olive green, with dark mottlings and a dark spot on each scale; a black opercular spot; eye red and very large; rays of dorsal fin XI, 10; anal VI, 10; scales 5-39 to 43-12: Vermont to Manitoba; southward to Alabama, Louisiana and Texas; very common west of the Alleghenies.

5. Archoplites Gill. Body elliptical, compressed, elevated; mouth large, oblique, the lower jaw projecting; opercle emarginate; gill-rakers about 20; lingual teeth in 2 patches; scales strongly ctenoid; hinder margin of tail emarginate: 1 species.

A. interruptus (Girard). Sacramento perch. Length 500 mm.; head 2.6; epth 2.5; color blackish above, sometimes all over; sides silvery, with about 7 vertical blackish bars; a black opercular spot; rays of dorsal fin XII or XIII, 10; anal VI or VII, 10; scales 7-40 to 51-14: basin of the Sacramento and San Joaquin Rivers; the only percoid fish west of the Rockies.

6. Chænobryttus Gill. Similar to *Ambloplites;* opercle convex at the angle; hinder margin of tail emarginate; tongue with teeth: 1 species.

C. gulosus (Cuvier & Valenciennes). Warmouth (Fig. 51). Length 250 mm.; head 2.5; depth 2.25; color olive green, clouded with red or blue, yellow below; sides sometimes with scattered dark spots; rays of dorsal fin X, 9 or 10; anal III, 8 or 9; scales 6 or 7-40 to 46-11 or 12; dorsal spines low: Great Lakes to Florida, Georgia and Texas; westward to Iowa and Kansas; common in the south.

7. Enneacanthus Gill. Little sunfish. Body short and deep, compressed, ovoid; mouth small; tongue toothless; opercle with 2 flat points on its margin; lateral line sometimes interrupted; supplementary maxillary large; tail margin rounded behind: 2 species.

E. obesus (Baird). Length 125 mm.; head 2.6; depth 2; color olivaceous, with 5 to 8 blackish cross bars; purplish or golden spots on body and fins; a large black opercular spot; rays of dorsal fin IX, 10; anal III, 10; scales 4-28-10: Boston to Florida, coastwise; often common in weedy streams.

FIG. 51.—*Chænobryttus gulosus (from Fishes of Illinois).*

E. gloriosus (Holbrook). Length 70 mm.; head 2.75; depth 2.25; color dark olive, with numerous small round blue spots which often form irregular cross stripes; opercular spot blue; rays of dorsal fin IX, 10; anal III, 9; scales 3-30-9; body comparatively elongate: New York to Florida, in clear sluggish streams.

8. Mesogonistius Gill. Body short, deep, compressed; mouth small; supplementary maxillary small; opercle with 2 flat points; anal fin much smaller than the dorsal; tail rounded behind: 1 species.

M. chætodon (Baird). Black-banded sunfish. Length 100 mm.; head 3; depth 1.6; color clouded straw-color, the sides with 6 to 8 conspicuous, irregular black vertical bars; a black opercular spot; rays of dorsal fin X, 10; anal III, 12; scales 4-28-10; body oval: New Jersey to Georgia, in sluggish streams.

9. Lepomis Rafinesque. Sunfish. Body ovate, compressed; back elevated; mouth small or moderate; suplementary maxillary reduced to a rudiment or wanting; gill-rakers short; opercle ending behind in a long black convex flap; hinder margin of tail concave; lower pharyngeals (Fig. 52) narrow, with sharp teeth; palatines with teeth: 2 species.

L. auritus (L.). Red belly. Length 200 mm.; head (without flap) 3; depth 2 to 2.5; color olive; belly and lower fins orange red; opercular flap very long and narrow; rays of dorsal fin X, 11 or 12; anal III, 8 to 10; scales 6-43 to 48-15; scales on cheek in 7 rows: Maine to Louisana, east of the Alleghenies; common.

L. solis (Cuvier and Valenciennes). Similar to above; scales on cheek in 4 to 6 rows; last rays of dorsal fin with a large dark spot; head 3.6; depth 2; scales 51 in lateral line: Virginia to Louisiana.

10. Apomotis Rafinesque. Like *Lepomis*, but with a well-developed supplemental maxillary: 3 species.

FIG. 52.—Lower left pharyngeal of *Helioperca incisor; a*, upper aspect; *b*, lateral aspect (*from Fishes of Illinois*).

A. cyanellus (Raf.). Green sunfish. Length 175 mm.; head 3; depth 2.5; color olivaceous, with a brassy lustre on the sides, yellow below; each scale usually with a sky-blue spot; eye red; rays of dorsal fin X, 11; anal III. 9; scales 7-45 to 55-16: Great Lakes to Mexico, not east of the Alleghenies; very common towards the south.

A. punctatus (Cuvier & Valenciennes). Length 150 mm.; head 3; depth 2; color olivaceous, everywhere with numerous minute brown dots; rays of dorsal fin X, 11; anal III, 10; scales 6-40 to 45-13: South Carolina to Florida, in lowland streams.

11. Lethogrammus Hubbs. Like *Lepomis*, but with an incomplete lateral line: 1 species.

L. symmetricus (Forbes). Length 75 mm.; head 2.75; depth 2.25; color dark green, each scale with a brown spot at its base; a black opercular spot present; rays of dorsal fin X, 10; anal III, 9; scales 6-35-10; mouth moderate, with projecting lower jaw; hinder margin of tail convex: Illinois to Texas; not rare southwards.

12. Sclerotis Hubbs. Similar to *Lepomis*, but with the opercular flap truncate and with a stiff margin: 1 species.

S. miniatus (Jordan). Length 150 mm.; head 2.75; depth 2.25; sides of male with about 14 rows of red spots; middle of the side with a few scales with black spots; belly orange with red spots; rays of dorsal fin X, 10; anal III, 9; scales 4-40-11: Texas to Indiana River, Florida; north to southern Illinois; in lowland streams; common near New Orleans.

13. Xenotes Jordan. Like *Lepomis*, but without palatine teeth; gill-rakers rudimentary; pectoral fins rounded: 2 species.

X. megalotis (Raf.). Long-eared sunfish. Length 200 mm.; head (without flap) 3; depth 1.6 to 2.5; color blue above, orange below; sides with orange spots; head with blue stripes and reticulations; opercular flap very long and broad; rays of dorsal fin X, 10 to 12; anal III, 8 to 10; scales 5-36 to 45-14: Great Lakes to Texas and Florida; westward to Minnesota; eastward to North Carolina; common.

14. Allotis Hubbs. Like *Lepomis*, but without palatine teeth and with enlarged sensory cavities in the cranial and facial bones: 1 species.

A. humilis (Girard). Spotted sunfish. Length 75 mm.; head 2.75; depth 2.25; color bluish with greenish specks posteriorly; opercle

a   b

FIG. 53.—Lower left pharyngeal of *Eupomotis gibbosus: a,* upper aspect; *b,* lateral aspect
(from Fishes of Illinois).

with 4 red bands; sides with many rounds orange spots; belly pink; eye red; rays of dorsal fin X, 10 or 11; anal III, 8 or 9; scales 5-34 to 42-11: Ohio and Kentucky to Dakota; southward to Texas; locally common.

15. Helioperca Jordan. Like *Lepomis*, but without palatine teeth; gill-rakers long; pectoral fins pointed: 2 species.

H. macrochira (Raf.). Length 125 mm.; head 3; depth 2.3; color blue with many orange spots which cover nearly the entire surface, so arranged that the ground color forms a series of vertical bars; no blue stripes on the cheek; rays of dorsal fin X, 12; anal III, 10; scales 44: Ohio Valley and southwestward to Arkansas; rare.

H. incisor (Cuvier and Valenciennes) Bluegill. Length 300 mm.; head 3; depth 2; color olive green; belly yellow or brown; sides with greenish cross bars; no blue stripes on the cheeks or red on the fins; a black on the base of the last rays of the dorsal fin; rays of dorsal fin X, 11 or 12; anal III, 10 to 12; scales 7-43 to 52-16: Great Lakes and Minnesota to Florida and the Rio Grande; east of the Alleghenies from New Jersey southward; very common in quiet streams and ponds.

16. Eupomotis Gill & Jordan. Sunfish. Very similar to *Lepomis,* but with lower pharyngeal bones (Fig. 53) broad and concave and with blunt teeth; no supplementary maxillary: 3 species.

Key to the Species of Eupomotis

a$_1$ No scarlet on the opercular flap.

  b$_2$ Border of opercular flap blood red in male, pale in female; scales

    34 to 39...*E. heros.*

    b$_3$ Border of opercular flap orange; scales 42 to 44............*E. holbrookii.*

a$_2$ Lower posterior border of opercular flap scarlet.................*E. gibbosus.*

E. heros (Baird & Girard). Head 3; depth 2.4; color dark greenish above, yellowish below; rays of dorsal fin X, 11; anal III, 11; scales 6-34 to 39-14: Indiana to Florida and the Rio Grande basin; rare.

E. holbrookii (Cuvier & Valenciennes). Length 250 mm.; head 3 to 3.5; depth 2 to 2.25; color dusky olive; silvery below; throat yellow; rays of dorsal fin X, 10 to 12; anal III, 9 to 11; scales 6-44 or 45-14: Virginia to Florida; common in lowland streams.

E. gibbosus (L.). Common sunfish; pumpkin-seed. Length 200 mm.; head 3 to 3.25; depth 1.75 to 2; color greenish olive above, shaded with bluish; sides spotted with orange; belly orange yellow; rays of dorsal fin X, 10 to 12; anal III, 10 or 11; scales 6-40 to 47-13; body ovate: Maine to Minnesota; southward east of the Alleghenies to Florida, but rather rare towards the south; in the northern parts only of the Mississippi Valley; very common, especially in ponds; eggs deposited in a nest made in shallow water by the male, who scoops out a depression in the bottom about a foot in diameter and several inches deep, which he guards after the eggs are laid and the young are hatched.

17. Micropterus Lacépède. Black bass. Body elongate; mouth very large, oblique; lower jaw projecting; supplementary maxillary bone broad; scales small, ctenoid; lateral line complete; dorsal fin with a deep notch between the spinous and the soft-rayed scaly portions; hinder margin of tail concave: 2 species, both important game and good fishes.

M. dolomieu Lac. Small-mouthed black bass. Length 600 mm.; weight up to 7 lbs.; scales on the cheek in about 17 rows; head 2.5; depth 3.3; color a uniform dull green, with a golden lustre; 3 longitudinal bands of the head back of the eye; young with dark spots; rays of dorsal fin X, 13 to 15; anal III, 10 to 12; scales 11-72 to 75-17: St. Lawrence River to Dakota; southward to South Carolina and Texas; common, especially in clear, cool streams and lakes; introduced into New England and many other places.

M. pseudaplites Hubbs. Similar to the above; scales on the cheek larger; side with a black band (fading with age); scales 59 to 66; soft rays of fins 11 or 12: Valley of the Ohio River in Kentucky and Ohio; south to Kansas and Texas; common.

18. Huro Cuvier. Similar to *Micropterus*, but with the pyloric cæca mostly branched; mouth very large; maxillary extending beyond the eye; soft portion of the dorsal and anal fins scaleless: 1 species.

H. salmoides (Lac.). Large-mouthed black bass. Length 750 mm.; extreme weight 20 lbs.; head 3 to 3.5; depth 3 to 3.25; color dark green, silvery below; adult plain, young with a broad blackish lateral band; 3 longitudinal bands on the head back of the eye; rays of dorsal fin X, 12 to 13; anal III, 10 or 11; scales 8-68-16: Great Lakes region to Dakota; southward to Florida and Mexico; common, especially in lakes and sluggish waters.

a   b

Fig. 54.—Black bass heads: *a*, head of *Micropterus dolomieu; b*, head of *Huro salmoides (from Jordan & Evermann).*

4. Family Percidæ.—The perch. Body elongate or elliptical; scales ctenoid and small; lateral line complete; mouth terminal or inferior; opercle ending in a flat spine; branchiostegals 7; 2 dorsal fins, anterior with about 13 spines; anal fin with 2 spines; ventral fins thoracic, with rays I, 5; air bladder small; pyloric cæca few: over 100 species, inhabiting the fresh waters of the northern hemisphere; 3 United States genera.

1. Perca L. Body elliptical, compressed; cheek scaly; opercle mostly naked and armed with a single spine; preopercle serrated; mouth terminal; branchiostegals 7; pseudobranchiæ small, but well developed; pyloric cæca 3; caudal margin concave: 3 species, *P. fluviatilis* occurring in Europe, and *P. schrenki* in Asia.

P. flavescens (Mitchill). Yellow perch; common perch. Length 300 mm.; head 3.25; depth 3.25; back elevated; color dark olive green above; sides yellow with 6 to 8 broad dark transverse bars; belly bright yellow; lower fins orange; rays of dorsal fins XIII-I, 14; anal II, 7 or 8; scales 5-55-17: Nova Scotia to South Carolina, in coastwise streams; throughout the Great Lakes region and westware to Iowa and Dakota; not found from central Ohio southwestward; very common; introduced on the Pacific slope. The perch spawns in the spring, laying its eggs in a single mass which stretches out ribbon-like, sometimes 7 feet or more.

2. Stizostedion Rafinesque. Body elongate; fusiform; head long; premaxillaries protractile; top of head scaly; mouth large; jaws equal; tail forked; ventral fins well separated; lateral line continuous; branchiostegals 7; pseudobranchiæ well developed: 2 species, both important food and game fishes.

S. vitreum (Mitchill). Wall-eye pike; pike-perch (Fig. 55). Length up to 900 mm.; weight up to 25 lbs.; head 3.6; depth 4.5; color dark olive green, blotched with darker; belly pinkish; anterior dorsal fin with

FIG. 55.—*Stizostedion vitreum (from Jordan & Evermann)*.

a large black spot on its hinder part; rays of dorsal fins XII to XVI-21; anal II, 12 to 14; scales 10-110 to 132-25; pyloric cæca 3, of nearly equal length; sides of head almost naked: Vermont and Pennsylvania to Saskatchewan; southward to Georgia; northward to Hudson Bay; very common northward.

S. glaucum Hubbs. Similar to above, but smaller; color grayish blue; length 450 mm.: Lake Erie.

3. Cynoperca Gill and Jordan. Like *Stizostedion;* pyloric cæca 4 to 8, of unequal length: 1 species.

C. canadensis (Smith). Sauger; sand pike. Length 450 mm.; head 3.5; depth 4.5 to 6; color olive gray; sides brassy or orange, with dark mottlings; spinous dorsal fin with 3 irregular rows of black spots; rays of dorsal fins XI to XV-I, 18; anal II, 11 or 12; scales 9-100 to 125-27; pyloric cæca 4 to 8, of unequal length; sides of head scaly: Great Lakes and St. Lawrence regions; westward to Montana; southward to Tennessee and Arkansas.

Subspecies of C. canadensis

C. c. grisea (DeKay). Head less completely scaled; head bones and opercles smoother: Great Lakes and southward.

C. c. borea (Girard).   Head slender: upper Missouri.

Family 5.   Etheostomidæ.—The darters.   Body small, elongate; scales ctenoid; air bladder small and often wanting; teeth all sharp, and usually present on the vomer and palatines; gills 4; branchiostegals 6; pyloric cæca 2 or 3; 2 dorsal fins, the anterior with many spines; anal fin with 2 (rarely 1) spines: about 30 genera and 100 species, all American; very small, mostly brightly colored fishes living in small clear streams, largely in mountainous regions in the eastern States.

Key to the Genera Here Included

a_1 With a pig-like snout which projects beyond the mouth.... 1. *Percina.*
a_2 No such snout present.
  b_1 Top of skull between the eyes rather flattened or depressed,
     not strongly convex.
    c_1 Body not hyaline and extremely slender.
      d_1 Premaxillaries not protractile.
        e_1 Belly with enlarged caducous scales, or (if
           absent), more or less bare.
          f_1 Palatine teeth present...................... 2. *Alvordius;*
                                          4. *Serraria.*
          f_2 Palatine teeth absent...................... 3. *Ericosoma.*
        e_2 Belly with ordinary scales which are never shed.. 5. *Hadropterus.*
                                          6. *Swainia.*
                                        7. *Hypohomus.*
      d_2 Premaxillaries proctractile.
        e_1 Two anal spines present.
          f_1 Gill membranes but slightly connected.......11. *Doration.*
          f_2 Gill membranes broadly connected across the
            isthmus.
            g_1 Belly behind the ventral fins with scales
               like the sides........................10. *Ulocentra.*
                                12. *Etheostoma.*
            g_2 Belly behind the ventral fins more or less
               scaleless............................. 8. *Cottogaster.*
                                 9. *Imostoma.*
        e_2 But 1 anal spine present.
          f_1 Lateral line complete.....................13. *Boleosoma.*
          f_2 Lateral line incomplete...................14. *Vaillantia.*
    c_2 Body hyaline and extremely slender and elongate.
      d_1 Premaxillaries not protractile...................15. *Crystallaria.*
      d_2 Premaxillaries protractile.
        e_1 But 1 anal spine present.....................17. *Vigil.*
        e_2 Two anal spines present.....................16. *Ammocrypta.*
                                    18. *Ioa.*
  b_2 Top of the head between eyes not depressed but more or
     less strongly convex; premaxillaries never protractile;

belly with ordinary scales; ventral fins inserted close
together.

c_1 Lateral line complete.

d_1 Anal fin large, approaching the soft portion of the
dorsal in size.................................19. *Poecilichthys.*

d_2 Anal fin small, much smaller than the soft dorsal...20. *Nanostoma.*

21. *Nothonotus.*

c_2 Lateral line more or less incomplete.

d_1 Gill membranes not connected...................22. *Oligocephalus.*

d_2 Gill membranes broadly connected across the
isthmus.

e_1 Anal spines 2...............................23. *Claricola.*

24. *Catonotus.*

26. *Hololepis.*

e_2 But 1 anal spine present.......................25. *Psychromaster.*

28. *Alvarius.*

c_3 Lateral line wanting.............................27. *Microperca.*

1. Percina Haldeman. Body slender, elongate, slightly compressed; midventral line with enlarged plates, which may fall off leaving a naked strip; caudal margin concave; mouth overhung by snout; teeth on vomer and palatines; lateral line continuous; air bladder and pseudobranchiæ rudimentary: 2 species.

P. caprodes (Rafinesque). Log-perch. Length 200 mm.; head 4 to 4.7; depth 5 to 6.5; color yellowish green, with about 15 black transverse bars extending from the back to the belly and alternating with shorter ones; a round spot at the base of the tail fin; rays of dorsal fin XIII to XV-12 to 17; anal II, 9 to 12; scales 9-90 to 95-15: Great Lakes region to North Carolina, Mississippi and the Rio Grande; in Atlantic coastal streams southward to North Carolina; in large, clear streams; generally common.

P. rex Jordan & Evermann. Length 150 mm.; head 4; depth 4.6; scales 11-83 to 85-19; anterior dorsal fin with a broad orange band towards the margin: Roanoke River; rare.

2. Alvordius Girard. Black-sided darters. Body very small, elongate, cylindrical, brightly colored, but without any red or blue, and with a series of large dark more or less confluent blotches along the lateral line and rounded blotches on the back; mouth terminal; teeth on jaws and vomer and usually the palatines; midventral area with enlarged scales, or with large plates which in most species may be shed, leaving the belly naked; fins large; ventral fins well separated: about 9 species.

A. evermanni (Mœnkhaus). Length 100 mm.; head 4; depth 5; color olive, marbled; sides with 13 or 14 blotches; rays of dorsal fins

XIII-14; anal II-12; scales 8-69-8 to 12; cheeks and opercles scaly: northern Indiana and Illinois; rare.

A. *phoxocephalus* (Nelson). Length 100 mm.; head 4; depth 5.5 to 6; color yellowish brown, with the lateral blotches elongate; cheek and opercle scaly; rays of dorsal fins XI or XII-12 to 14; anal II, 8 or 9; scales 12-68-14; head very long and slender; a strong opercular spine; pyloric cæca 2: Ohio to Iowa; southward to Tennessee and Oklahoma; in sandy rivers; locally common.

A. *macrocephalus* (Cope). Length 75 mm.; head 3.5 to 4; depth 6 or 7; color light brown, with 9 spots on the side; rays of dorsal fins XV-12 to 14; anal II, 9 to 11; scales 11-77-15; cheek naked or with

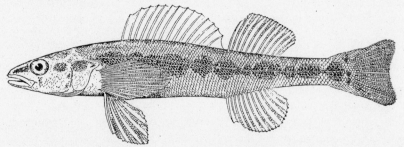

Fig. 56.—*Alvordius maculatus* (from *Jordan & Evermann*).

rudimentary scales; opercle with small cycloid scales; a small spot at the base of the tail fin: west slope of the Alleghenies, from Pennsylvania southwards; in clear rivers; scarce; not in brooks.

A. *maculatus* Girard (Fig. 56). Length 100 mm.; head 4; depth 5 or 6; color yellowish or greenish, with about 7 elongate blotches along the sides; rays of dorsal fins XIII to XV-11 to 13; anal II, 8 to 10; scales 9-65-17; cheek with small scales, opercle with larger ones; pyloric cæca 3: Great Lakes to Manitoba; eastward and southward to the James, the Ohio Valley and to Arkansas; common in clear streams; common in small brooks.

A. *peltatus* (Stauffer). Length 100 mm.; head 4; depth 5.6; color light yellow, with 6 large, squarish lateral blotches and faint bars between; cheek naked; opercle scaled above; rays of dorsal fins XII-12; anal II, 8; scales 6-52 to 56-9: southeastern Pennsylvania to South Carolina, in coastwise streams; locally common.

A. *ouachitæ* (Jordan & Gilbert). Length 60 mm.; head 4; depth 6.5; color olivaceous, with about 5 rather black bars extending downward from the back to the lateral line and 8 or 9 dusky quadrate lateral blotches; rays of dorsal fins XI or XII-13; anal II, 10; scales 6-52 to 60-10: southern Indiana to Arkansas; not rare.

A. roanoka (Jordan & Jenkins). Length 60 mm.; head 4; depth 4.75; color light yellow, with dark green markings and 10 or 11 vertical green lateral confluent bars; anterior dorsal fin with a median band of bright yellow; female pale; rays of dorsal fins X or XI-11; anal II, 8 or 9; scales 5-48-9; body robust: southern Virginia and North Carolina; common.

3. Ericosoma Jordan. Similar to *Alvordius*, but without palatine teeth; ventrals not widely separate; males with lower fins tuberculate in the spring: 1 species.

E. evides (Jordan & Copeland). Length 75 mm.; head 4.3; depth 5.3; color extremely brilliant, olivaceous or yellow above, mottled with darker with about 7 broad transverse green (male) or black (female) bars extending from the back down the sides, connected by an orange-brown lateral line; rays of dorsal fins XI-10; anal II, 8 or 9; scales 9-52 to 67-9 to 11; cheeks not scaly: Indiana, in the Maumee and Wabash basins, to central Iowa; southward to Arkansas and North Carolina; often common.

4. Serraria Gilbert. Similar to *Alvordius*, but with serrate preopercle: 1 species.

S. sciera (Swain). Length 75 mm.; head 4 to 4.8; depth 5 or 6; color yellowish olive, everywhere vaguely blotched with black; top of head, dorsal anal and caudal fins black; preopercle serrate; cheeks and opercles scaly; gill membranes united; rays of dorsal fins XIII-13 or 14; anal II, 9; scales 7-65 to 70-17; fins very large: northern Indiana to Tennessee and Texas.

5. Hadropterus Agassiz. Like *Alvordius*, belly with a series of large persistent scales: 1 species.

H. nigrofasciatus Agassiz. Length 150 mm.; head 4; depth 5; color dark olive; sides with 12 narrow vertical bars, confluent along the middle; no red or blue; body stout, compressed; fins large; dorsal fins XII-11 or 12; anal II, 9 or 10; scales 7-58-15: South Carolina to Louisiana, in larger clear streams; often common.

6. Swainia Jordan and Evermann. Gill membranes united; belly with ordinary scales; a conspicuous shoulder spot: 1 species.

S. squamata (Gilbert & Swain). Length 125 mm.; body elongate; head 3.7; depth 5.5; color yellowish olive, with 10 broad dusky bars across the back, and an equal number along the lateral line; a conspicuous black shoulder spot; rays of the dorsal fins XIV-13; anal II, 10; scales 10-82-18; cheeks and opercle scaly; gill membranes broadly united across the isthmus: upper Tennessee River basin; rare.

7. Hypohomus Cope. Like *Swainia*, but with gill membranes separate and no shoulder spot: 4 species.

H. aurantiacus (Cope). Length 150 mm.; head 4.25; depth 6; color olive, with a row of confluent blotches along the side joined by a dark lateral band; chin and throat deep orange; rays of dorsal fins XV-15; anal II, 11; scales 14-85-15: upper Tennessee basin.

H. cymatotænia (Gilbert & Meek). Length 125 mm.; head 4 to 4.25; depth 5; body robust; color greenish, with fine dots and 2 pale streaks along the sides; a black spot at the base of the tail fin; rays of dorsal fins XII to XIV-12 to 14; anal II, 10; scales 7-64 to 70-12: southern Missouri.

8. Cottogaster Putnam. Body slender; snout blunt; scales ctenoid; midventral space naked anteriorly or with enlarged caducous scales; lateral line continuous; premaxillaries protractile: 2 species.

FIG. 57.—*Imostoma shumardi (from Fishes of Illinois).*

C. uranidea (Jordan & Gilbert). Length 50 mm.; head 3.5; depth 5.6; color greenish olive; back with 4 conspicuous broad black cross bands and 11 dark blotches below the lateral line; cheeks mostly naked; opercle scaly; rays of dorsal fins X or XI-13; anal II, 10 or 11; scales 6-48 to 56-10: southern Indiana to Alabama and Arkansas, in lowland streams.

C. copelandi (Jordan). Length 75 mm.; head 3.75; depth 5.5 to 6.5; color brownish olive, with a series of small black blotches along the lateral line forming an interrupted lateral band; a black spot on the anterior dorsal fin; cheek naked; opercle with a few scales; rays of dorsal fins X to XII-10 to 12; anal II, 8 or 9; scales 6-44 to 56-8: Lake Champlain to Lake Huron and southwestward to Tennessee and southern Missouri; abundant in central Indiana; in clear brooks.

9. Imostoma Jordan. Like *Cottogaster*, but with scaly cheeks; midventral plates not enlarged: 3 species.

I. shumardi (Girard) (Fig. 57). Length 75 mm.; head 3.4; depth 5; color dark, vaguely blotched with darker, with a large black spo att the base of the anterior dorsal fin; caudal and pectoral fins barred; rays of dorsal fins IX to XI-13 to 15; anal II, 10 to 12; scales 6-48 to 60-11: Manitoba to Kentucky and Arkansas; the Great Lakes region; common.

10. **Ulocentra** Jordan.   Darters.   Body elongate; head short and thick; scales on belly like those on the sides; premaxillaries protractile; ventral fins close together: 6 species, several rare.

U. histrio (Jordan & Gilbert).   Length 50 mm.; head 4 to 4.25; depth 5 to 5.5; color very dark green, with 7 light dorsal cross bars usually alternating with bars beneath the lateral line; fins all barred; head naked; rays of dorsal fins X-13; anal II, 7; scales 6-52-11: southern Indiana and Kentucky to Arkansas; common.

U. simotera (Cope).   Length 75 mm.; head 4 to 4.6; depth 4 to 5; color green; sides with dark blotches; belly yellow; dorsal fins variegated; back spotted with red; rays of dorsal fins X-11; anal II, 7; scales 10-52-12; snout very short: western Virginia and eastern Kentucky to Alabama; very common in clear streams.

U. longimana (Jordan).   Length 60 mm.; head 4.4; depth 5; color green, with 10 small irregular spots on the sides and about 5 cross blotches on the back; cheeks and breast naked; opercles scaly; rays of dorsal fins X-13; anal II, 8; scales 5-44-7: Virginia; abundant in rocky streams.

U. podostemona (Jordan & Jenkins).   Length 50 mm.; head 4.4; depth 5.6; color yellowish green, with 7 or 8 dark spots along the sides and 5 or 6 larger ones along the back; fins barred; cheeks and breast naked; opercles scaly; rays of dorsal fins X-12; anal II, 8; scales 4-35-8: Roanoke River; common.

11. **Doration** Jordan.   Similar to *Boleosoma*, but with an incomplete lateral line and with 2 anal spines: 1 species.

D. stigmæa (Jord.).   Length 60 mm.; head 4.25; depth 5; color olivaceous, speckled above; sides with 8 dark green blotches below the lateral line; rays of dorsal fins X to XIII-12; anal II, 7; scales 5-46 to 55-10; opercle and cheek scaly; lateral line incomplete: Tennessee and Georgia to Arkansas and Louisiana; rather common in pine woods.

12. **Etheostoma** Rafinesque.   Body slender; head very blunt; mouth very small, inferior; premaxillaries protractile; gill membranes joined across the isthmus: 1 species.

E. blennioides Rafinesque.   Green-sided darter (Fig. 58).   Length 125 mm.; head 4.5; depth 4.75-6; color olive green; sides with about 8 double transverse bars and dotted with orange; second dorsal and anal fins bluish green; rays of dorsal fins XII to XIV-12 to 15; anal II,

8 or 9; scales 6-58 to 78-14: Michigan to the Alabama basin and Kansas; common.

13. Boleosoma DeKay.   Body elongate; head pointed; premaxillaries protractile; vomer teeth present; scales large; belly with ordinary

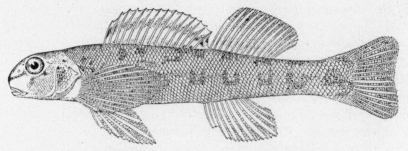

FIG. 58.—*Etheostoma blennioides* (*from Fishes of Illinois*).

scales; ventral fins well separated; anal fin with but one spine; no red or blue in the coloration; pyloric cæca mostly 6: 5 species.

B. nigrum (Rafinesque).   Johnny darter (Fig. 59).   Length 60 mm.; head 4.2; depth 5 or 6; color pale olivaceous; back speckled with brown; sides with numerous small black blotches; males in spring

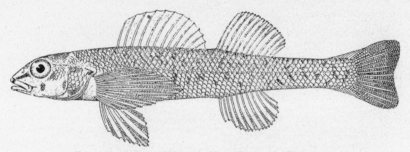

FIG. 59.—*Boleosoma nigrum* (*from Jordan & Evermann*).

black anteriorly; opercles scaly; rays of dorsal fins IX-12; anal I, 7 to 9; scales 5-44 to 55-9; scales rarely 35 to 40: eastern and central States; western Pennsylvania to Colorado; Oklahoma to Manitoba; very common in most streams, especially in small ones among weeds.

Subspecies of B. nigrum

B. n. olmstedi (Storer).   Length 85 mm.; soft dorsal fin with 13 to 15 rays; cheek scaly: coastwise streams; south to Virginia.

B. n. effulgens (Girard).   Cheek and breast naked; color metallic green: Maryland to North Carolina.

B. n. vexillare Jord.   Cheek naked; rays of dorsal fins VIII or IX-10 to 12; anal I, 7; scales 4-35 to 47-6: Virginia; common.

B. n. maculaticeps Cope. Head spotted; cheek naked: Catawba River, North Carolina; common.

B. susanæ Jordan & Swain. Length 50 mm.; head 4; depth 65.; color as in *B. nigrum;* rays of dorsal fins VIII-10 or 11; anal I, 8; scales 4-45 to 50-6; head naked; body very slender: upper Cumberland River, Kentucky; common.

14. Vaillantia Jordan. Similar to *Boleosoma,* but with incomplete lateral line: 1 species.

V. camura (Forbes). Length 60 mm.; head 4 to 4.5; depth 5.5 to 6.5; color as in *B. nigrum;* rays of dorsal fins IX or X-10 or 11; anal I, 7 or 8; scales 5 or 6-56 to 65-11; lateral line ending near middle of body; cheek and opercle scaly: Indiana to Iowa; southward to Alabama and Texas; common towards the south.

FIG. 60.—*Vigil pellucidus (from Fishes of Illinois).*

15. Crystallaria Jordan & Gilbert. Body elongate and very slender and hyaline; lateral line complete; cheek and opercle scaly; tail forked; but 1 anal spine; premaxillaries not protractile; throat and belly naked: 1 species.

C. asprella (Jordan). Length 100 mm.; eyes very large; head 4 to 4.5; depth 7 or 8; color olive, mottled, with 4 or 5 dark cross bands on the back and a dark lateral band; rays of dorsal fins XII to XIV-13 to 15; anal I, 12 to 14; scales 7 to 10-98-10 (83 to 85 in specimens from Alabama): southern Indiana and Illinois to Alabama and Arkansas, in swift streams.

16. Ammocrypta Jordan. Similar to *Crystallaria,* but with very protractile premaxillaries: 1 species, which has the habit of burying itself in the sand.

A. beani Jord. Length 60 mm.; head 3.75; depth 7.5; color translucent, without bars or spots; anterior dorsal fin spotted; rays of dorsal fins VIII to X-10 or 11; anal I, 9 or 10; scales 65; head and body naked, except the caudal peduncle: Alabama to Louisiana; common in pine woods.

17. Vigil Jordan. Body very elongate, slender and hyaline; belly almost bare; premaxillaries protractile; anal spine single: 3 species, which bury themselves in the sand.

V. pellucidus (Baird). Sand darter (Fig. 60). Length 75 mm.; head 4 to 4.75; depth 7 to 8.5; body translucent; nose very sharp; a series of small spots along the back and another along each side; cheek and opercle scaly; rays of dorsal fins X-10; anal I, 8 to 10; scales 67 to 78: Lake Erie to Minnesota; southward to Kentucky and Texas; common in clear, sandy streams.

V. vivax (Hay).   A dusky bar across the base of the soft dorsal fin: Mississippi to Arkansas and Texas.

18. Ioa Jordan & Brayton.   Similar to *Vigil*, but with 2 spines in the anal fin: 2 species.

I. vitrea (Cope).   Length 50 mm.; head 4 to 4.5; depth 7 to 7.5; color translucent, with small dark spots on the back and sides; rays of dorsal fins VII to IX-11 to 14; anal II, 6 to 9; scales 50 to 62; belly partly naked: eastern Virginia and North Carolina; common.

19. Poecilichthys Agassiz.   Body elongate and brightly colored; belly with ordinary scales; gill membranes broadly joined across the isthmus; premaxillaries not protractile; ventral fins well separated: 1 species.

P. variatus (Kirtland).   Body moderately elongate; head short and blunt and very rugose; length 100 mm.; head 3.5 to 4.4; depth 4.8 to 5.5; color greenish; sides and belly orange, with 5 bands posteriorly; anterior dorsal fin with a blue band; female paler; fins very large; rays of dorsal fins XII to XIV-11 to 13; anal II, 7 to 9; scales 8-51 to 63-12: Ohio basin to Arkansas; rare.

20. Nanostoma Putnam.—Similar to *Poecilichthys*, but with a small anal fin, much smaller than the soft part of the dorsal: 7 species.

N. swannanoa (Jordan & Evermann).   Body robust; length 75 mm.; head 4.3; depth 6; head naked, very short and blunt; color green, with 6 distinct dark cross blotches on the back and 8 or 10 on the sides; cheeks, opercles and breast naked; rays of dorsal fins XI or XII-12 to 14; anal II, 9; scales 6-48 to 57-7 or 8: upper waters of the Tennessee River; common.

N. thalassinum (Jordan & Brayton).   Length 60 mm.; head 3.6; depth 4.75 to 5; color dark green, blotches above and with 6 to 9 dark vertical bars; dorsal fins reddish; females duller; head and throat naked; rays of dorsal fins IX to XI-10 to 12; anal II, 7 or 8; scales 5-40 to 48-7: Santee River basin; very abundant.

N. zonale (Cope) (Fig. 61).   Body slender; length 75 mm.; head 4 or 5; depth 5 or 6; color olivaceous, with large dorsal spots which connect with a lateral band from which 8 bands encircle the belly; rays of dorsal fins X or XI-10 to 12; anal II, 6 to 8; scales 6-48 to 53-9; cheeks, opercles and throat more or less scaly: Mississippi Valley, from Ohio to Iowa; southward to Alabama and Louisiana; abundant; very variable.

21. Nothonotus Agassiz. Similar to *Poecilichthys*, but with the ventral fins close together at the base and with the gill membranes scarcely joined across the isthmus: 7 species.

N. camurus (Cope). Blue-breasted darter. Body stout; length 60 mm.; head 4; depth 4.5; color dark olive, sprinkled with crimson dots; throat and breast deep blue; posterior dorsal, anal and caudal fins crimson, bordered by yellow and blue; rays of dorsal fins XI-13; anal II, 8; scales 7-50 to 58-8; cheeks and opercles naked; body stout; head blunt: Indiana and Ohio to Tennessee, in swift waters; not common.

Fig. 61.—*Nanostoma zonale* (*from Fishes of Illinois*).

N. maculatus (Kirt.). Body elongate with a large tail fin; length 60 mm.; head 4; depth 5.25; color black above, olive below; throat blue; back and sides with crimson dots; anterior dorsal fin with a black spot; tail fin with 2 crimson spots at the base; cheeks naked; opercles scaly; rays of dorsal fins XII-12 or 13; anal II, 8 or 9; scales 9-56 to 63-14: northern Ohio and Indiana to northern Alabama and Tennessee: rare.

N. cinereus (Storer). Body slender; length 100 mm.; head 3.5; depth 5.5; color light yellow, with 4 dark cross bars on the back and a series of about 12 dark spots along the lateral line; rays of dorsal fins XI or XII-11 to 13; anal II, 8; scales 8-57 to 60-9; opercles scaly; cheeks, breast and nape naked: Tennessee and Cumberland Rivers; rare.

N. rufilineatus (Cope). Body stout; length 75 mm.; head 4; depth 4.5 to 5; color green, with narrow longitudinal stripes and quadrate red spots on the sides; breast blue; opercles scaly; cheeks, nape and breast naked; fins variegated, all bordered with scarlet; rays of dorsal fins X to XII-11 to 13; anal II, 8 or 9; scales 6-45 to 48-7: upper tributaries of the Tennessee, Cumberland and Green Rivers; very common.

N. jordani (Gilbert). Similar to *N. rufilineatus;* color olivaceous, with 8 black cross bars on the back and 9 or 10 irregular blotches on the side; nape and opercles scaly; cheeks and breast naked; shoulder with an enlarged black scale: tributaries of the Coosa River, Alabama; common.

22. Oligocephalus Girard.   Body elongate and brightly colored; lateral line more or less incomplete; ventrals close together at the base; gill membranes not joined across the isthmus; anal spines 2:7 species.

O. exilis (Girard).   Length 50 mm.; body slender; head 3.8; depth 4 to 5.5; color light green, blotches with darker; sides with 10 or 11 large brown spots alternating with black ones; cheeks, opercles and nape scaly; top of head and breast naked; rays of dorsal fins VII to X-10 or 11; anal II, 6 to 8; scales 5-55 to 63-11: Michigan, Iowa and Nebraska, and northward into Canada; common.

O. jessiæ (J. & B.).   Length 45 mm.; head 4; depth 4.75; cheeks and opercles scaly; color brownish, with a light lateral band, above and below which are light spots; rays of dorsal fins X to XII-12 to 14; anal II, 7 to 9; scales 6-47 to 55-8: Michigan to Iowa; southward to Mississippi and Texas; common.

O. luteovinctus (Gilbert & Swain).   Body compressed; length 50 mm.; head 3.6; depth 4.5 to 5; color light olive, with 7 cross bars; sides with 9 greenish blotches alternating with yellowish bands; cheeks and opercles scaly; rays of dorsal fins IX or X-13; anal II, 7 or 8; scales 6-49 to 55-11; tail very slender: Stone River, Tennessee; rare.

O. cœruleus (Storer).   Rainbow darter.   Body stout; length 60 mm.; head 3.75; depth 4.25; color olivaceous, blotched with darker; sides with about 12 oblique blue bars with orange between; cheeks blue; breast and throat orange; fins mostly orange and blue; rays of dorsal fins X-12 to 14; anal II, 7 or 8; scales 5-37 to 50-10; neck and breast naked: valleys of the Mississippi and Great Lakes and southwestward to Texas; very common in small streams.

O. punctulatus (Agassiz).   Body slender; length 50 mm.; head 3.3; depth 5.75; color dark green, with indistinct darker bars; head punctulate; belly red; a black spot on shoulder; rays of dorsal fins X or XI-14; anal II, 8 or 9; scales 9-63 to 80-16; breast, cheeks and opercles naked: Ozark region; not common.

O. cragini (Gilb.).   Length 40 mm.; head 3.3; depth 4.75; color olivaceous, mottled; lower half of sides specked with black; sides with a series of small spots; a conspicuous shoulder spot; cheeks and opercles naked; rays of dorsal fins VIII or IX-10 to 12; anal II, 6 or 7; scales 6-46 to 55: western portion of Arkansas River basin, in Colorado; in small brooks; the only darter reaching the base of the Rockies.

23. Claricola Jordan and Evermann.   Similar to *Oligocephalus*, but with the gill membranes broadly joined across the isthmus (except in *C. squamiceps*), and with a large black shoulder scale: 4 species.

C. whipplii (Girard). Body rather deep, compressed; length 60 mm.; head 3.5; depth 4.5 to 5; color grayish, mottled with darker and about 12 indistinct dusky bars; sides with small scarlet spots and 2 orange spots at the base of the tail fin; a black shoulder spot; rays of dorsal fins XI-11 or 12; anal II, 7 or 8; scales 8-60 to 70; lateral line incomplete; opercles with a few large scales: lower Arkansas basin; common.

C. squamiceps (Jordan). Body robust; length 75 mm.; head 3 to 4; depth 4.25 to 5; color dusky olive, with about 10 diffuse blackish cross bands; a pinkish streak along the lateral line; no red or blue; cheeks, opercles, nape and breast usually scaly; rays of dorsal fins VIII to XI-9 to 12; anal II, 7 or 8; scales 6-48 to 60-12: southern Indiana to Georgia and western Florida; common southward.

24. Catonotus Agassiz. Similar to *Claricola*, but with a projecting lower jaw: 1 species.

N. flabellaris (Raf.). Fan-tailed darter. Body slender; head long and pointed; length 60 mm.; head 3.5 to 4; depth 4.5 to 5.5; color rather dark, body covered with fine specks which form dark cross blotches in the male; a conspicuous shoulder spot; no red or blue; rays of dorsal fins VIII-12 to 14; anal II, 7 to 9; scales 7-50-7; lower jaw strongly projecting; head naked; tail fin large: New England to northern Alabama; westward to Iowa; abundant in swift waters; variable.

Subspecies of C. flabellaris

C. f. lineolatus (Agassiz). Longitudinal lines of dark dots present: northern Indiana and Missouri to Minnesota.

C. f. cumberlandicus (Jordan & Swain). Coloration plain, except for the black shoulder spot: Cumberland Mountains.

25. Psychromaster Jordan & Evermann. Body robust; a single anal spine present; the top of the head scaly; lateral line curved and incomplete: 1 species.

P. tuscumbia (Gilbert & Swain). Body heavy and robust, with an elevated back; length 50 mm.; head 3.5; depth 4; color grayish or greenish, mottled or speckled with black; 6 broad dorsal bars and 8 or 10 black blotches along the lateral line; fins barred; cheeks and opercles scaly; rays of dorsal fins IX or X-11 to 13; anal I, 8; scales 6-48 to 50-10: northern Alabama; abundant.

26. Hololepis Agassiz. Lateral line incomplete, being strongly curved upward anteriorly; gill membranes not joined; ventral fins close together at the base: 2 species.

H. barratti (Holbrook). Body compressed, elongate; length 75 mm.; head 3.6; depth 4.6; color dark brown, with bright red and blackish mottlings on the sides and back; a small black shoulder spot; rays of dorsal fins IX to XII-9 to 12; anal II, 7; scales 3-48 to 56-10; cheeks, top of head, breast, nape and opercles scaly: Virginia to Florida, in swamps and lowland streams of the coastal plain; not common.

H. fusiformis (Girard). Body elongate and compressed; length 50 mm.; head 4; depth 6; color very variable, olivaceous, blotched with dusky; a black spot below and another in front of the eye; rays of dorsal fins IX or X-9 to 12; anal II, 6; scales 3-43 to 50-12; cheek, opercle and nape scaly: entire eastern and central States; westward to Minnesota and the Rio Grande, in lowland streams and ponds.

27. Microperca Putnam. No lateral line: 3 species.

Key to the Species of Microperca and Alvarius

a$_1$ Checks and opercles scaly.....................................*M. prælaris.*
a$_2$ Cheeks naked.
  b$_1$ Anal spines 2; in the northwest...........................*M. punctulata.*
  b$_2$ Anal spine 1; in the south...............................*A. fonticola.*

M. prælaris Hay. Length 40 mm.; head 4; depth 4.5; color olive, speckled with brown; 10 spots along the sides; rays of dorsal fins VIII, 11; anal II, 6; scales 36: Alabama to Arkansas, in lowland streams.

M. punctulata Putn. Length 30 mm.; head 3.75; depth 4.5 to 5; color light olive, with sides speckled and vaguely barred; rays of dorsal fins VI or VII-10; anal II, 6; scales 34 to 37-9; cheeks, nape and breast naked; opercles with a few scales: Michigan to Minnesota; southward to Arkansas; common in clear weedy streams and ponds, especially in the Great Lakes basin; the smallest of the darters.

28. Alvarius Girard. Lateral line present anteriorly; dorsal fins short; anal spine single; head naked: 2 species.

A. fonticola Jordan & Gilbert. Length 30 mm.; head 3.3 to 4; depth 4.5 to 5; color light olive, with 8 cross blotches on the back and horizontal lines on the sides; rays of dorsal fins VI to VII-8 to 10; anal I, 7; scales 34: Arkansas and Texas, in clear rocky streams; scarce.

Family 6. Moronidæ.—River bass. Body elliptical, more or less compressed; scales ctenoid; lateral line present; tail forked; branchiostegals normally 7; pseudobranchiæ large; spines of anal fin 3; cheeks and opercles always scaly; teeth on vomers and palatines: about 70 genera and 400 species, mostly marine; 4 genera and species in fresh water, which are important food and game fishes.

1. **Roccus** Mitchill. Body deep and compressed; lower jaw projecting; two separate dorsal fins present; teeth on the base of the tongue: 1 species.

R. saxatilis (Walbaum). Striped bass. Length up to 1,500 mm.; weight up to 90 lbs.; head 3.25 to 3.5; depth 3.5; color olivaceous, silvery, with 7 to 8 narrow longitudinal stripes on the middle and upper portions of the body; 2 patches of teeth at the base of the tongue; rays of dorsal fins IX-I, 12; anal III, 11; scales 8-67-11: Atlantic Ocean from New Brunswick to Louisiana, entering the rivers in the spring to spawn; occasionally in Lake Ontario; introduced into California; abundant.

2. **Lepibema** Rafinesque. Similar to *Roccus*, but with but one patch of teeth at the base of the tongue: 1 species.

L. chrysops (Rafinesque). White bass. Length 375 mm.; head 3.5; depth 2.5; back with a high arch; color silvery, with about 6 narrow dark longitudinal stripes on the upper and middle portions of the body; 1 patch of teeth at the base of the tongue; rays of dorsal fins IX-I, 14; anal III, 11 or 12; scales 10-55 to 65-15: Great Lakes region to Manitoba; southward in Mississippi Valley to Arkansas; in deeper waters; abundant.

3. **Chrysoperca** Fowler. Similar to *Roccus;* base of tongue toothless; the spinous and the soft dorsal fins joined, but slightly: 1 species.

C. interrupta Gill. Yellow bass. Length 300 mm.; head 3; depth 2.6; color brassy yellow, with 7 distinct black longitudinal lines, those below the lateral line interrupted posteriorly; rays of dorsal fins IX-I, 12; anal III, 9 or 10; scales 7-50 to 54-11: lower Mississippi Valley, northward to the Ohio River and to central Indiana and Illinois; westward to the Kansas River; common towards the south in large rivers and lakes.

4. **Morone** Mitchill. Similar to *Chrysoperca;* dorsal fins well connected; longitudinal stripes faint: 1 species.

M. americana (Gmelin). White perch. Length 250 mm.; head 3; depth 3; color dark olivaceous; sides silvery, usually with faint paler streaks; rays of dorsal fins IX-I, 12; anal III, 8 or 9; scales 8-50 to 55-12: Atlantic Ocean; abundant in brackish pools and in river mouths, also often in fresh water ponds, from Nova Scotia to Florida.

Family 7. Sciænidæ.—The drums. Body compressed, more or less elongate; back elevated; scales ctenoid; lateral line continuous and extending on to the tail fin; premaxillaries protractile; dorsal fin single, deeply notched or separated into two fins; air bladder large and often complex, enabling the fish to make drumming sounds; no teeth on the palatines, vomer, pterygoids or tongue; branchiostegals 7: about 30 genera and 150 species, mostly in warm seas; a few in fresh water, 1 in the United States.

Aplodinotus Rafinesque. With the characters of the family: 1 species.

A. grunniens Raf. Sheephead (Fig. 62). Length up to 1,100 mm.; weight up to 50 lbs.; head 3.3; depth 3; color silvery; dusky above; rays of dorsal fins IX-I, 25 to 30; anal II, 7; scales 9-55-13; lower pharyngeals very large, with blunt teeth; head scaly: Great Lakes

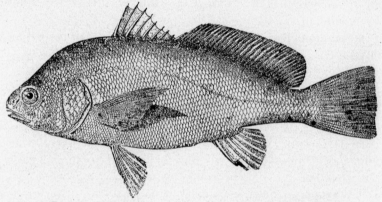

FIG. 62.—*Aplodinotus grunniens (from Jordan & Evermann)*.

to Alabama and Texas, between the Alleghenies and the Great Plains; common in large streams and lakes; an inferior food fish in the north, but not in the south.

Order 15. Holconoti.—The surf fishes. Viviparous fishes with united pharyngeals, an increased number of vertebræ, cycloid scales and many rays in the soft dorsal and anal fins: 1 family.

Family Embiotocidæ.—Body elliptical, compressed cheeks, opercles and interopercles scaly; lateral line continuous; branchiostegals 5 or 6: 17 genera and about 20 species, all marine but one.

Hysterocarpus Gibbons. Body ovate; back elevated; dorsal fin single, the spinous portion very long; anal fin very long: 1 species.

H. traski Gibbons. Length 100 mm.; head 3.3; depth 2; color brown above; sides yellowish, with fine dots; throat and belly yellow; rays of dorsal fin XVI to XVIII, 11; anal III, 22: rivers of central California; locally abundant.

Order 16. Cataphracti.—The mailed cheeked fishes. Fishes with a bony process of the suborbital ring extending across the cheek to or towards the preopercle: 22 families, most of them marine, 1 in fresh water.

Family Cottidæ.—Sculpins. Body elongate, tapering backward from the broad head; body not uniformly scaled but either naked or armed with scales, bony plates or spines; lateral line present; ventral fins thoracic; dorsal fins either separate or connected; anal fins without spines; pseudobranchiæ present; air-bladder usually wanting: about 30 genera and 90 species, mostly marine; many species in fresh water.

Key to the Fresh Water Genera of Cottidæ

a_1 Ventral fins with 4 soft rays....................................1. *Cottus.*
a_2 Ventral fins with 3 soft rays....................................2. *Triglopsis.*

1. Cottus L. Fresh-water sculpins. Body smooth, sometimes with prickles; preopercle with a spine at its angle and usually 2 or 3 spines below it; villiform teeth on the vomer, jaws and sometimes the palatines; gill openings separated by a wide isthmus; pectoral fins large; dorsal fins usually nearly or quite separate: numerous species, in the northern hemisphere.

Key to the Species of Cottus

a_1 Palatine bones with teeth; the two dorsal fins usually very
slightly connected at base, or not at all.
  b_1 Anal rays 15 to 20.
    c_1 Vent midway between tip of snout and base of tail.......*C. asper.*
    c_2 Vent nearer the tail than the tip of the snout...........*C. gulosus.*
  b_2 Anal rays 11 to 13.
    c_1 In the far-western States.
      d_1 In the Columbia River basin......................*C. rhotheus.*
                                 C. bendirei.
      d_1 In the Rocky Mountain region....................*C. punctulatus.*
                                   C. semiscaber.
    c_2 In the eastern and central States.....................*C. bairdi.*
                                   C. ricei.
a_2 Palatine bones without teeth.
  b_1 In the Far-western States.
    c_1 In the Klamath Lakes region, Oregon..................*C. klamathensis.*
                                   C. tenuis.
    c_2 In the Columbia River basin.........................*C. beldingi.*
    c_3 In the Colorado River basin.........................*C. annæ.*
  b_2 In eastern and central States...........................*C. cognotus.*

C. asper Richardson. Length 300 mm.; head 3.25; depth 4.5; color grayish olive, mottled and spotted with blackish; prickles coarse and stiff; rays of dorsal fins IX or X, 19 to 21; anal 17 or 18: San Francisco Bay to Alaska; Cascade Range; abundant in cold streams.

C. gulosus (Girard). Rifflefish. Length 150 mm.; head 3; depth 4.5; color grayish olive, mottled with darker; rays of dorsal fin VIII or

IX, 19 to 21; anal 16 to 18: southeastern Oregon; Coast Range, California, Sacramento River region; Alaska; very common.

C. rhotheus Rosa Smith.   Length 100 mm.; head 3; depth 4.5; color dark gray, spotted and mottled; rays of dorsal fins VII or VIII, 16 or 17; anal 11 or 12: Columbia River basin; common.

C. punctulatus (Gill).   Length 125 mm.; head 3; depth 4.75; color olivaceous, spotted with black and with 5 or 6 dark lateral cross bars; rays of dorsal fins VII or VIII, 17 or 18; anal 11 or 12: head waters of Green River, Wyoming; southeastern Oregon; common.

C. semiscaber (Cope).   Rocky Mountain bullhead.   Length 100 mm.; head 3; depth 4.5; color gray, with inconspicuous cross bars on the sides; rays of dorsal fins VIII, 17 or 18; anal 12 or 13: New Mexico and Wyoming into Montana and Washington; common.

FIG. 63.—*Cottus bairdi (from Fishes of Illinois).*

C. bairdi Girard.   Miller's thumb (Fig. 63).   Length 150 mm.; head 3.3; depth 4 to 6; color olivaceous, bared or speckled with darker; rays of dorsal fins VI to VIII, 16 or 17; anal about 12: middle or northern States from New York to the Dakotas; southward along the Alleghenies to Alabama; very common in clear brooks and lakes; very variable.

C. ricei (Nelson).   Length 60 mm.; head 3.6; depth 5.3; color olivaceous; finely speckled; rays of dorsal fin VIII, 17; anal 12: Great Lakes; in deep water only.

C. klamathensis Gilbert.   Length 130 mm.; head 3; depth 4 to 4.3; color brownish olive, much blotched with darker; rays of dorsal fin VII, 19; anal 14; the 2 dorsal fins broadly joined; lateral line very incomplete; preopercle with a single short spine: Klamath Lakes, Oregon; very common.

C. beldingii Eigenmann.   Length 100 mm.; head 4; depth 5; color mottled black and white, with 6 blackish cross bars on the back, the first across the head behind the eyes; rays of dorsal fin VI to VIII, 15 to 18; anal 11 to 13: abundant east of the Cascades, Columbia River basin.

C. annæ Jordan and Sparks. Length 75 mm.; head 3.5; depth 5; color light gray, somewhat mottled; rays of dorsal fin VII or VIII, 17 or 18; anal 12; mouth very small; preopercle with 1 blunt spine and no others: Colorado River basin; common.

C. bendirei (Bean). Length 75 mm.; color dark brown, lighter on the throat and belly; rays of dorsal fins VIII, 16; anal, 12; palatines with teeth; preopercle with 4 spines: Columbia basin in Oregon and Idaho.

C. tenuis (Evermann and Meek). Length 75 mm.; head 3.8; depth 7; color dark above and pale beneath; under side of head speckled; rays of dorsal fins VI-I, 17; anal 15; body very slender: Klamath Lakes, Oregon.

C. cognatus Richardson. Head 3.5; depth 5; color olivaceous, mottled; upper edge of spinous dorsal fin red in life; rays of dorsal fins VIII, 16; anal 12: Great Lakes to New England and New York; West Virginia; Alaska; common.

2. Triglopsis Girard. Body and head slender; skin naked; lateral line chain-like; teeth on vomer, but not on palatines; a small distinct slit behind the last gill; preopercular spines 4: 1 species.

T. thompsoni Girard. Length 75 mm.; head 3; depth 6 color olivaceous, with dark blotches; eyes very large; rays of dorsal fins VIII, 18; anal 15; dorsal fins separate; the soft dorsal and the anal fins very large: deep waters of the Great Lakes; not common.

Order 17. Gobioidea.—Ventral fins thoracic, I, 4 or I, 5; pseudobranchiæ present; dorsal fins separate or united; dorsal spines few and weak; soft dorsal and anal long; caudal fin rounded: 2 families of marine fishes, with a few fresh water representatives.

Family Gobiidæ.—Gobies. Body mostly elongate, naked or covered with ctenoid scales; ventral fins close together, usually united; no lateral line; no pyloric cæca: 600 species, a very few in fresh water; shore fishes in tropical regions.

Dormitator Gill. Body scaled, short, robust; head scaled, broad, blunt and flat; mouth small, oblique; scales large; fins large: 1 species.

D. maculatus (Bloch). Length 600 mm.; head 3.2; depth 3; color dark gray or brown with lighter spots; dorsal fins separate and with parallel black bands; rays of dorsal fins VII-I, 8 or 9; anal I, 9 or 10; scales 33: both coasts of America from North Carolina and Cape St. Lucas to Brazil, in fresh and brackish water.

CLASS 2. AMPHIBIANS (AMPHIBIA; BATRACHIA)*

The amphibians are cold-blooded vertebrates which, so far as the American species are concerned, are devoid of scales and other special integumental coverings and have no claws or nails on their digits. Their eggs are usually deposited in the water or in wet places where the young animals live, breathing by means of integumental gills, while they undergo a metamorphosis which transforms them into the more or less terrestrial adults.

Amphibians occupy a place in the zoological system intermediate between fishes and reptiles, being physiologically like the former when young and the latter when adult. They resemble fishes and differ from the higher vertebrates chiefly in the possession of gill-slits and exclusively aquatic respiration during a part or all of their lives, by the absence of allantois and amnion, the possession of a single ventral aorta through which the blood leaves the heart, and of ten instead of twelve cranial nerves. They differ from fishes and resemble the higher vertebrates chiefly in the absence of dermal scales (except in the *Apoda*), in the possession of pentadactyle limbs, of lungs, and a more or less terrestrial life-habit, and in the reduction of the bones of the head.

History.—It has apparently been a difficult matter to fix the position of the amphibians in the zoological system. Linnæus originated the term *Amphibia*, but included in it also reptiles, and many ganoid and cyclostomate fishes. This tendency to group amphibians and reptiles together existed also among subsequent authors for almost a hundred years, although Blainville as early as 1816 clearly indicated the proper relations of the two classes; the common group was called by some authors the *Reptilia* and by others the *Amphibia*, the possession of scales being the distinctive feature which marked the former group. Milne-Edwards, Cope and Huxley were among the first authors to see matters more clearly, and to speak definitely of *Amphibia* and *Reptilia* as two distinct and equivalent classes. In recent times the systematic study of amphibians has attracted relatively few authors. G. A. and E. G. Boulenger have been among the most influential. In this country the most important have been Spencer F. Baird and Edward D. Cope, each of whom devoted a life-time to the study of the

* Revised by Dr. E. R. Dunn.

group. Cope's *Batrachia of North America* is perhaps the most comprehensive and fundamental single work treating it.

Number and Distribution.—About 1,800 species of amphibians are known, of which 150 species are *Caudata*, or salamanders, and 1,600 species are *Salientia*, or frogs and toads. The burrowing, limbless *Apoda*, which are confined to tropical America, Africa and India, number about 50 species. The *Caudata* occupy principally the temperate and subtropical portions of Europe, Asia and America, penetrating only into the extreme northern parts of Africa, and not occurring at all in Australia and the East Indian archipelago. The *Salientia* inhabit the entire world, except the polar regions and the smaller oceanic islands.

The amphibian fauna of the United States is very rich, a feature in which it parallels the distribution of other animal groups with a similar habitat, namely, fresh water fish and fresh water mollusks. A comparison of the number of species of amphibians inhabiting New York State and Germany or Great Britain will illustrate the statement: in Germany the *Caudata* are represented by 4 species and in New York by 15; Great Britain possesses 3 species of *Salientia*, while New York has 13.

Key to the Orders of Amphibia in the United States

a_1 Body elongate with a tail which persists throughout life;
    salamanders..1. *Caudata* (p. 135).
a_2 Body of adult short and tailless; young with a long tail
    which disappears in the metamorphosis; frogs and toads. 2. *Salientia* (p. 156).

Order 1. Caudata (*Urodela*).—Salamanders. Amphibians with an elongate body and usually two pairs of weak limbs. The vertebræ are numerous and are accompanied by ribs. The skin is without scales and is very glandular, the secretion in some species being poisonous. The eyes are small and the eye-lids are not present in the lower forms. The ear is entirely internal, as in fishes, there being no tympanum or tympanic cavity. The body muscles have a conspicuously segmental arrangement, like those of fishes, the vertical grooves which separate the muscle segments of the trunk being usually easily seen on the outside of the body, and called the *costal grooves* (Fig. 72). Teeth may be present on the maxillaries, premaxillaries, vomers, pterygoids, parasphenoid and mandibles. The eggs are usually deposited in the water and the larvæ are aquatic, being provided with three pairs of external gills, which are expansions of the outer integument and not homologous to the gills of fishes. These gills disappear during the metamorphosis, except in *Necturus, Typhlomolge, Pseudobranchus* and *Siren*. In some of the *Plethodontidæ* the greater part of the larval stage is spent in the egg and the young are terrestrial from the time of birth and without gills. The lower *Caudata* are aquatic animals throughout life, the higher ones are mostly terrestrial as adults, but must still live in moist places.

The 150 species of *Caudata* are grouped in 2 suborders and are found mostly in the temperate parts of the northern hemisphere; about 99 species occur in North America and 69 species in the United States.

On the Identification of Caudate Amphibia.—The descriptions of salmanders in this book apply to adult animals. The most important descriptive features are the shape and appearance of the body and its

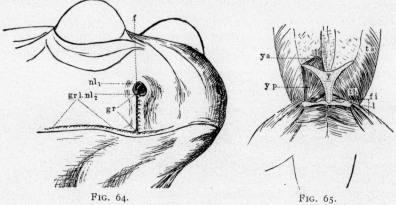

FIG. 64.   FIG. 65.

FIG. 64.—The naso-labial groove of *Desmognathus fuscus*, *f*, crescentic fold which closes the nostril when the head is submerged; *gr*, naso-labial groove which drains the nostril when the head emerges from the water; *grl*, labial groove; *nl*, orifices of glands (*from Whipple*).

FIG. 65.—The ypsiloid cartilage of *Triturus viridescens*: *l*, pubis; *y*, ypsiloid cartilage; the other letters refer to muscles (*from Whipple*).

color, the length of the body in millimeters, including the tail, the length of the tail, the number of costal grooves between the fore and hind limbs, the number of digits, and the position of the teeth, especially those of the vomers and parasphenoid. The *naso-labial groove*, a glandular groove passing from the nostril to the lip (Fig. 64), and the plantar tubercles, which are elevations on the palms and soles, are also often important. Several features of the internal structure are important in a full analysis of the various groups, although a knowledge of them is not usually necessary for the identification of species; these are the shape of the vertebræ, the form and condition of the cranial bones and cartilages, the presence or absence of the lungs and of the cartilage which may lie in the ventral body wall just anterior to the pubis and is called the *ypsiloid cartilage* (Fig. 65).

Key to the Suborders of the Caudata

a_1 Two pairs of legs present..........................1. *Mutabilia* (p. 137).

a_2 But one pair of legs present.........................2. *Meantes* (p. 155).

Suborder 1. Mutabilia.—Both pairs of limbs present; both jaws with teeth; a single ossification in the shoulder girdle: 7 families, grouped in 2 superfamilies.

Key to the Superfamilies and Families of Mutabilia

a_1 Prearticular and angular bones in lower jaw separate; adult
with second epibranchial; female without spermatheca;
fertilization external.....................*Superfamily A. Cryptobranchidea.*

   b_1 Large flattened, river dwelling forms; teeth on prevomer
close to and parallel to those on maxilla............1. *Cryptobranchidæ.*

a_2 Prearticular and angular bones fused; adult without second
epibranchial; female with spermatheca; fertilization
internal................................*Superfamily B. Salamandroidea.*

   b_2 Smaller in size; more or less cylindrical forms; larvæ,
if small, with 5 toes.

      c_1 Ypsiloid cartilage and lungs present; no naso-labial
groove; no parasphenoid teeth.

         d_1 Vomerine teeth in 2 longitudinal rows, diverging
posteriorly; costal grooves not marked........2. *Pleurodelidæ.*

         d_2 Vomerine teeth in transverse series; costal grooves
marked...................................3. *Ambystomidæ.*

      c_2 Ypsiloid cartilage and lungs absent; naso-labial
groove present in adults; parasphenoid teeth present in adults.................................4. *Plethodontidæ.*

   b_3 Eel-like in form, and of larger size; larvæ, if large, with
4 toes.

      c_1 Legs minute, with 2 to 3 toes.....................5. *Amphiumidæ.*

      c_2 Toes 4 on all feet...............................6. *Proteidæ.*

Family 1. Cryptobranchidæ.—Giant salamanders. Body stout and of large size; a pair of small gill-slits usually persistent; vertebræ amphicœlous; carpus and tarsus cartilaginous; no eyelids; vomerine teeth form an arched series parallel with the jaws: 2 genera, one of which, *Megalobactrachus*, is found in China and Japan and contains but one species, *M. japonicus* (Hoeven), which grows to a length of 6 feet and is the largest salamander.

Cryptobranchus F. S. Leuckart. Fore legs with 4 and hind legs with 5 toes each; gill slits always persistent: 1 species.

C. alleganiensis (Daudin). Hellbender. Body dark brown in color; head and trunk depressed, tail compressed; prominent lateral fold present; length 480 mm.; tail 160 mm.: western New York and central Pennsylvania to Georgia and Louisiana; westward to Iowa; Mississippi drainage; Susquehanna; aquatic; often common.

Family 2. Pleurodelidæ.—Body of medium size; teeth on the maxillaries and premaxillaries; vomerine teeth in 2 longitudinal series, converging anteriorly; vertebræ opisthocœlous; carpus and tarsus ossified; lungs and ypsiloid cartilage present; no naso-labial groove: about 10 genera, all in the old world, one of which is represented in America.

Triturus Rafinesque (*Diemyctylus* Raf.). Newts. Tongue attached by nearly its whole lower surface; digits 4-5: about 12 species in Europe, Asia and America, 4 species in the United States. These salamanders can float in water without swimming movements, because of their lungs.

Key to the American Species of Triturus

a₁ Species east of the Rockies.
  b₁ Red markings on the side of the body.
    c₁ Circular, black-edged red spots on the sides............*T. v. viridescens*.
    c₂ A continuous or broken red line edged with black, on the
       side...*T. v. symmetrica*.
  b₂ No red markings present; on the Gulf coastal plain........*T. louisianensis*.
a₂ Species west of the Rockies...............................*T. torosus*.

T. viridescens Raf. Spotted salamander; newt (Fig. 66). Body of

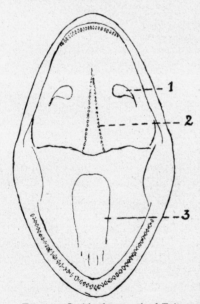

adult elongate; tail with a prominent keel above and below; color olive green above, yellowish beneath, sprinkled everywhere with black dots except on the belly, and with a row of 2 to 6 or more round red black-edged spots on the side of the trunk; length 90 mm.; tail 44 mm.: eastern and central States and Canada, from Hudson Bay to Florida and Texas; westward to Wisconsin and Oklahoma; common. The adult animals are aquatic, living in ponds and streams containing vegetation. The eggs are few in number and are attached separately to vegetation. There are two larval stages, in the first of which the animal is aquatic, with gills and the color of the adult, and in the second it is terrestrial,

FIG. 66.—Inside the mouth of *Triturus viridescens*: 1, inner nares; 2, vomerine teeth; 3, tongue (*from Hay*).

without gills and bright red in color and smaller in size, but is spotted like the adult and without a keeled tail. The first stage lasts 3 or 4 months; the second lasts 2 or 3 years, and at the end of it the animal again becomes aquatic.

Subspecies of T. viridescens

T. v. viridescens Raf. Eastern States and Canada.

T. v. symmetricus (Harlan). Similar to *T. viridescens*, but with the red spots forming a continuous or a broken line: coastal plain, North Carolina to Florida.

T. louisianensis (Wolterstorff). Similar to *T. viridescens*, except that the red spots are inconspicuous or absent, and are not ringed with black: Gulf Coast to Tennessee and Kansas.

T. torosus (Eschscholtz). Body rather stout; tail long, with a wide keel above and below; color brown above and yellow beneath; length 170 mm.; tail 92 mm.: Pacific slope, from Alaska to Lower California, in ponds and streams; no terrestrial form present.

Family 3. Ambystomidæ.—Body of medium size; digits 4-5; a transverse series of teeth, more or less interrupted, on the hinder margin of the vomers; tongue thick, free in front; vertebræ amphicœlous; carpus and tarsus ossified; eyelids present; lungs and ypsiloid cartilage present; costal grooves prominent: 3 genera in the United States; habitat usually terrestrial.

Key to the United States Genera of Ambystomidæ

a₁ Lungs rudimentary; ypsiloid cartilage aborted; on Pacific slope. 1. *Rhyacotriton*.
a₂ Lungs and ypsiloid cartilage (Fig. 65) well developed.
  b₁ Tail dorsally thin and flattened.........................2. *Dicamptodon*.
  b₂ Tail dorsally thick and glandular......................3. *Ambystoma*.

1. Rhyacotriton Dunn. Lungs very small; ypsiloid cartilage aborted; nasal bones absent: 1 species.

R. olympicus (Gaige). Color black above; length 125 mm.: Olympic Mountains, Washington, in mountain streams.

2. Dicamptodon Strauch. Lungs and ypsiloid cartilage normal: nasal bones present: 1 species.

D. ensatus (Eschscholtz) (*Chondrotus tenebrosus* Baird & Girard). Body very large and massive; legs stout; color reddish brown, mottled above; length 250 mm.; tail 100 mm.; costal grooves 12, obscure; parasphenoid narrow: coastal region of Pacific slope, from southern California to British Columbia.

3. Ambystoma Tschudi. Lungs and ypsiloid cartilage well developed; premaxillary fontanelle small or wanting; nasals present;

parasphenoid broad: about species in the United States. These salamanders can float in water without swimming movements, because of their lungs. *A. mexicanum* Shaw, the axylotl, which lives in a lake near Mexico City, becomes sexually mature and breeds as a larva, never transforming. It retains its gills and never leaves the water.

Key to the United States Species of Ambystoma

a_1 Species east of the Rockies.
  b_1 Costal grooves 10 to 12; vomerine teeth in 1, 3 or 4 patches,
      running across the mouth behind the nares (Fig. 70).
    c_1 Two plantar tubercles (Fig. 69) present.
      d_1 Costal grooves 10............................*A. talpoideum.*
      d_2 Costal grooves 12............................*A. tigrinum.*
    c_2 One plantar tubercle present or none.
      d_1 Costal grooves 11.
        e_1 Body with black and white bars..............*A. opacum.*
        e_2 Body black with 2 rows of yellow spots.........*A. maculatum.*
      d_2 Costal grooves 12; toes very long.................*A. jeffersonianum.*
  b_2 Costal grooves 14; teeth in 2 patches (Fig. 71).
    c_1 Definite color markings in form of cross bars.
      d_1 Body black with narrow white cross lines..........*A. cingulatum.*
      d_2 Body dark brown with broad yellow cross bars.....*A. annulatum.*
    c_2 Black with whitish dots............................*A. texanum.*
a_2 Species in the Rockies and far-west.
  b_1 Four phalanges in the fourth toe of hind foot.
    c_1 Body mottled with black and yellow; no dorsal stripe...*A. tigrinum.*
    c_2 A light dorsal stripe present........................*A. macrodactylum.*
  b_2 Three phalanges in the fourth toe of hind foot..........*A. gracile.*

A. talpoideum (Holbrook). Mole salamander. Body short, stout, depressed, gray or dark brown in color dotted with gray; head very broad; length 90 mm.; tail 37 mm.; costal grooves 10; vomerine teeth in 3 patches: southern States from North Carolina to Louisiana and up the Mississippi Valley to Illinois.

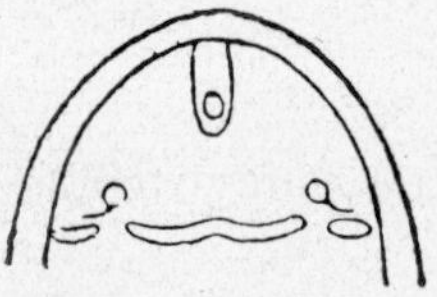

FIG. 67.—Roof of mouth of *Ambystoma opacum*, showing vomerine teeth (*from Cope*).

A. opacum (Gravenhorst). Marbled salamander (Fig. 67). Body thick, cylindrical, black above with about 14 grayish bars which may be confluent; costal grooves 11; length 95 mm.; tail 38 mm.; plantar tubercles indistinct; vomerine teeth in 3 patches: eastern States from central Massachusetts and New York to Florida; westward to Missouri and Texas; in relatively dry and often sandy locations, under stones and logs.

A. maculatum (Shaw) (*A. punctatum* L.). Spotted salamander (Fig. 68). Body stout; color black above, with a series of round yellow spots on the side, about 3 being on the head, 8 or 9 on the tail and 8 or 9 on the trunk; length 160 mm.; tail 77 mm.; costal grooves 11; skin

FIG. 68.—*Ambystoma maculatum* (*from Fowler*).

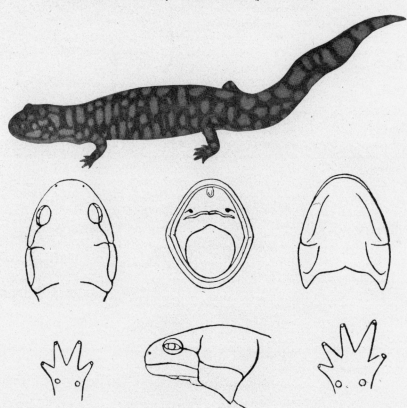

FIG. 69.—(Above) *Ambystoma tigrinum* (*from Fowler*): (below) head, inside of mouth and inner surface of feet of same (*from Cope*).

pitted with numerous minute pores which exude a milky secretion: eastern and central America from Nova Scotia to Florida; westward to Wisconsin, Kansas and Texas.

A. tigrinum (Green). Tiger salamander (Fig. 69). Body thick and massive, dark brown in color, with many large rounded or irregular yellow spots which may be confluent; length 250 mm.; tail 125 mm.; costal grooves 12; vomerine teeth in one long transverse band: the entire United States, except New England and the Appalachian region; the Mexican Plateau; common west of the Appalachians. The larva was formally supposed occasionally to become sexually mature and to breed.

A. jeffersonianum (Green) (Fig. 70). Body long and slender, brownish or blackish in color, with pale dots which may be wanting; digits very long; no plantar tubercles, or

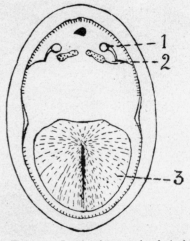

FIG. 70.—Roof of mouth of *Ambystoma jeffersonianum*: 1, inner nares; 2, vomerine teeth (*from Cope*).

FIG. 71.—Inside the mouth of *Ambystoma texanum*: 1, inner nares; 2, vomerine teeth; 3, tongue (*from Hay*).

a single indistinct one; length 150 mm.; tail 75 mm.; costal grooves 12: northeastern States and Canada; northward to Hudson Bay; southward and westward to Virginia and Illinois; common northward.

A. cingulatum Cope. Body slender, black in color, speckled, with gray underneath, and a series of narrow gray rings encircling it from the eyes to the tip of the tail; head elongate; length 85 mm.; costal grooves 14: South Carolina to northern Florida and Alabama.

A. texanum (Matthes) (*A. microstomum* Cope) (Fig. 71). Body elongate, slender, brown or blackish in color, with numerous grayish spots on the sides; limbs weak; digits very long; length 150 mm.; tail 65 mm.; costal grooves 14: central States, Ohio to Texas; often common.

A. gracile (Baird). Body stout and reddish brown or blackish in color, with or without spots; length 180 mm.; tail 102 mm.; costal grooves 11; no plantar tubercles; eyes very large; vomerine teeth in 4 small patches, forming a transverse series: California to British Columbia.

A. macrodactylum Baird (*A. stejnegeri* Ruthven). Body elongate and slender, brownish in color, with a broad lighter dorsal stripe;

length 100 mm.; tail 50 mm.; costal grooves 12; vomerine teeth in 3 or 4 transverse patches; digits very long: northern California to British Columbia and eastward into Montana and Iowa.

A. annulatum Cope. Body slender; tail very long; color dark brown above, with about 15 light cross bands, very light beneath; length 186 mm.; tail 94 mm.; costal grooves 13; tail with 31 grooves; vomerine teeth in 2 patches: Arkansas and Missouri; rare.

Family 4. Plethodontidæ.—Body of medium or small size and without gills or gill slits in the adult state, except in certain cave dwelling species; parasphenoid and vomerine teeth present (Fig. 72); costal grooves 11 to 21; vertebræ amphicœlous or opisthocœlous; carpus and tarsus cartilaginous; lungs absent; ypsiloid cartilage absent; naso-labial groove present (Fig. 64): about 16 genera and 50 species, all American but two, which occur in Italy. These salamanders cannot float in water without swimming motions, and are, with few exceptions, terrestrial animals, living in shaded, moist localities near or in small streams. In several genera the larvæ are also terrestrial, losing their gills before they hatch, or very soon after, and never entering the water; the larvæ of *Desmognathus*, however, make for the water, in which they live about a year.

Key to the Genera of Plethodontidæ

a₁ Blind, white, cave-dwelling salamanders.
   b₁ Adult without gills; in Missouri...................... 9. *Typhlotriton*.
   b₂ Adult with gills; in Texas............................10. *Typhlomolge*.
a₂ Salamanders which are not blind or white in color.
   b₁ Tongue attached at its anterior margin.
      c₁ Hind foot with 5 toes.
         d₁ Teeth not confined to the front of the jaw.
            e₁ With a light line running from the eye to the angle
               of the mouth............................. 1. *Desmognathus*.
            e₂ No such line present.
               f₁ Vomerine teeth absent.................... 2. *Leurognathus*.
               f₂ Vomerine teeth present.
                  g₁ Vomerine teeth continuous with the para-
                     sphenoid teeth...................... 8. *Stereochilus*.
                  g₂ Vomerine teeth separated from the para-
                     sphenoid teeth.
                     h₁ Palm without plantar tubercles....... 3. *Plethodon*.
                     h₂ Palm with 2 plantar tubercles........ 5. *Ensatina*.
         d₂ Front teeth alone present and projecting from the
           closed mouth.............................. 6. *Aneides*.
      c₂ Hind foot with 4 toes.
         d₁ In the eastern States.......................... 4. *Hemidactylium*.
         d₂ On the Pacific slope........................... 7. *Batrachoseps*.

b_2 Tongue free at its anterior margin, being attached by
a central pedicle (Fig. 77).
  c_1 Toes not webbed.
    d_1 With a light line running from the eye to the
nostril.....................................11. *Gyrinophilus.*
    d_2 No such line present.
      e_1 Vomerine teeth continuous with parasphenoid
teeth; color red..........................12. *Pseudotriton.*
      e_2 Vomerine teeth separate from the parasphenoid
teeth (Fig. 80)..........................13. *Eurycea.*
  c_2 Toes webbed...................................14. *Hydromantes.*

1. **Desmognathus** Baird. Body of medium or small size; tongue
attached, except by its lateral margins; premaxillaries united; vertebræ
opisthocœlous; vomerine teeth wanting in adult males of some species;
a light line from the eye to the angle of the mouth: 3 species.

Key to the Species of Desmognathus

a_1 Belly mottled..*D. fuscus.*
a_2 Belly uniformily colored.
  b_1 Belly black.......................................*D. quadramaculatus.*
  b_2 Belly light.......................................*D. phoca.*

D. fuscus (Rafinesque) (Fig. 72). Body rather stout, brown above,
mottled below; length 115 mm.; tail 58 mm.; costal grooves 14; vomerine
teeth not present in mature males; parasphenoid teeth in 2 separated
patches: southern Canada to the Gulf; westward to Illinois, Tennessee
and Louisiana; common.

Key to the Subspecies of D. fuscus

a_1 Semiaquatic forms; tail keeled above.
  b_1 In the northern, central and eastern states..............*D. f. fuscus.*
  b_2 In the South Atlantic and coastal plains................*D. f. auriculatus.*
  b_3 West of the Mississippi...............................*D. f. brimleyorum.*
a_2 Terrestrial forms; tail cylindrical; size small.
  b_1 Back mottled: southern Blue Ridge....................*D. f. carolinensis.*
  b_2 Back with a regular pale stripe: mountains of West Virginia
to New York....................................*D. f. ochraphœus.*

Subspecies of D. fuscus

D. f. fuscus (Raf.). Belly light; no spots on the sides: New Brunswick to Gulf Coast and southeastern Virginia, except in the higher
mountains.

D. f. auriculatus (Holbrook). Belly dark; a row of light spots on
the sides: coastal plain of the Atlantic and Gulf from Virginia to
Florida.

D. f. brimleyorum Stejneger. Body slender and similar to *D. f. auriculatus* in color; belly light; size and teeth similar to *D. f. fuscus:* Oklahoma, Texas and Arkansas; rare.

D. f. carolinensis Dunn. Belly dark; a tubercle at the anterior angle of the eye: West Virginia to Georgia; in the mountains.

D. f. ochrophæus Cope. Body small; tail without keel; color variable, with a very dark, broad lateral band; length 94 mm.; tail

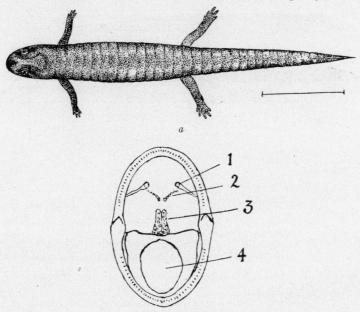

FIG. 72.—*Desmognathus fuscus: a,* dorsal aspect (*from Fowler*); *b,* inside of the mouth: 1, inner nares; 2, vomerine teeth; 3, parasphenoid teeth; 4, tongue (*from Hay*).

46 mm.; costal grooves 14; vomerine teeth absent in adult male; parasphenoid patches separated: New York to Georgia; habits terrestrial.

D. quadramaculatus (Holbrook). Body large, black above and below; length 175 mm.; tail 82 mm.; costal grooves 12 to 14; parasphenoid teeth in 2 patches which are confluent anteriorly; vomerine teeth always present: southwest Virginia to northern Georgia, in the mountains; the most aquatic of the genus.

D. phoca (Matthes) (Fig. 73). Body large, uniformly colored, more or less mottled, with a light belly; tail long; length 135 mm.; tail 71 mm.; costal grooves 13 or 14; vomerine teeth always present; parasphenoid teeth in 2 patches, confluent anteriorly: Pennsylvania to Georgia; in the mountains; common.

2. Leurognathus Moore.   Body of large size; internal nares very inconspicuous and twice as far apart as the nostrils; vertebræ opisthocœlous; vomerine teeth absent: 1 species.

L. marmorata Moore.   Body 128 mm. long; tail 53 mm.; parasphenoid teeth in 2 patches which touch anteriorly; costal grooves 13; tail keeled; color brownish above; belly black in old specimens: North Carolina mountains; rare; aquatic.

FIG. 73.—*Desmognathus phoca (from Dunn).*

3. Plethodon Tschudi.   Body slender and elongate; tongue attached except at its lateral margins; vertebræ amphicœlous; premaxillaries separate; parasphenoid and vomerine teeth present, the 2 parasphenoid patches in contact throughout; toes 4-5: about 15 species, all American.   Both adults and larvæ are largely terrestrial, living in damp places, under stones and logs, the larvæ in some species losing their gills while still in the egg, and never entering the water.   The eggs are sometimes carried in the mouth of the female.

Key to the Species of Plethodon

a_1 Species occurring east of the Pacific slope.
  b_1 Color not uniformly plumbeous, and with spots or stripes.
    c_1 With a broad middorsal red stripe.
      d_1 Costal grooves 19; stripe straight....................*P. cinereus.*
      d_2 Costal grooves 17; stripe zigzag.....................*P. dorsalis.*
    c_2 No such stripe present; costal grooves 14.
      d_1 Back blackish, dotted with white...................*P. glutinosus.*
      d_2 Back red or chestnut..............................*P. yonahlossee.*
  b_2 Color uniformly plumbeous.
    c_1 Body without color markings.
      d_1 Belly mottled; costal grooves 19....................*P. cinereus.*
      d_2 Belly plain.
        e_1 Costal grooves 14................................*P. metcalfi.*
        e_2 Costal grooves 17..............................*P. wehrlei.*
    c_2 Body with color markings.
      d_1 Legs red..*P. shermani.*
      d_2 With a yellow stripe from eye to gular fold..........*P. jordani.*

a_2 Species occurring on the Pacific slope.

    b_1 Digits not webbed.

        c_1 Costal grooves 14.....................................*P. vehiculum.*

        c_2 Costal grooves 16.....................................*P. elongatus.*

    b_2 Digits webbed; costal grooves 12 or 13.....................*P. vandykei.*

P. cinereus (Green). Red-backed salamander; dusky salamander (Fig. 74). Body very slender, cylindrical and elongate, and dark brown or dark gray in color with a broad, light reddish stripe running down the back, which is sometimes wanting, there being thus two distinct color phases; under parts mottled; length 90 mm.; tail 45 mm.; costal grooves 19; vomerine teeth not extending laterally beyond the inner nares:

FIG. 74.—*Plethodon cinereus (from Fowler).*

Canada and States east of the Mississippi; Missouri and Arkansas; very common towards the north; both larvæ and adults terrestrial.

P. dorsalis Cope. Similar to *P. cinereus* but with 17 costal grooves, and a zigzag dorsal stripe: southern portions of Ohio, Indiana and Illinois to Alabama.

P. glutinosus (Green) (Fig. 75). Body rather stout, depressed, blackish in color with whitish blotches and dots; length 138 mm.; tail 67 mm.; costal grooves 14; vomerine teeth extending laterally beyond the internal nares: eastern and central States and New York; westward to Wisconsin and central Texas; southward to the Gulf States; terrestrial; common in upland districts.

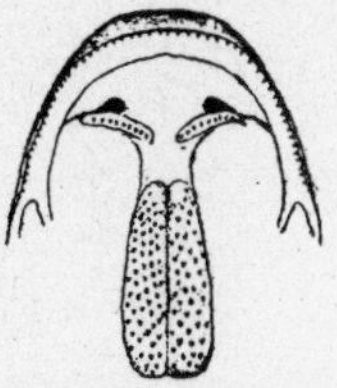

FIG. 75.—The roof of the mouth of *Plethodon glutinosus (from Dunn).*

P. yonahlossee Dunn. Similar to *P. glutinosus,* but with a chestnut red dorsal coloration and with paired red spots: mountains of North Carolina and southwest Virginia.

P. metcalfi Brimley. Similar to *P. glutinosus,* but slenderer; color plain plumbeous, paler beneath; length 108 mm.; tail 53 mm.; costal grooves 14; vomerine teeth in 2 short curved transverse rows: mountains of North Carolina; often very common.

P. wehrlei Fowler and Dunn. Similar to *P. metcalfi;* dorsal surface with paired spots; costal grooves 17; toes webbed: central and western Pennsylvania, West Virginia and southwest New York.

P. shermani Stejneger. Similar to *P. metcalfi*, but with red legs; length 104 mm.; tail 56 mm.; costal grooves 14: western North Carolina.

P. jordani Blatchley. Similar to *P. metcalfi;* color black, with a red or yellow stripe on the side of the head between the eye and the gular fold; legs sometimes dotted with red; costal grooves 14: mountains of Tennessee and North Carolina.

P. vehiculum (Cooper) (*P. intermedius* Baird). Similar to *P. cinereus* in color; length 90 mm.; tail 38 mm.; costal grooves 14: California to Vancouver Island.

P. elongatus Van Denburgh. Similar to *P. vehiculum*, but with 16 costal grooves; length 117 mm.; tail 58 mm.: northern California.

P. vandykei Van Denburgh. Similar to *P. intermedius*, but stouter and with 13 or 14 costal grooves; back clay-colored, dotted with black; lower surfaces black; length 116 mm.; tail 56 mm.; toes partly webbed: western Washington.

4. Hemidactylium Tschudi. Like *Plethodon*, but with 4 toes on the hind foot: 1 species.

H. scutatum (Schlegel). Body small, cylindrical, dark chestnut above, white beneath with large black spots; tail with a basal constriction; length 80 mm.; tail 46 mm.; costal grooves 14: eastern and central States and Canada; northward into Massachusetts; westward into Michigan, Illinois and Arkansas; southward into the Gulf States; terrestrial; locally common.

5. Ensatina Gray. Similar to *Plethodon*, but with a basal constriction of the tail and with 2 plantar tubercles on the palm: 4 species, 1 (*E. platensis*) in Uruguay and Argentina.

E. eschscholtzi Gray. Body depressed, brown or orange in color; tail short and slender; limbs long; length 115 mm.; tail 50 mm.; costal grooves 11; parasphenoid patches of teeth diverging posteriorly, confluent anteriorly: Pacific slope from Los Angeles to Puget Sound.

E. croceater (Cope). Body large, black in color with large yellow dorsal spots; bright orange beneath; costal grooves 13; length 145 mm.; tail 87 mm.: southern California.

6. Aneides Baird. Similar to *Plethodon*, but differs in that there is but one premaxillary and the maxillary and mandibular teeth are few in number and confined to the anterior portion of the arch; vomerine teeth on a ridge between the internal nares: 4 species.

Key to the Species of Aneides

a_1 On the Pacific slope.

  b_1 Teeth not flattened; color black......................*A. flairpunctatus.*
  b_2 Teeth flattened.

c₁ Color brown, not mottled; light below..............*A. lugubris.*
c₂ Color mottled brown and black; dark below..........*A. ferreus.*
a₂ In the southeastern States.............................*A. æneus.*

A. lugubris (Hallowell). Body light yellow above with yellowish spots and yellow beneath; length 75 mm.; tail 35 mm.; snout very prominent; eyes bulging; anterior teeth projecting from the closed mouth; costal grooves 13: California; common; adults and larvæ terrestrial, the latter being without functional gills.

A. ferreus (Cope). Body slender, black above, with gray on the sides and brown beneath; length 90 mm.; tail 37 mm.; costal grooves 14: northern California to British Columbia.

A. flairpunctatus Strauch (*A. iecanus* Cope). Body robust, black in color, with minute light specks; length 53 mm.; costal grooves 13; parasphenoid teeth in a single patch: northern California.

A. æneus (Cope and Packard). Body rather stout; color dark, mottled coppery and black; length 118 mm.; tail 66 mm.; costal grooves 14: Virginia and West Virginia to Georgia.

7. Batrachoseps Bonaparte. Similar to *Plethodon*, but with 4 toes on the hind foot and but one premaxillary: 2 species; Pacific slope.

Key to These Species

a₁ Back lighter than the sides....................................*B. attenuatus.*
a₂ Back not lighter than the sides.............................*B. pacificus.*

B. attenuatus (Eschscholtz). Body slender, with very weak legs and a long tail; color brown above and below but darker on the belly and the sides; length 111 mm.; tail 64 mm.; costal grooves 19; leg spanning 3 costal folds; parasphenoid and vomerine teeth in 1 patch each: Pacific slope west of the Coast Range from Oregon to Lower California; very common.

B. pacificus (Cope). Body elongate, brown above, yellowish beneath; length 70 mm.; tail 37 mm.; costal grooves 18; hind leg spanning 6 costal folds; inner digits of both pairs of legs rudimentary: southern California.

Subspecies of B. pacificus

B. p. pacificus (Cope). Islands off the coast.
B. p. major Camp. Body large, pale in color, light yellowish beneath; hind leg spanning 4 costal folds; costal folds 18; length 134 mm.; tail 74 mm.: southern California.

8. Stereochilus Cope. Tongue attached at its anterior margin; vomerine teeth confluent with parasphenoid teeth; 1 premaxillary: 1 species.

S. marginatus (Hallowell). Body slender, yellowish brown in color, with numerous brown lines along the sides; belly yellow, specked with brown; length 79 mm.; tail 35 mm.; costal grooves 17; tail compressed: Dismal Swamp to Georgia; aquatic.

9. Typhlotriton Stejneger. Body of medium size; tongue attached anteriorly; eyes concealed under the skin: 1 species.

T. spelæus Stej. Body white, 120 mm. long; costal grooves 16: in caves in Missouri and Kansas.

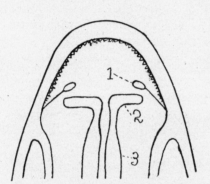 

Fig. 76.—Roof of mouth of *Gyrinophilus porphyriticus:* 1, inner nares; 2, vomerine teeth; 3, parasphenoid teeth (*from Cope*).

Fig. 77.—Head of *Pseudotriton*, showing the tongue (*after Hurter*).

10. Typhlomolge Stejneger. Body elongate, with very long legs and persistent gills; eyes concealed under the skin: 1 species.

T. rathbuni Stej. Body white, and with the general structure of a sexually mature *Eurycea* larva; length 102 mm.; length of legs 20 mm.: in wells in San Marcos, Texas.

11. Gyrinophilus Cope. Body elongate; tongue free anteriorly; premaxillaries distinct; vomerine teeth continuous with the parasphenoid: 2 species.

G. porphyriticus (Green) (Fig. 76). Body large and purplish brown in color, blotched with gray; belly whitish; length 163 mm.; tail 60 mm.; costal grooves 15; eye connected with nostril by a conspicuous light colored ridge: northeastern States; common; aquatic.

G. danielsi (Blatchley). Body elongate; color light chocolate brown above, with widely scattered dots of black which are wanting on the hinder two-thirds of the tail, light brown beneath; length 160 mm.; tail 65 mm.; costal grooves 16: North Carolina to Georgia; Tennessee.

12. Pseudotriton Baird (*Spelerpes* Rafinesque). Body elongate, red in color; tail short and compressed; tongue free all round, being attached by a slender pedicle only (Fig. 77); but 1 premaxillary; vomerine teeth continuous with the parasphenoid (Fig. 78): 2 species.

Key to the Species of Pseudotriton

a_1 A few scattered black spots present.........................*P. montanus.*
a_2 Many black spots close together............................*P. ruber.*

P. montanus Baird. Body elongate, cylindrical, brownish salmon in color, with a few circular spots; under parts pale salmon; length 140 mm.; tail 62 mm.; the 2 patches of parasphenoid teeth in contact anteriorly: Pennsylvania to the Gulf.

Subspecies of P. montanus

P. m. montanus Baird. Costal grooves 17: Pennsylvania, Virginia and Kentucky to Georgia.

P. m. flavissimus Hallowell. Costal grooves 16 to 18: Gulf States, from Georgia to Louisiana.

P. ruber (Sonnini). Red salamander (Fig. 78). Body rather stout and dark salmon red in color, with numerous black spots, very large specimens often showing more black than red; length 140 mm.; tail 53 mm.; costal grooves 16:

FIG. 78.—*Pseudotriton ruber (from Fowler)*: a, roof of mouth (*from Dunn*).

eastern States from Maine to Florida; westward to Louisiana, Illinois and Wisconsin; very common.

Subspecies of P. ruber

P. r. ruber (Sonnini). Spots of adult running together; chin blackish: eastern States; New York and Indiana to northern Georgia and Mississippi.

P. r. schencki (Brimley). Spots of adult separate; chin black: mountains of North Carolina.

P. r. nitidus Dunn. Spots of adult separate; no black on the chin or on the hinder half of the tail; length 97 mm.; tail 36 mm.: mountains of Virginia and North Carolina.

13. Eurycea Rafinesque.   (*Spelerpes* Rafinesque.) Body elongate, mostly yellow or orange in color; tail long and compressed; vomerine teeth separate from the parasphenoid (Fig. 80); tongue free all round, being attached by a slender pedicle only (Fig. 77): 7 species.

Key to the Species of Eurycea

a_1 Digits on hind leg 5.
  b_1 Color yellow.
    c_1 Tail with longitudinal stripes.
      d_1 Tail with 2 lateral and no dorsal stripes............*E. bislineata.*
      d_2 Tail with 2 lateral and 1 dorsal stripe..............*E. guttolineata.*
    c_2 Tail barred...*E. longicauda.*
  b_2 Color orange; tail spotted.............................*E. lucifuga.*
  b_3 Color black or brown.
    c_1 Costal grooves 13; color black......................*E. melanopleura.*
    c_2 Costal grooves 20; color brown......................*E. multiplicata.*
a_2 Digits on hind leg 4.....................................*E. quadridigitata.*

E. bislineata (Green) (Fig. 79).   Body small, yellow above and below, with a dark line along each side of the back; length 72 mm.; tail 40 mm.;

FIG. 79.—*Eurycea bislineata wilderæ (from Dunn).*

costal grooves 14 or 15; digits very long: northern New England to Florida; westward to Lake Superior and Louisiana; very common.

Subspecies of E. bislineata

E. b. bislineata (Green).   Costal grooves 15: northern New England to Indiana; southward to Virginia and Tennessee.

E. b. cirrigera (Green).   Sides dusky, with white dots below the lateral band; costal grooves 14; upper lip of male with cirri: North Carolina to Louisiana.

E. b. wilderæ Dunn.   Black lateral line broken or absent on the hinder half of tail; male with cirri; costal grooves 15: mountains of Virginia and North Carolina.

E. guttolineata (Holbrook).   Body similar to *E. bislineata,* but with a mottled belly and 3 dark dorsal longitudinal lines; length 130 mm.; tail 75 mm.; costal grooves 13: Virginia to Georgia; westward to Louisiana.

E. longicauda (Green). Body slender, with a very long tail and bright yellow or reddish in color, with small black spots on the back and sides which form bars on the tail, and unspotted underneath; length 130 mm.; tail 80 mm.; costal grooves 13: Pennsylvania to Tennessee; westward to Missouri.

E. lucifuga Rafinesque (*E. maculicauda* Cope) (Fig. 80). Body slender, elongate, orange in color densely spotted with black; legs very long; length 152 mm.; tail 90 mm.: West Virginia to Missouri; northward into Indiana and Illinois; often in caves.

E. quadridigitata (Holbrook). Dwarf salamander. Body small, yellowish above, with a dark line running along each side of the back; length 82 mm.; tail 47 mm.; costal grooves 15; 4 toes on each foot: North Carolina to Florida; westward to Texas.

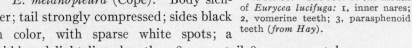

Fig. 80.—The roof of the mouth of *Eurycea lucifuga*: 1, inner nares; 2, vomerine teeth; 3, parasphenoid teeth (*from Hay*).

E. melanopleura (Cope). Body slender; tail strongly compressed; sides black in color, with sparse white spots; a middorsal light line; length 148 mm.; tail 83 mm.; costal grooves 13: Missouri, Kansas and Arkansas.

E. multiplicata (Cope). Body small, brown in color, paler below; length 80 mm.; tail 170 mm.; costal grooves 20: Arkansas, Missouri and Kansas to New Mexico.

14. Hydromantes Gistel. Toes webbed; tongue free all round; 2 premaxillaries present; parasphenoid patches separate: 3 species, 2 in Italy.

H. platycephalus (Camp). Body elongate; tail cylindrical, rather short; color dark chocolate, mottled with black; length 106 mm.; tail 35 mm.; costal folds 12: Yosemite National Park, California.

ON THE IDENTIFICATION OF THE LARVÆ OF THE PLETHODONTIDÆ

Aquatic larvæ are known to occur in the genera *Desmognathus*, *Leurognathus*, *Hemidactylum*, *Typhlotriton*, *Typhlomolge* (a permanent larva), *Grinophilus*, *Pseudotriton* and *Eurycea;* these larval forms have all been identified in the eastern and middle western States. They may be distinguished from the larvæ *Ambystomidæ* and *Pleurodelidæ* which inhabit the same region by the presence of a dorsal fin on the body of the larva in these two families; also in the Plethodont larva the legs develop before hatching. This fin is absent in the larvæ of the *Plethodon-*

tidæ, except in *Hemidactylium*, in which the larva has an extremely short larval life.   It is also much smaller than the larva of the *Ambystomidæ* and the *Pleurodelidæ* and has 4 digits on the hind feet.

Key to the Larvæ of the Plethodontidæ (except Hemidactylium)

a₁ Blind, white larvæ; costal grooves 12; legs very
    long.....................................*Typhlomolge.*
a₂ Eyes functional; body pigmented; legs normal.
  b₁ Gills short, glistening white; legs very stout.
    c₁ Definite color-pattern of light dorsal spots.*Desmognathus fuscus.*
    c₂ No definite color-pattern.
      d₁ Chin and throat light; eyes smaller,
        lateral...........................*Desmognathus quadramaculatus.*
      d₂ Chin and throat pigmented; eyes
        larger, more dorsal...............*Leurognathus marmorata.*
  b₂ Gills longer, not glistening white; legs slimmer.
    c₁ Back and sides the same color.
      d₁ Sides irregularly streaked............*Stereochilus.*
      d₂ Sides not so streaked.
        e₁ Chin and throat pigmented; head
          longer........................ *Gyrinophilus.*
        e₂ Chin and throat not pigmented;
          head shorter.
          f₁ Costal grooves 16..............*Pseudotriton ruber.*
          f₂ Costal grooves 17..............*Pseudotriton montanus.*
          f₃ Costal grooves 18..............*Typhlotriton.*
    c₂ Back lighter than the sides..............*Eurycea.*
      d₁ Digits on hind leg 5.
        e₁ No sharp demarcation between the
          lighter back and the darker sides;
          a gray band on the sides;
          costal grooves 14–15............*Eurycea lucifuga.*
        e₂ A sharp and uninterrupted demar-
          cation between the lighter back
          and the darker sides; sides black;
          costal grooves 13–14.
          f₁ A definite stripe on side.........*Eurycea guttolineata.*
          f₂ No definite stripe on side.......*Eurycea longicauda.*
                      Eurycea melanopleura.
        e₃ A sharp but broken demarcation
          between the lighter back and the
          darker sides.
          f₁ Costal grooves 14–15..........*Eurycea bislineata.*
          f₂ Costal grooves 20..............*Eurycea multiplicata.*
      d₂ Digits on hind leg 4.................*Eurycea quadridigitata.*

Family 5.   Amphiumidæ.—Body serpentine in form, with about

100 vertebræ; a pair of small gill slits; vertebræ amphicœlous; carpus

and tarsus cartilaginous; no eyelids; vomerine teeth prominent, forming an arched series parallel with those of the jaw; 2 pairs of weak legs; tail short, compressed: 1 genus.

Amphiuma Garden. With the characters of the family: 2 species.

A. means Gard. Congo snake. Body dark brown above, light below; length 886 mm.; tail 182 mm.; 2 toes on each foot; costal grooves about 60: Virginia to Florida and westward to Louisiana; in swamps, sometimes on the land; eggs about 150 in number and with a diameter of 9 mm.

A. tridactylum Cuvier. Similar to *A. means* but more distinctly bicolored and larger and with 3 toes on each foot: northern Florida to southern Louisiana, and up the Mississippi Valley to Missouri.

Family 6. Proteidæ.—Body elongate, with 2 pairs of weak legs, each leg having 4 toes; 3 pairs of gills and 2 pairs of gill slits persistent throughout life, the animals being permanent larvæ and completely aquatic; pubis with an anterior projection: 2 genera, the species of one of which, *Proteus*, are found in caves in southern Europe, and are blind and colorless.

Necturus Rafinesque. Toes 4 on all four feet; eyes very small: 2 species.

N. maculosus (Raf.). Mudpuppy; waterdog. Body subcylindrical; head flattened, with a fold of skin across the throat; tail compressed; color of adult dark brown above, lighter beneath, more or less spotted and splotched with darker brown and black; young striped; length 360 mm.; tail 110 mm.; extreme length 600 mm.: valleys of the Great Lakes and the Mississippi north of the Gulf States; Lake Champlain; Susquehanna River and the upper Hudson; Manitoba; southward into northern Alabama and Arkansas; often very common in rivers and lakes.

Subspecies of N. maculosus

N. m. maculosus (Raf.). Distribution as above.

N. m. lewisi Brimley. Size very small: in the Atlantic piedmont drainage of the Carolinas.

N. punctatus (Gibbes). Head short, elevated; length 170 mm.; tail 50 mm.; color pale, unspotted: North and South Carolina, in rivers of the coastal plain.

Suborder 2. Meantes.—Three pairs of gills persistent throughout life; maxillaries wanting; vertebræ amphicœlous; no hind legs; no teeth on the jaws; 2 ossifications in the shoulder girdle: 1 family.

Family Sirenidæ.—Body verye longate, eel-shaped; hind legs and pelvis wanting; carpus cartilaginous; 3 pairs of external gills which atrophy in the young and grow again in the adult; 1 or 3 pairs of gill slits; eyes very small; 2 patches of teeth on prevomer; premaxillaries and mandibles toothless and with horny sheaths: 2 genera and species.

Key to the Genera of Sirenidæ

a₁ Leg with 4 toes..1. *Siren*.
a₂ Leg with 3 toes..2. *Pseudobranchus*.

1. Siren L.   Four toes on each leg; 3 pairs of gill-slits present: 1 species.

S. lacertina L. Mud eel.   Body dark gray above, lighter beneath, more or less cylindrical in shape; head flattened; snout truncate; tail compressed; lateral grooves 31 to 37; length 700 mm.; tail 240 mm.; fore leg 38 mm.: south Atlantic and Gulf States, from District of Columbia and central North Carolina to the Rio Grande, and north-wards in the valley of the Mississippi to Alton, Illinois and Lafayette, Indiana; in swamps; often common.

2. Pseudobranchus Gray.   Three toes on each leg; 1 pair of gill slits: 1 species.

P. striatus (LeConte).   Body light with dark stripes; snout pointed; mouth very small; length 150 mm.; tail 65 mm.; fore leg 4 mm.; gills often covered by a fold of skin: South Carolina to Florida; in swamps; not common.

Order 2. Salientia (*Anura*).—Frogs and toads. Amphibians with two pairs of well developed legs and without a tail in the adult stage, but with a long tail and weak legs during some stage of the larval life (American forms).   The body is short and compact, there being in most cases nine vertebræ, and either no ribs or three very short ones; in addition to the vertebræ is the *urostyle*, a bone which is homologous to the caudal vertebræ and extends backward from the pelvic girdle.   The hind legs are usually long and muscular.   The head is generally very large; the eyes are large and protruding, and the eyelids well developed; the tympanum is flush with the surface of the skin.   Just behind the eye and behind and above the tympanum in the toads is a conspicuous raised glandular area called the *parotoid gland* (Fig. 81).   The general surface of the skin is glandular, and is either smooth or tubercular and warty.   The color is often bright, and metachrosis is very general. The male, in most forms, has a large vocal sack which opens into the mouth by one or two slits in its floor, by means of which it can produce a call which is often very loud; they can, however, croak without the aid of their vocal sacks, and some species do not have them.   The tongus is absent in the tropical family *Pipidæ*, but in most of the others it ie well developed and attached in front, the hinder end being free so that it can be thrown forward; it is in this manner that the animal captures the insects and other small animals on which it feeds. The eggs are usually laid in the water and the tadpoles which emerge from them have external integumental gills and a swimming tail, but no legs. In the metamorphosis which follows, the gills and tail are absorbed, the legs and lungs develop, the head and mouth change their form and relative size, and the animal becomes adult and fitted for a terrestrial life.

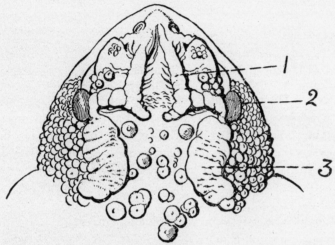

Fig. 81.—Upper surface of head of *Bufo americanus:* 1, cranial crests; 2, tympanum; 3, parotoid glands (*after Surface*).

About 1,600 species of *Salientia* are known, which occur in all the geographical regions of the earth, about 60 species being in the United States, grouped in 6 families.

On the Identification of the Salientia.—The descriptions of frogs and toads in this book apply to both adults and larvæ, and inasmuch as the animals in these two stages of development differ radically in form and appearance, the descriptions of the two stages are given separately.

1. The Adult.—There is a general uniformity in the shape of the body of the various species of frogs and toads, and the most important descriptive features are the following; the length in millimeters and color of the body, the size and shape of the head, the length of the hind legs, the character of the digits, the number of which is four in the fore foot and five in the hind, the character of the skin, whether it is smooth, tubercular or warty, the presence and character of the parotoid gland, the tympanum and the teeth. For a complete analysis of the main group several internal structures are important—the ribs, vertebræ, sacrum and pectoral girdle.

Key to the Families of the Salientia

a_1 Ribs present...1. *Discoglossidæ.*
a_2 Ribs absent; no anal processes.
    b_1 Pupil of eye vertical; parotoid glands present..............2. *Pelobatidæ.*
    b_2 Pupil of eye horizontal or round.
        c_1 Parotoid glands present (Fig. 81) toads................3. *Bufonidæ.*
        c_2 Parotoid glands absent.
            d_1 Expanded adhesive disks at ends of digits; tree toads
                (Figs. 88 and 89)...............................4. *Hylidæ.*
            d_2 No such disks present.
                e_1 Upper jaw with teeth; frogs; waist narrow; legs long.5. *Ranidæ.*
                e_2 Upper jaw without teeth; waist wide; legs short.....6. *Microhylidæ.*

Family 1.   Discoglossidæ.—Ribs present; vertebræ opisthocœlous; male with tail-like process; female with short anal tube; tongue with but little movement; pelvic girdle arciferous (coracoids and precoracoids overlapping midventrally); larvæ with a midventral spiracle: 5 genera, 1 in New Zealand, 3 in the Palearctic region and 1 in western America.

Ascaphus Stejneger.   Tympanum and Eustachian tube wanting; tongue free behind; sternum cartilaginous; maxillary and vomerine teeth present; parotoid gland well developed: 1 species.

A. truei Stej.   Color reddish brown or slate gray above, with a few blackish markings, and whitish beneath; a black streak from the nostril through the eye and along the lower border of the parotoid gland; length 40 mm.; length of hind leg 59 mm.: Washington, western Montana Oregon and northern California.

Family 2.   Pelobatidæ.—Spadefoot toads.   Body of medium size; head broad and short; eyes prominent; maxillary teeth present; pelvic girdle arciferous (coracoids and precoracoids overlapping midventrally); heel with a prominent spur which is used in digging: 5 genera and 70 species, in the Nearctic and Palearctic regions; 1 genus in the United States.

Scaphiopus Holbrook.   Body toad-like; tympanum present; hind feet partly webbed; vomerine teeth present: 3 species, in the United States.

Key to the Species of Scaphiopus

a_1 In the eastern and Gulf States; parotoid glands and tympanum
    distinct..*S. holbrookii.*

a$_2$ In the western States; parotoid glands and tympanum indistinct.

  b$_1$ In the Pacific States and eastward to Texas and Dakota......*S. hammondii.*

  b$_2$ In Texas and along the Mexican border....................*S. couchii.*

S. holbrookii (Harlan). Common spadefoot (Fig. 82). Body either smooth or covered with small tubercles and brown, yellowish or greenish in color, sometimes with a curved yellow line extending back from the shoulder; belly dirty white; iris golden; length 68 mm.; hind leg 76 mm.: eastern States from Massachusetts to Florida; Gulf States and Texas, and northward into Arkansas; common, but rarely seen because it spends the day in a hole in the ground which it digs with its hind feet, emerging in the night-time to feed.

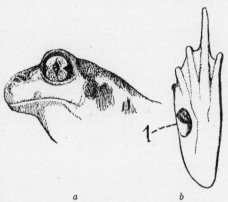

S. hammondii Baird. Body brown or gray in color, often with several irregular dorsal stripes of lighter color; tubercles

FIG. 82.—*a*, Left side of the head of the spadefoot toad. *b*, Hind foot of spadefoot: 1, spur *(from Surface).*

with red; throat of male black; length 60 mm.; hind leg 70 mm.: western America from the Pacific eastward into Texas and Dakota.

S. couchii Baird. Body greenish or brownish in color, mottled with lighter; belly whitish; dorsal surface with black tubercles, which are sometimes yellow on the hinder parts of the back and legs; length 60 mm.; hind leg 60 mm.: Texas to Arizona.

Family 3. Bufonidæ.—Toes 4-5; pectoral girdle arciferous (coracoids and precoracoids overlapping midventrally); presacral vertebræ 8: about 100 species, in all parts of the world; 4 genera in the United States.

Key to the Genera of the Bufonidæ

a$_1$ Hind toes webbed; no teeth on upper jaw................1. *Bufo.*

a$_2$ Hind toes not webbed; teeth on upper jaw; no parotoid glands.

  b$_1$ Toes without disks; vomerine teeth present...........2. *Leptodactylus.*

  b$_2$ Toes with small disks.

    c$_1$ Vomerine teeth present.........................3. *Eleutherodactylus.*

    c$_2$ No vomerine teeth..............................4. *Syrrhophus.*

1. Bufo Laurenti.—Pupil horizontal; a pair of prominent longitudinal ridges called the *cranial crests* lie between the eyes, which pass back to or along the parotoid glands (Fig. 81); prominent plantar tubercles often present on the digits; eggs laid in a long chord of jelly which is usually deposited on the bottom of some shallow pool: nearly 100 species; 15 in the United States.

Key to the United States Species of Bufo

a_1 In the States east of the Mississippi.
  b_1 In the northeastern States.
    c_1 Profile of snout sloping; back with a single wart to a color spot..*B. americanus.*
    c_2 Profile of snout abrupt; back with more than one wart to a color spot......................................*B. fowleri.*
  b_2 In the southern States.
    c_1 Cranial crests very prominent (Fig. 85)................*B. terrestris.*
    c_2 Cranial crests inconspicuous..........................*B. quercicus.*
a_2 In the States west of the Mississippi.
  b_1 In the central western States.
    c_1 Belly spotted.
      d_1 Cranial crests divergent (Fig. 81)...................*B. americanus.*
      d_2 Cranial crests parallel..............................*B. hemiophrys.*
    c_2 Belly unspotted.......................................*B. woodhousii.*
  b_2 In the southwestern States.
    c_1 Cranial crests absent.
      d_1 Parotoid glands small, and oval or round.
        e_1 Plantar tubercles small..........................*B. punctatus.*
        e_2 Plantar tubercles large, with cutting edges.........*B. compactilis.*
      d_2 Parotoid glands large and long......................*B. debilis.*
    c_2 Cranial crests present.
      d_1 Cranial crests sharp-edged and high.................*B. valliceps.*
      d_2 Cranial crests thick, confluent between the nostrils....*B. cognatus.*
      d_3 Cranial crests curved around the eyes................*B. alvarius.*
  b_3 On the Pacific slope.
    c_1 With a light middorsal line; skin rough.................*B. boreas.*
    c_2 Without a light middorsal line; skin very smooth........*B. canorus.*

B. americanus Holbrook. Common toad (Figs. 81 and 83). Body heavy and squat and variable in color, being usually gray or yellowish brown, more or less mottled or spotted; throat of male black; under parts white, spotted; parotoids elongate and reniform; cranial crests divergent; length 70 mm.; hind leg 85 mm.; female much larger: North America east of the Rockies; northward to Hudson Bay and Great Bear Lake.

B. fowleri Hinckley. Common toad (Fig. 84). Body rather slender, greenish or yellowish gray in color, spotted or striped with brown; under parts white; throat of male black; parotoids narrow and not reniform; cranial crests parallel; length 75 mm.: central New England to Georgia; westward to Michigan and Texas.

B. terrestris Bonnaterre (Fig. 85). Color dusky, with a pale mid-dorsal line and an irregular row of yellowish spots on the flank; belly yellowish white; length 70 mm.; cranial crests prominent, each ending in a knob: North Carolina to Florida and westward to the Mississippi.

B. quercicus Holb. Body small, brown in color, with a light middorsal line on each side of which are 3 or 4 pairs of black blotches; underneath white; length 27 mm.; parotoids long and oval: North Carolina to Florida; the smallest species.

FIG. 83.—Under surface of *Bufo americanus* (*from Dickerson*).

B. hemiophrys Cope. Color brown, with a yellowish middorsal line, on each side of which are 2 or 3 rows of brown spots; cranial crests parallel; belly spotted; length 60 mm.: North Dakota and Manitoba.

B. woodhousii Girard (Fig. 86). Color brown, with a pale middorsal line and 3 pairs of brown spots; belly yellow; length 90 mm.; head short, with thickened cranial crests posteriorly: Texas to Kansas and Montana; westward to Nevada and eastern California.

B. punctatus Baird and Girard. Body small and slender; color light brown above and yellowish white beneath; length 52 mm.; parotoid gland small and round: western Texas to southern California.

B. compactilis Wiegmann.   Color greenish brown; belly greenish or yellowish; length 72 mm.: New Mexico and Arizona.

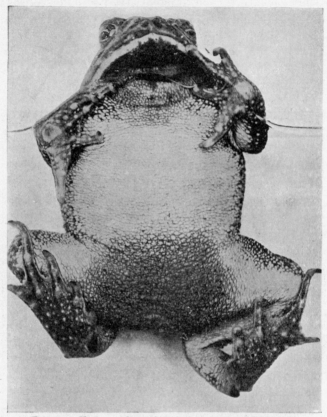

FIG. 84.—Under surface of *Bufo fowleri* (*from Dickerson*).

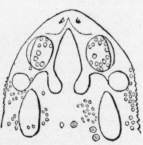

FIG. 85.—Upper surface of head of *Bufo terrestris* (*from Cope*).

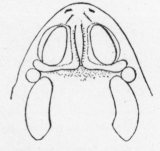

FIG. 86.—Upper surface of head of *Bufo woodhousei* (*from Cope*).

B. debilis Gir.   Similar to *B. punctatus* but with very large parotoid glands, which are elongate and not round; legs with black cross bands:

Texas to California; northward into Colorado; southward into Mexico; rather common.

B. valliceps Wieg.   Color chestnut brown above, with a dark cross band behind the orbits and a dark lateral band; legs cross barred; length 85 mm.: Louisiana and Texas.

B. cognatus Say.   Body large, dusky brown in color, with a yellowish middorsal line from which project irregular lateral lines to the right and left, giving the back a blotchy appearance; white underneath; length 85 mm.; parotoid glands short and wide: western plains from Kansas, Nebraska and Texas to southern California.

Subspecies of B. cognatus

B. c. cognatus Say.   Wyoming to Texas; west to the Rockies.

B. c. californicus Camp.   Southwestern California.

B. alvarius Gir.   Color dark green or brown; belly whitish; length 165 mm.; parotoid gland a long oval: southern Arizona and California; very rare.

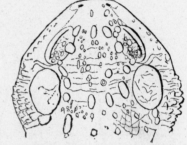

FIG. 87.—Upper surface of head of *Bufo boreas* (*from Cope*).

B. boreas B. and G. (Fig. 87).   Body very large, either uniformly dusky brown in color with a light middorsal line or with numerous spots on a yellow or green ground; white underneath, spotted with black; length 124 mm.; parotoid round or oval; no cranial crests: Pacific slope from Alaska to Lower California; eastward to Utah; common.

Subspecies of B. boreas

B. b. boreas B. and G.   Colors dark; web extending to tip of toes: northern California to Alaska.

B. b. halophilus B. and G.   Body small, slender; color light brown above; web deeply notched, 3 phalanges of fourth toe being free: central California to Lower California.

B. canorus Camp.   Coloration dimorphic, the female being irregularly blotched and the male specked with black; length 69 mm.; hind leg 82 mm.; parotoids very large and circular; no cranial crests: Yosemite National Park, California, at elevations above 7,000 feet.

2. Leptodactylus Fitzinger.   Toes without discs; vomerine teeth present; also a bony sternal style: many tropical American species; 1 in Texas.

L. albilebris (Gunther). A white stripe along the upper jaws; dorsolateral ridges present; color obscurely mottled above; toes with a dermal fringe; length 35 to 49 mm.: extreme southern Texas.

3. Eleutherodactylus Duméril & Bibron. Vomerine teeth present; body relatively slim; skin smooth or tubercular but not warty; digits not webbed; terminal phalanges with a transverse limb which supports dermal disk; 3 species in the United States.

E. latrans (Cope). Skin smooth; color brownish gray, with large brown spots; grayish white beneath; length 94 mm.; hind leg 115 mm.; pupil horizontal: San Antonio, Texas.

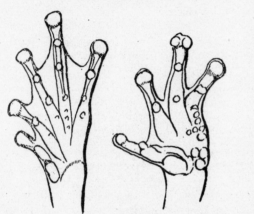 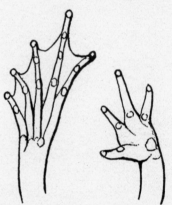

Fɪɢ. 88.—Hind and fore foot of *Hyla versicolor*   Fɪɢ. 89.—Hind and fore foot of *Acris*
(*from Surface*).   *crepitans (from Surface)*.

E. ricordii (D. and B.). Skin slightly tubercular; length 25 mm.: Florida.

4. Syrrhophus Cope. Like *Eleutherodactylus*, but without vomerine teeth: 2 species in the United States.

S. marnocki Cope. Color purplish brown, spotted; length 38 mm.; hind leg 45 mm.: San Antonio, Texas.

Family 4. Hylidæ.—Tree toads; tree frogs. Small *Salientia* which live in trees, bushes or in dense foliage on the ground and return to the water only in the spring time to breed; maxillary and vomerine teeth present; no parotoid glands; pelvic girdle arciferous (coracoids and precoracoids overlapping midventrally); digits expanded at their tips to form glandular disks, the sticky secretion of which assists the animal in climbing; front toes sometimes slightly webbed, hind toes usually fully webbed; eggs of American species laid in small masses in the water: about 190 species, most of which are in the Neotropic region; 23 species in the United States, which often show a remarkable metachrosis.

Key to the United States Genera of Hylidæ

a_1 Finger and toe disks conspicuous (Fig. 88)..................1. *Hyla.*
a_2 Finger and toe disks very small (Fig. 89).
   b_1 Hind toes fully webbed.....................................2. *Acris.*
   b_2 Hind toes slightly webbed...............................3. *Pseudacris.*

1. Hyla Laurenti.   Hind toes webbed; skin smooth in most species; belly granulated; pupil round or horizontal: about 14 species in the United States.

Key to the United States Species of Hyla

a_1 Eastern species.
   b_1 Fingers webbed at the base.
      c_1 A white spot under the eye............................*H. versicolor.*
      c_2 No white spot under the eye..........................*H. femoralis.*
   b_2 Fingers not webbed.
      c_1 Color bright green; no dorsal markings.
         d_1 No dark lateral markings...........................*H. cinerea.*
         d_2 With a dark lateral band..........................*H. andersonii.*
      c_2 Brownish, dorsal markings present.
         d_1 Large, circular dark dots above.....................*H. gratiosa.*
         d_2 Small, irregular markings above.
            e_1 With a dark X on the back......................*H. crucifer.*
            e_2 With the spots on the back elongate and in lines....*H. squirella.*
a_2 Western species.
   b_1 With a large white spot below the eye; fingers webbed........*H. baudinii.*
   b_2 No spot below the eye; fingers free; size medium to small.
      c_1 With dark spots above................................*H. arenicolor.*
      c_2 With linear markings above..........................*H. regilla.*

H. versicolor LeConte.   Common tree toad (Fig. 88 and 90). Body rather stout, with a rough, warty skin and very variable in color, varying from white or gray to deep brown or bright green and more or less mottled, with usually an oblique dark band above and a light spot beneath each eye and a large dark irregularly star-shaped patch on the back between the fore legs; length 50 mm.; hind leg 80 mm.: North America, west to Minnesota, Kansas and Texas; northward to southern Canada; southward into the Gulf States.

H. crucifer Wied (*H. pickeringii* Storer).   Spring peeper (Fig. 91). Body small and delicate and varying in color from deep brown to yellow, reddish, green or gray, with an oblique cross-shaped mark on the back and usually a V-shaped mark between the eyes; length 28 mm.; hind leg 45 mm.: eastern and central America; northward to New Brunswick; westward to Manitoba; southward to Georgia, Louisiana and Kansas;

the earliest frog to make its appearance in the spring; usually found on or near the ground.

H. squirella Latreille.   Body small, green or brown in color with or without spots; a dark line runs from the nostril to the eye and a light line along the jaw and under the eye to the shoulder; length 30 mm.: Virginia to Florida; westward to Texas and northward to Indiana.

H. andersonii. Baird.   Body small, unspotted bright green in color edged on the sides of the body by a band of white; gray beneath; length 40 mm.: New Jersey to South Carolina; rare.

FIG.   90.—*Hyla versicolor* (*from Dickerson*).

FIG. 91.—*Hyla crucifer* (*from Park Museum Bulletin*).

H. cinerea (Schneider).   Body slender, dark brownish green, bright green or greenish yellow in color, with or without a conspicuous white or yellowish band along each side; length 45 mm.; legs very long: Maryland to Florida; the Gulf States and up the valley of the Mississippi to Illinois; common.

Subspecies of H. cinerea

H. c. cinerea (Schneider).   With a light stripe along the side: Dismal Swamp, south and west.

H. c. evittata Miller.   Without a light stripe: Chesapeake Bay, on tidal flats, on aquatic vegetation; abundant.

H. gratiosa LeC.   Body very large; skin of back granulated or glandular; color green or brown, entire back generally covered with large spots; length 60 mm.: South Carolina to Florida and Louisiana.

H. baudinii Duméril & Bibron.   Body large, very dark brown, green or gray in color, without spots when the shade is light or dark, but otherwise with a broad mark extending from between the eyes to the middle of the back; length 55 mm.: southwestern Texas.

H. femoralis Lat.   Body small, and brown or gray in color, with a triangular spot between the eyes and a large irregular blotch on the back and also a dark line on each side of the body; length 35 mm.: southeast Virginia to Florida; the Gulf States; in pine trees.

H. arenicolor Cope. Body robust, gray in color with or without two or three rows of round brown spots on the back; length 42 mm.; skin rough; fingers not webbed: southwestern States from Texas and Utah into southern California.

H. regilla Baird and Girard. Pacific tree frog. Body small, and gray, green, brown or red in color, with a wide black band from the nostril through the eye to the shoulder; either without markings or with elongated black blotches on the back and a V-shaped spot on the head; length 53 mm.: Pacific slope from Vancouver Island to Cape St. Lucas; Idaho, Nevada, Arizona; ranging from sea level to 10,000 feet elevation; in low bushes, trees, moist places on the ground, and in burrows of animals.

2. Acris Duméril and Bibron. Similar to *Hyla*, except that the digital disks are minute; hind toes webbed: 7 species.

A. crepitans Baird (*A. gryllus* Le Conte). Cricket frog (Figs. 89 and 92). Body small, with a warty skin and variable in color, being some shade of brown or gray with a black triangular patch between the eyes, the apex of which is directed backwards, and usually 2 or 3

FIG. 92.—*Acris crepitans (from Park Museum Bulletin).*

oblique spots on each side of the back; eyes orange; length 25 mm.; hind legs 40 mm.; toes webbed; a fold of skin over the tympanum and one across the breast: eastern and central America; northward to southern New York and Connecticut; westward to Texas and Dakota; a diurnal frog which lives in the grass and near marshy places, but not in trees.

3. Pseudacris Fitzinger (*Chrophilus* Baird). Swamp cricket frogs. Similar to *Hyla*, but without webs between the toes or very short ones, and with very small digital disks: 7 species and subspecies.

Key to the Species of Pseudacris

a_1 Size larger; dorsal markings present.
    b_1 A median stripe or row of spots..........................*P. nigrita.*
    b_2 No median stripe or row of spots.
        c_1 In the Appalachian area..........................*P. brachyphona.*
        c_2 In the southwestern states.........................*P. ornata.*
a_2 Size very small; a black stripe through the eye; no dorsal
    markings...*P. ocularis.*

P. nigrita (LeConte). Body coarsely granulated above and beneath, with a narrow, pointed head and long legs; color varying from black to salmon, with 3 dark dorsal stripes or rows of spots; length 30 mm.: eastern and central States.

Subspecies of P. nigrita

P. n. nigrita (LeConte). Spots outlined with lighter: North Carolina to Mississippi.

P. n. feriarum (Baird). Color greenish brown or gray, creamy underneath; legs longer; hind leg 40 mm. long: Virginia to New York, east of the mountains.

P. n. triseriata (Wied). Legs shorter; color light ash, usually with 5 or 6 brown stripes: central States, from the Alleghenies to Arizona and Idaho.

P. brachyphona (Cope). A black triangle present between the eyes, and a black band through each eye; 2 broad curved dorsal stripes; length 30 mm.: Pennsylvania to Tennessee, in the mountains.

P. ornata (Holbrook). Body smooth, gray, green or reddish brown in color, with or without elongated dark spots and with a black band on each side of the body; several bright yellow spots on the sides posteriorly; length 35 mm.: Florida and South Carolina to Texas.

P. ocularis (Holb.). Color chestnut, with a dark stripe through the eye; length 17 mm.; upper jaw edged with white: South Carolina and Georgia; the smallest American tree toad.

Family 5. Ranidæ.—Frogs. Medium sized or large *Salientia;* skin smooth; maxillary and usually vomerine teeth present; pectoral girdle firmisternal (coracoids and precoracoids do not overlap midventrally); sacral transverse processes cylindrical; toes 4–5; no parotoid glands: about 270 species, in all the geographical regions, four-fifths of which are in Africa and India; 1 genus and about 15 species in the United States.

Rana L. Toes webbed; fingers not webbed; first finger of male swollen, especially in the spring at breeding time; vomerine teeth present; a pair of conspicuous dorso-lateral glandular ridges (Figs. 93, 94 and 95) run the length of the back in most species: about 120 species, widely distributed throughout the world; 15 species in the United States, mostly diurnal and more or less terrestrial animals which live in moist situations on the ground near the water, to which they return to breed, and often also, when alarmed, for protection. The eggs are laid in the water in large jelly masses attached usually to sticks or vegetation. The tadpoles usually complete their metamorphosis the year in which they are born, but the green-frog and the bullfrog do not become adult until the following, or in many cases, the second year. The principal food of frogs is insects, worms and snails. Frogs have a considerable economic importance in consequence of the demand for the hind legs for food, large quantities of which appear in the fish markets of the large cities.

Key to the United States Species of Rana

a_1 In the States east of the Sierra Nevadas.
  b_1 Dorso-lateral ridges present (Fig. 95).
    c_1 With conspicuous rounded, elongate or squarish spots between the dorso-lateral ridges.
      d_1 Skin smooth, with usually 2 rows of spots between the dorso-lateral folds.
        e_1 Spots rounded or elongate; color tone of body green......................................*R. pipiens.*
        e_2 Spots squarish; color tone of body brown.......*R. palustris.*
      d_2 Skin warty; numerous spots on the back and sides.
        e_1 Total length three times the length of head.....*R. areolata.*
        e_2 Total length two and a half times the length of head......................................*R. æsopus.*
    c_2 Without large spots on the back.
      d_1 Large aquatic frogs; head green...................*R. clamitans.*
      d_2 Small wood-frogs; head brown.
        e_1 Length of leg to the heel exceeds total length of body......................................*R. sylvatica.*
        e_2 Length of leg to the heel less than or equal to total length of body..............................*R. cantabrigensis.*
  b_2 Dorso-lateral ridges absent.
    c_1 Very large frogs, upwards of 200 mm. long...........*R. catesbeiana.*
    c_2 Smaller, medium sized frogs, under 100 mm. long.
      d_1 In the northern and eastern States.
        e_1 Back mottled................................*R. septentrionalis.*
        e_2 Back plain, not mottled......................*R. virgatipes.*
      d_2 In the Gulf States............................*R. gryilo.*
a_2 On the Pacific slope and in the Rocky Mountain region.
  b_1 Dorsolateral ridges distinct the full length of the body.
    c_1 A dark cheek patch present.
      d_1 Cheek patch brown; white stripe from the snout to the shoulder...............,..................*R. pretiosa.*
      d_2 Cheek patch black; white stripe from the eye to the shoulder....................................*R. aurora.*
    c_2 No dark cheek patch..............................*R. onca*
  b_2 Dorsolateral ridges absent or indistinct or broken..........*R. boylii.*

R. pipiens Schreber. Leopard frog (Fig. 93). Body green, gray or brown above with light-colored dorso-lateral ridges, between which are 1 to 3 irregular rows of elongate or rounded dark spots, each edged with yellow or white; similar spots on the flanks and legs; belly white; length

90 mm.; hind leg 150 mm.: North America, east of Sierras; absent from much of the Appalachian and piedmont regions; southward into Mexico; the commonest frog; in ponds, marshes and meadows, often at a considerable distance from water.

R. palustris LeConte. Pickerel frog (Fig. 94). Body pale brown above, with 2 light dorso-lateral ridges, between which are 2 rows of

Fig. 93.—*Rana pipiens (from Park Museum Bulletin).*   Fig. 94.—*Rana palustris (from Park Museum Bulletin).*

large squarish or rounded spots; the sides and legs with similar spots; beneath white in front and yellowish behind; length 70 mm.; leg 115 mm.: North America, from the Atlantic to Wisconsin, Kansas and Louisiana in small streams and ponds or in adjacent meadows.

R. clamitans Latreille. Green-frog; spring-frog. Body large, usually green on the head and shoulders and brown posteriorly, and

Fig. 95.—*Rana sylvatica (from Dickerson).*

with small irregular spots; dorso-lateral ridges light; sides and legs with dark bars and spots; throat of male yellow, of female white; belly white; length 100 mm.; hind leg 150 mm.: America, from the Atlantic to the Great Plains; common in ponds and streams; except the bullfrog, the most aquatic and the largest frog; development of tadpole completed in the second summer.

R. catesbeiana Shaw.   Bullfrog.   Body very large, green or greenish brown in color, being usually greener on the head and shoulders than more posteriorly; legs spotted or barred; beneath white; length 200 mm.; hind leg 250 mm.: America from the Atlantic to the Rockies, in ponds and streams; the largest and most aquatic frog, apparently rarely leaving the water; development of tadpole completed in the second or third summer; often common.

R. sylvatica LeC.   Wood-frog (Fig. 95).   Body small and slender, with long hind legs, and brown or faun color, often with a yellowish or reddish tone; a wide dark bank on the ear passing forward to the eye, and in some cases to the snout, and backward to the shoulder; legs

FIG. 96.—*Rana areolata* (*from Dickerson*).

often barred; dorso-lateral ridges light; length 48 mm.; hind leg 86 mm.: America from the Atlantic to the Great Plains; southward to South Carolina; northward to Quebec; common in the east; rare in the west; the least aquatic of the frogs, being found usually in damp woods.

R. areolata Baird & Girard (Fig. 96).   Body brown or olive in color, mottled or speckled with lighter and covered with rounded dark spots; skin rough and warty; length 75 mm.; hind leg 150 mm.: Texas, and northward in the Valley of the Mississippi into Illinois and Indiana.

R. æsopus Cope.   Gopher frog.   Body short and squat, with a very large head; color gray or brown, with large black spots on the back and side; length 62 mm.; hind leg 74 mm.: South Carolina to Florida and Louisiana; often hiding in holes in the ground.

R. cantabrigensis Baird.   Body small and similar to *R. sylvatica* in size and coloration, but with shorter legs; length 52 mm.; hind leg 70 mm.: northern North America from Michigan to Alaska and Hudson Bay; habits similar to those of *R. sylvatica*.

R. septentrionalis Baird. Mink frog. Body small, rather stout, light olive in color with mottlings of darker; legs blotched or banded; belly light yellow; length 56 mm.; hind leg 97 mm.: Canada; northern New England to Minnesota.

R. virgatipes Cope. Body small, with short legs and large ear and eye; color brown, with 4 narrow longitudinal stripes; throat yellow; sides yellowish brown, with large spots; belly white, spotted with brown; length 55 mm.: in pine barrens, New Jersey to Georgia.

R. grylio Stejneger. Body large, green in color in front and olive behind, with many irregular black spots; beneath light, unspotted except posteriorly; length 125 mm.; tympanum large: Georgia and Florida to Louisiana.

R. aurora B. and G. Body brown, yellowish or olive in color, often with numerous small darker spots; sides and hind legs reddish orange; belly light, mottled; skin smooth; length 75 mm.; hind leg 125 mm.: Pacific slope from Lower California to Vancouver Island; common towards the north.

Subspecies of R. aurora

R. a. aurora (B. and G.). Skin smooth: northern forms.

R. a. draytoni (B. and G.). Skin rough: southern forms.

R. onca Cope. Body rather small, green or brownish in color, with several irregular rows of dark spots on the back and sides; belly white; length 60 mm.; legs short; skin smooth: Utah and Nevada.

R. boylii B. and G. Body small, with a warty skin and very long legs; color brown, olive or red, with obscure round brown spots; beneath white anteriorly, yellow posteriorly; dorso-lateral ridges broad and inconspicuous; length 45 mm.; hind leg 75 mm.: California and Oregon; terrestrial.

Subspecies of R. boylii

R. b. boylii Baird. A light patch on the forehead: southwestern Oregon and California.

R. b. mucosa Camp. Size large; ground color yellow or light brown; no light patch on the forehead: in the mountains of southern California.

R. b. sierræ Camp. No light patch on the head; head narrow; hind leg short: southern Sierra Nevadas.

R. pretiosa (B. and G.). Body large, yellowish or reddish brown in color with 2 rows of irregular black spots between the dorso-lateral ridges; beneath light, marbled with gray; flanks and under surface of legs red; length 75 mm.: Montana and Utah, and westward to the Pacific coast; common; entirely aquatic.

Family 6. Microhylidæ.—Narrow-mouthed toads. Head narrow and pointed; mouth small; no maxillary or mandibular teeth; pelvic girdle firmisternal (coracoids and precoracoids fused midventrally) tropical toads with 4 species and 2 genera in the United States.

Key to the United States Genera of Microhylidæ

a_1 Foot with one small tubercle..............................1. *Microhyla*.
a_2 Foot with two large tubercles..............................2. *Hypopachus*.

1. Microhyla Tschudi (*Gastrophyne* Fitzinger). Head very narrow and pointed, much narrower than the body; skin smooth or glandular, but not warty: 3 United States species.

M. carolinensis (Holbrook) (Fig. 97). Size very small; body stout; color dark brown to gray, with two reddish dorso-lateral stripes bordered by dark brown; back and sides speckled with black; length 25 mm.; hind leg 28 mm.: Virginia to Florida, and westward to Texas; northward in the Mississippi Valley to southern Indiana.

M. areolata (Strecker). Color light gray above, marbled with brown; under surface light gray, with closely placed pale spots; skin of back highly glandular; length 22 mm.: southeastern Texas.

FIG. 97.—*Microhyla carolinensis* (*from Dickerson*).

M. olivacea (Hallowell) (*G. texensis* Girard). Color gray or brownish above, speckled or spotted with black spots tending to form longitudinal rows; skin of back smooth: Texas, New Mexico, Oklahoma, Kansas.

2. Hypopachus Keferstein. Head small; body large; limbs short; no vomerine teeth: 6 species.

H. cuneus Cope. Color light brown or grayish brown, sometimes tinged with olive, with a pale median vertebral line; length 41 mm.; hind leg 46 mm.: southwestern Texas.

2. The Eggs and Larvæ. In the identification of the freshly laid egg-masses of frogs and toads the first feature to be examined is the form

and condition of the jelly in which the eggs are imbedded and its location
in the water; the time of the year when the eggs are found is also of
importance, whether in the early spring, the later spring or the summer.
The egg is a spherical body ranging from 0.9 mm. to 2.4 mm. in diameter, in the different species, which has two distinct surfaces, the dark,
pigmented upper surface, or animal pole, and the white or yellow under
surface, or vegital pole; the pigmented portion is much the larger in
extent.   The egg is surrounded immediately by a spherical envelope of
jelly, inside of which and next to the egg is, in most species, a second or
inner envelope.

Key to the Eggs of some of the common Eastern Frogs and Toads

a_1 Eggs laid in a single row within a long spiral chord of jelly
which lies on the bottom or is looped around plants or
sticks; diameter of chord 3.4 to 4 mm.; number of eggs
4,000 to 7,000; season of egg laying April, May and June. *Bufo americanus.*
a_2 Eggs laid in a mass or singly.
  b_1 Eggs laid in a firm consistant mass around sticks, twigs,
etc., or free, and usually near the surface of the water.
    c_1 Inner jelly envelope of egg small and distinct.
      d_1 Vegital pole of egg yellow; animal pole brown;
egg mass globular; season of egg laying April
and first half of May; number of eggs 2,000 to
3,000 . . . . *Rana palustris.*
      d_2 Vegital pole of egg white; animal pole brown;
egg mass elongate; season of egg laying latter
part of March to middle of May; number of
eggs 3,500 to 4,500 . . . . *Rana pipiens.*
    c_2 Inner jelly envelope of egg large and indistinct, or
apparently absent; vegital pole of egg white; animal pole black; egg mass globular; season of egg
laying middle of March to end of April; number
of eggs 2,000 to 3,000 . . . . *Rana sylvatica.*
  b_2 Eggs laid in large loose masses or in small bunches or
singly.
    c_1 Eggs laid in large loose masses at or near the surface
of the water; vegital pole of egg white; animal pole
black.
      d_1 Eggs laid usually in one continuous film, one or
two eggs thick, on the surface of the water,
among plants; season of egg laying latter part
of May to middle of August; inner jelly envelope of egg distinct, elliptical in shape; number
of eggs 3,500 to 4,000 . . . . *Rana clamitans.*
      d_2 Eggs laid either in a wide film or in an irregular
mass attached to vegitation or to sticks; season

of egg laying middle of June to middle of July;
no individual jelly envelope to egg; number of
eggs 12,000 to 20,000......................*Rana catesbeiana.*
c_2 Eggs laid in small bunches or singly.
  d_1 Egg with 2 jelly envelopes, the inner one distinct;
  vegital pole of egg yellowish or cream; eggs
  laid in small bunches (4 to 25) on surface of
  water either attached or free; season of egg
  laying middle of May to middle of June; num-
  ber of eggs 1,500 to 2,000...................*Hyla versicolor.*
  d_2 Egg with but one jelly envelope; vegital pole of
  egg white.
    e_1 Eggs laid in bunches (20 to 100) attached to
    sticks and grass beneath the surface of the
    water; season of egg laying middle of March
    to middle of April; number of eggs 500 to
    800.....................................*Pseudacris triseriatus.*
    e_2 Eggs laid singly or in small bunches (4 to 12)
    attached to grass beneath the surface of the
    water; season of egg laying middle of March
    to May; number of eggs 800 to 1,000......*Hyla crucifer.*

In the identification of the well-grown tadpoles the features to be
first noticed are the relative size and color of the body and the relative
size and color of the tail. The position of the spiracle, through which
the respiratory water is discharged, the position of the anus and the
number of rows of labial teeth, which are situated above and below the
mouth, are also important.

Key to the Tadpoles of some of the common Eastern Frogs and Toads

a_1 Anus median; spiracle sinistral; tail cloudy, translucent,
rounded at the end; belly very dark, iridescent; greatest
length 28 mm...*Bufo americanus.*
a_2 Anus dextral; spiracle sinistral; greatest length over 30 mm.
  b_1 Eyes lateral in position, being visible from the ventral as
  well as from the dorsal aspect of the body; upper caudal
  crest extends almost to the eyes.
    c_1 Tail covered with black blotches and scarlet or ver-
    milion in color; belly white......................*Hyla versicolor.*
    c_2 Tail heavily pigmented with black blotches on the outer
    edges; belly cream, iridescent....................*Hyla crucifer.*
  b_2 Eyes dorsal in position; upper caudal crest not extending
  beyond the spiracle.
    c_1 Labial teeth, 3 or 4 rows above the mouth and 4 rows
    below it; a creamy line along the upper jaw region;
    belly pinkish; greatest length 47 mm..............*Rana sylvatica.*
    c_2 Labial teeth, 2 or 3 rows above the mouth and 3 rows
    below it.

d_1 Tail spotted with black; belly straw color, not iridescent; greatest length 145 mm....................*Rana catesbeiana.*

d_2 Tail greenish, mottled with brown; belly cream color; greatest length 84 mm....................*Rana clamitans.*

d_3 Caudal crest very dark purplish black, mottled; belly conspicuously iridescent; greatest length 74 mm..*Rana palustris.*

d_4 Caudal crest very light, translucent, with a few scattered dots; belly deep cream with a bronzy iridescence; greatest length 84 mm..............*Rana pipiens.*

CLASS 3.   REPTILES (Reptilia)*

The reptiles are cold-blooded vertebrates whose bodies are covered with horny scales or plates, and which have claws on their digits.   The legs are well developed, when present, and are often adapted for rapid running, but they do not usually support the body above the ground except during locomotion.   Respiration is always pulmonary.   The skeleton, including the skull, is well developed and ossified, the skull articulating by a single condyle.   The eggs are large and are usually laid on or in the ground, even when the animals are aquatic, although many species are ovoviviparous, and the embryo is meroblastic and provided with an amnion and allantois; the young animals resemble the parents, when born, there being no postnatal metamorphosis.

History.—The cold-blooded, egg-laying quadrupeds were named *Amphibia* by Linnæus, and subdivided into two orders, the *Serpentia* and *Reptilia*, the latter order including turtles, frogs and lizards.   Opinion fluctuated as to the exact relation existing between amphibians and reptiles for almost a century, although Blainville as early as 1816 correctly defined them, until near the middle of the last century the anatomical and embryological studies of Johannes Müller, Gegenbaur and others definitely established the two groups as distinct and equivalent classes.

The foundation of our knowledge of American reptiles was laid principally by John Edward Holbrook, Spencer F. Baird and Edward D. Cope, the work of Cope on *The Crocodilians, Lizards and Snakes of North America* being the most important single one on the subject; in more recent times the works of Leonhard Stejneger have been very important.

Number of Species and Distribution.—About 5,500 species of reptiles are known at the present time, most of which live in the warmer regions of the world.   There are no reptiles in Arctic regions, and but few in the colder portions of the Temperate zone.   About 300 species are known in the United States, which are grouped in 4 orders.

Key to the Orders of Reptiles

a₁ Jaws with teeth.
   b₁ Teeth set in alveoli; anus a longitudinal slit.........1. *Crocodilia* (p. 178).

* Revised by Dr. E. R. Dunn.

b₂ Teeth not set in alveoli; anus a transverse slit.

    c₁ Two pairs of limbs present (rarely absent); eyelids, external ear-opening and tympanum usually present; lizards...2. *Lacertilia* (p. 179).

    c₂ Limbs absent; eyelids, external ear-opening and tympanum absent; snakes......................3. *Serpentes* (p. 196).

a₂ Jaws without teeth; turtles.........................4. *Testudinata* (p. 225).

Order 1. Crocodilia.—The crocodiles and alligators are elongated, aquatic reptiles of large size, whose bodies are covered with scales and plates and which have two pairs of short legs and a laterally compressed tail.   There are five digits on the fore leg and four on the hind leg, the latter being webbed and the former usually so.   Only the three inner digits of each foot have claws.   The scales are arranged in transverse rows, the dorsal ones having high keels and being supported beneath by corresponding plates of dermal bone.   The head is compactly built; the quadrate bone is immovable and the palate is bony.   The jaws are powerful and the teeth are set in alveoli.   The tympanum is exposed, but is protected by a movable fold of the skin.   The nostrils lie close together and each can be closed by a valve.   The eye has an upper and a lower lid and a nictitating membrane.   The order contains a single family.

Habits and Distribution.—The Crocodilia live in streams and ponds in the warmer parts of the earth.   The American crocodile and the marine crocodile of the East Indies also enter salt water, and may be found far from land.   All are carnivorous and feed on all kinds of vertebrate animals.   They are oviparous, the eggs, which have a hard shell and somewhat resemble goose eggs, being laid in large nests, where they are guarded by the female while the sun incubates them.   Most species hibernate or æstivate in the mud for two or three months or more each year.

Family Crocodylidæ.—With the characters of the order: about 8 genera and 25 species, of which 2 genera and species occur in the United States.

Key to the Genera of United States Crocodilia

a₁ Snout broad (Fig. 98), the closed mouth not showing the fourth mandibular tooth.......................................1. *Alligator.*

a₂ Snout pointed; fourth mandibular tooth exposed..............2. *Crocodylus.*

1. Alligator Cuvier (Fig. 98).   Head broad; snout blunt; fourth mandibular tooth fits into a pit in the upper jaw; nasal aperture separated by a bony septum: 2 species, one in the Yang-tse-kiang, China.

A. mississippiensis (Daudin). Alligator. Body from 2 to 5 m. long, of which half is the tail; weight up to 500 lbs.; color dark brown or blackish, lighter or blotched on the sides and beneath; 19 to 20 teeth on each side of each jaw: North Carolina to the Gulf and westward to the Rio Grande; in the Mississippi as far north as Rodney, Miss.; 20 to 40 eggs in a nest, which hatch in about 2 months. The alligator has a loud voice, which can be heard a mile or more.

FIG. 98.—Heads of American alligator and American crocodile; alligator on left (*from Reese after Ditmars*).

2. **Crocodylus** Laurenti (Fig. 98). Head long and pointed; fourth mandibular tooth fits into a notch in the upper jaw and is exposed when the mouth is closed; nasal aperture not divided: 8 species, in America, Africa, Asia and Australia. Of these the Nile crocodile, *C. niloticus*, which may attain a length of 6 m., is the best known; the marine crocodile, *C. porosus*, which is found from India to Australia, is the largest species, attaining a length of 10 m.

C. acutus Cuvier. Body up to 7 m. long and slender; average adult length 3.5 m.; color olive green or gray: southern Florida and the greater Antilles, except Porto Rico, to Ecuador; in salt marshes; not common.

Order 2. Lacertilia (*Sauria*). Lizards. Elongated reptiles whose bodies are covered with scales, and with usually two pairs of pentadactyle limbs and a transverse anal opening. The head is of firmer structure than in the snakes, the two halves of the lower jaw being immovably bound together and the upper jaw being firmly joined with the cranium; the quadrate bone is, however, movable as in the snakes. The tympanum is not at the surface, and the ear-opening is often protected by special scales. The eye has a upper and a lower lid and a nictitating membrane. Most lizards possess the vestiges of a pineal eye, which often appears on the top of the head just back of the paired eyes. Teeth are always present and are either acrodont or pleurodont, and are often present on the gums as well as the jaws.

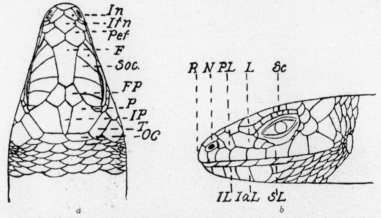

FIG. 99.—Head of a lizard (*Eumeces fasciatus*): *a*, dorsal view; *b*, lateral view: *F*, frontal; *FP*, frontoparietal; *IaL*, infralabial; *Ifn*, interfrontonasal; *IL*, lower labial; *In*, internasal; *IP*, interparietal; *L*, loreal; *N*, nasal; *Oc*, occipital; *P*, parietal; *Pef*, prefrontal; *PL*, preloreal; *R*, rostral; *Sc*, superciliary; *SL*, upper labial; *Soc*, supraocular; *T*, temporal *from Cope*).

The tongue is well developed and usually protractile, and may be bifid or not. The tail is mostly long and fragile and easily broken off; it grows again, but the lost vertebæ are not regenerated. Most lizards lay eggs; a few are ovoviviparous.

Habits and Distribution.—Lizards feed mainly on insects and worms, and are mostly active, terrestrial animals. The larger species feed also on birds, small mammals and eggs. A number of species are vegetarians. Metachrosis is common, and in some species, as the chameleon, very remarkable. About 2,700 species are known, which inhabit the warmer regions of the earth. About 100 species are known in this country, ranging, in one or two cases, as far north as Canada: they are grouped in 9 families.

On the Identification of Lizards.—The size and general form, whether elongate or not, or large or small, are first to be observed, together with the length of the head, body and tail in millimeters and that of the tail alone. The color markings are also important, but it must be remembered that many lizards are extremely variable in color, as well as exhibiting metachrosis in a high degree. Young animals also often differ totally from the adult in coloration. The character of the scales or plates and the differences between those on the back and the belly are sometimes important, as well as the number of transverse and longitudinal rows. Those immediately in front of the anus are often of characteristic form and number. The plates on the head are usually characteristic and a description of them often enters into a detailed description (Fig. 99), the supraocular scales over the eye, and the upper and lower labials, which bound the lips, being especially important. The character of the tongue is also usually to be noticed; in some families it is thick and little protractile, in others it is similar to the tongue of snakes and may be projected from the mouth as an important tactile organ. In most lizards a row, sometimes double, of conspicuous pores is present on the inner surface of the thigh; they are the *femoral pores* (Fig. 103). The teeth are usually conical and are never set in alveoli, but become ankylosed usually to the bone of the jaw, either by their base to the edge of the jaw bone, when they are spoken of as *acrodont teeth*, or by their side just inside the edge of the bone, when they are called *pleurodont teeth*.

Key to the Families of American Lacertilia

a_1 Legs present.
   b_1 Skin soft, with minute granular scales.................. 1. *Gekkonidæ.*
   b_2 Skin usually scaly.
      c_1 Tongue thick and not protractile................... 2. *Iguanidæ.*
      c_2 Tongue protractile.
         d_1 Conspicuous lateral fold present................. 3. *Anguidæ.*
         d_2 No such lateral fold.
            e_1 Body large and thick; no femoral pores........ 5. *Helodermatidæ.*
            e_2 Body very small and slender; femoral pores present or not.
               f_1 Femoral pores present.
                  g_1 No movable eyelids; pupils vertical...... 6. *Xantusiidæ.*
                  g_2 Eyelids movable; pupils round.......... 7. *Teiidæ.*
               f_2 Femoral pores absent.................... 8. *Scincidæ.*
a_2 Legs wanting; body vermiform.
   b_1 A conspicuous lateral fold; eye and ear opening present... 3. *Anguidæ.*
   b_2 No lateral fold present.
      c_1 Scales non-imbricate, in rings; no eye or ear opening.. 9. *Amphisbænidæ.*
      c_2 Scales imbricate, not in rings; no ear opening; eye partially concealed............................. 4. *Anniellidæ.*

Family 1.   Gekkonidæ.—Geckos.   Mostly small lizards with a soft skin covered with minute granular scales; digits usually flattened with adhesive disks; eyes large: 60 species, all tropical; 5 species in the United States, some adventitious, *Sphærodactylus cinereus* Mac Leay, a Cuban species, and *Hemidactylus turcicus* (L.), a Mediterranean species, having become established at Key West.

1. Sphærodactylus Wagler.   Digits expanded at their tips and without claws: 20 species in Mexico, Central America and the West Indies.

S. notatus Baird.   Reef gecko.   Body very small, 60 mm. long; color brownish yellow, with scattered reddish brown spots; scales on back strongly keeled: southern Florida, Cuba and Bahamas.

FIG. 100.—*Coleonyx variegatus (from Ditmars)*.

2. Coleonyx Gray.   Digits not dilated, with very small claws: 3 species.

C. variegatus (Baird).   The banded gecko (Fig. 100).   Body small, 130 mm. long, yellow in color, and either with about 13 broad brown transverse bands or with brown spots and blotches: Texas to California; rather common; not poisonous, although often so thought.

Family 2.   Iguanidæ.—Iguanas; swifts.   Tongue thick and non-protactile; scalation fine; teeth pleurodont; femoral pores usually present; eyelids well developed; pupil round: 50 genera and over 300 species, all American except a few East Indian, and tropical and sub-tropical; mostly insectivorous; 50 species in the United States.

Key to the Genera of Inguanidæ

a_1 Femoral pores absent, toes flattened (Fig. 101)............. 1. *Anolis.*
a_2 Femoral pores present, toes not flattened.
    b_1 A middorsal crest of enlarged scales present.............. 2. *Dipsosaurus.*
    b_2 No middorsal crest of enlarged scales present.
        c_1 Body lizard-like, head without horns.
            d_1 Tail blunt, superciliary scales not imbricate......... 3. *Sauromalus.*
            d_2 Tail long and attenuate; superciliary scales imbricate.

e_1 Upper labial scales oblique and imbricate.
f_1 Tympanum distinct; ear-opening evident.
g_1 A fringe of elongate scales on the toes...... 6. *Uma.*
g_2 No digital fringe present.................. 5. *Callisaurus.*
f_2 Tympanum hidden; ear-opening absent........ 7. *Holbrookia.*
e_2 Upper labial scales not oblique or imbricate.
f_1 Head plates small........................... 4. *Crotaphytus.*
f_2 Head plates large.
g_1 A collar of enlarged scales crossing the throat. 8. *Uta.*
g_2 No collar across the throat................ 9. *Sceloporus.*
c_2 Body broad and flat, toad-like; head with spines or horns. 10. *Phrynosoma.*

1. **Anolis** Daudin. Body slender and more or less compressed; head flattened; throat of male with a large ventral fold of skin which when dilated is fan-shaped: 120 species of arboreal, brilliantly colored lizards confined to tropical America; 1 species in the United States.

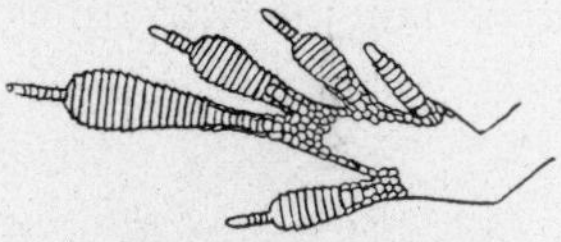

FIG. 101.—Foot of *Anolis carolinensis* (*from Ditmars*).

A. carolinensis Voigt. Chameleon (Fig. 101). Length 175 mm.; tail 120 mm.; color-changes very remarkable and equal to those of the true chameleon of southern Europe, the color being usually green or brown, yellow, gray or black; throat-fan, when dilated, crimson; middle portion of the toes expanded: coastal regions of the southern States, from the Neuse River, North Carolina, into Mexico; abundant; diurnal and insectivorous; easily tamed.

2. **Dipsosaurus** Hallowell. Large, thick-bodied lizards with a mid-dorsal crest of enlarged scales: 1 species.

D. dorsalis (Baird & Girard). Keel-backed lizard. Length 380 mm.; tail 250 mm.; color pale brown, with wavy longitudinal brown or black lines on the back: deserts of southwestern States and Mexico; herbivorous.

3. **Sauromalus** Duméril. Large, blunt-tailed lizards with very small imbricated scales; claws very thick and strong; a prominent neck-fold: 2 species, 1 in the United States.

S. obesus (Baird). Chuck-walla. Body thick and broad; length 300 mm.; tail 215 mm.; color black or dark brown; tail whitish; belly reddish: deserts of southwestern States; northward into Nevada and Utah; herbivorous; used for food; often abundant.

4. **Crotaphytus** Holbrook. Large, brightly-colored lizards with a very long, tapering tail and small granular scales and a neck-fold: 5 species, 4 in the United States.

Key to the Species of Crotaphytus

a_1 One or 2 rows of enlarged scales between the orbital area.
    b_1 A double black collar on the neck.........................*C. collaris.*
    b_2 No collar on the neck...................................*C. reticulatus.*
a_2 Several rows of small scales between the orbital areas.
    b_1 Snout short, truncate in profile............................*C. silus.*
    b_2 Snout longer..*C. wislizenii.*

C. collaris (Say). Collared lizard; mountain boomer. Body short; head very large; length 300 mm.; tail 200 mm.; color green or gray, with numerous white or yellow spots; behind the head are 2 black rings, separated by a white or yellowish space; throat usually orange: central and southern Missouri to central California and southwards; northward into Idaho and Oregon; in dry rocky places; omnivorous; often abundant; it sometimes runs on the hind legs, like a kangaroo.

FIG. 102.—*Callisaurus ventralis (from Cope).*

C. reticulatus Baird. Similar to *C. collaris* in form and size; color yellowish brown or gray, with a net-work of pale gray or yellow: southwestern Texas; rare.

C. wislizenii Baird and Girard. Leopard lizard. Length 300 mm.; tail 210 mm.; color brown, with black blotches and red dots; back and tail with yellowish or red transverse bands: the Great Basin from Idaho into southern California and Mexico, in desert places; abundant.

C. silus Stejneger. Similar to *C. wislizenii* but with a shorter and more truncate snout, and sharply defined light cross bands: San Joaquin Valley.

5. Callisaurus Blainville. Body stout; tail rather short; neckfold present: 4 species, 1 in the United States.

C. ventralis (Hallowell). Gridiron-tailed lizard (Fig. 102). Length 180 mm.; tail 100 mm.; color gray or greenish, thickly spotted with white; 2 rows of large spots on back; under surface of tail of male white, with 4 wide black bars: western Texas to California; northward into Utah and Nevada; in desert and arid regions; very common; when running it curls its tail over its back.

6. Uma Baird. Body rather stocky, with 2 rows of subdigital scales, and a lateral digital fringe of elongate scales: 1 species.

U. notata Baird. Length 220 mm.; tail 120 mm.; ground color black, with numerous large round, white spots, each with a black center; abdomen white, with a black spot on each side: deserts of southeastern California.

7. Holbrookia Girard. Spotted lizards. Small, rather slender, flattened lizards with very small scales; color pale, with 2 rows of dark blotches on the back, a row of more or less indistinct blotches on the side and 2 black bars on the lower portion of each side; upper labials imbricate; no external ear-opening: 7 species, 6 in the United States.

Key to the United States Species of Holbrookia

a_1 Tail flat, with broad black bands beneath.....................*H. texana.*
a_2 Tail round.
  b_1 Tail longer than the body in both sexes.
    c_1 Dorsal scales very small, convex or keeled; tail very long..*H. propinqua.*
    c_2 Dorsal scales larger, flat.
      d_1 Size large; femoral pores usually more than 12.........*H. elegans.*
      d_2 Size smaller; femoral pores usually less than 12........*H. pulchra.*
  b_2 Tail shorter than the body in females, and usually also in males.
    c_1 Black subcaudal spots usually present; dorsal spots sharply
     defined...*H. lacerata.*
    c_2 No subcaudal spots; dorsal spots not sharply outlined......*H. maculata.*

H. texana (Troschel). Length 150 mm.; tail with black cross bars on the under surface, almost exactly like *Callisaurus ventralis,* and held over the body when the animal is running; hind foot half the length of head and body: western Texas to eastern Arizona.

H. propinqua Baird and Girard. Length 120 mm.; tail 70 mm.; dorsal spots frequently wanting; tail proportionately long; upper labials 7: southern Texas.

H. elegans Bocourt. A large, smooth scaled form with sharply defined dorsal spots: deserts west of Tucson, Arizona.

H. pulchra Schmidt. A small, smooth scaled form with sharply defined dorsal spots: higher altitudes in mountains of southern Arizona.

H. lacerata Cope. Under surface of tail with black spots; dorsal spots large, sharply defined; length 106 mm.; tail 52 mm.: central Texas.

H. maculata Girard. Length 100 mm.; tail 50 mm.; coloration variable: Nebraska and Wyoming to Arizona, southward into Mexico; in dry, rocky places, feeding mainly on insects.

8. Uta Baird and Girard. Swifts. Small, flattened, active lizards with small scales; ear distinct; collar present; tail longer than the body: about 24 species in the southwestern United States and Mexico.

Key to the Species of Uta in the United States

a_1 Scales on the back uniform, not abruptly larger than those on
  the sides (Fig. 103).
  b_1 Scales on the back very small, perfectly smooth...........*U. mearnsi.*
  b_2 Scales on the back larger and more or less sharply keeled..*U. stansburiana.*

a₂ Scales on the back enlarged, sharply distinct from the smaller
    lateral scales (Fig. 104).
    b₁ Tail very long, more than twice the length of the head and
        body; usually without a median dorsal row of small
        scales..*U. graciosa.*
    b₂ Tail shorter; 1 or 2 rows of small scales on the middorsal
        line, between the rows of enlarged scales.
        c₁ Lateral caudal scales small and smooth...............*U. levis.*
        c₂ Lateral caudal scales larger and more sharply keeled.....*U. ornata.*

U. mearnsi Stejneger.   Size large; length 230 mm.; tail 150 mm.:
western border of the Colorado desert, in rocky situations.

U. stansburiana B. & G. (Fig. 103).   Length 120 mm.; tail 60 mm.;
color dark green or gray, with rows of small light and dark blotches on

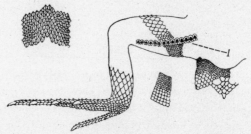

Fig. 103.—Femoral pores on hind leg and scales of back of *Uta stansburiana:* 1, femoral
pores (*from Cope*).

the back which are surrounded by scattered bluish dots: western Texas
to California; northward into Utah, Idaho and Oregon; very common in
deserts.

Subspecies of U. stansburiana

  U. s. stansburiana B. and G.   In northerly portion of range.
  U. s. stejnegeri Schmidt.   In the central portion of the range.

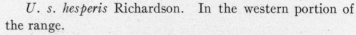

    U. s. hesperis Richardson.   In the western portion of
the range.

    U. graciosa (Hallowell).   Length 200 mm.; tail 140

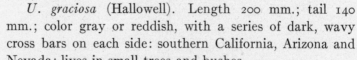

Fig. 104.
Scales of back
of *Uta ornata*
(*from Cope*).

mm.; color gray or reddish, with a series of dark, wavy
cross bars on each side: southern California, Arizona and
Nevada; lives in small trees and bushes.

    U. levis Stejneger.   Six middorsal rows of enlarged
scales; color uniform pale with markings: New Mexico, canyons southeastern Utah and western Colorado.

  U. ornata B. and G. (Fig. 104).   Length 150 mm.; color gray, with
wavy black cross bands: western Texas to southern California; northward into Utah.

Subspecies of U. ornata

U. o. ornata B. and G.   In Texas.

U. o. linearis Baird.   In southern Arizona.

U. o. symmetrica Baird.   In the Colorado desert.

9. Sceloporus Wiegmann.   Spiny swifts.   Small, active lizards with large-keeled, sharply pointed and bristling scales; large supraocular scales present; ear distinct; no neck fold: about 35 species, mostly in desert regions of tropical America, several species, not here mentioned, entering the United States from Mexico.

Key to the more common United States Species of Sceloporus

a_1 A single row of large supraocular scales, bordered on each
     side by a single row of small scales.
     b_1 Median row of small scales extending around forward
         two-thirds only of cresentic margin of supraocular
         scales..*S. clarkii.*
     b_2 Median row of small scales extending completely
         around cresentic margin........................*S. spinosus.*
a_2 A single row of large supraocular scales, bordered by a
     single median and 2 ventral rows of small scales (Fig.
     105).
     b_1 A broad black color on the sides of the neck..........*S. jarrovii.*
     b_2 No collar present.
         c_1 In the Great Basin and Pacific region.............*S. occidentalis.*
         c_2 In the Great Plains region and west to California...*S. consobrinus.*
         c_3 In central and east-central Florida................*S. woodi.*
a_3 Supraocular plates similar to a_2, but wrinkled and some-
     times with 3 ventral rows of small scales..............*S. undulatus.*
a_4 Two rows of supraocular scales, bordered above by 1 and
     below by 1 or 2 rows of small scales.
     b_1 A broad, black collar round the neck................*S. torquatus poinsetti.*
     b_2 No collar present..................................*S. graciosus.*

S. undulatus (Latreille).   Pine lizard; fence lizard; swift (Fig. 106). Length 140 mm.; tail 70 mm.; scales large and rough; color grayish or greenish, with a series of black, wavy cross bars on the back and a pale band extending backward from the eye on each side: from the Atlantic to the Pacific; from New Jersey, Michigan and Oregon southward; common; in dry, sandy places, especially in pinelands; tail very brittle.

S. clarkii Baird & Girard.   Length 220 mm.; tail 120 mm.; color gray or brown, with dark transverse bands; a green spot in each scale on the back; broad black collar interrupted above: New Mexico, Arizona and Mexico; common.

S. consobrinus B. and G.   Similar to *S. undulatus*, but with 2 pale lateral stripes instead of cross bars and smooth head scales: Dakota to Texas and westward to California; common.

S. spinosus Wiegmann.   Similar to *S. undulatus*, but 250 mm. long, with coarsely bristling scales, with a broad, pale band on each side and an oblong black patch on each shoulder: Florida to New Mexico and Mexico.

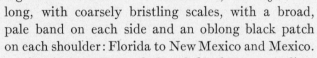

S. graciosus B. and G.   Color brown or olive, with 2 yellow stripes on each side enclosing a dark band and a round black spot in front of each fore leg: Great Basin region, from Oregon and Idaho to Nevada and southern California; common.

S. torquatus poinsetti B. and G.   Length 250 mm.; tail 110 mm.; body stout; tail short and blunt; scales very coarse and pointed; color dull olive with a broad, black collar bordered with yellow: Texas to Arizona and Mexico.

FIG. 105.—Head of *Sceloporus occidentalis* (*from Cope*).

S. jarrovii Cope.   Length 177 mm.; tail 80 mm.; color bluish black, with a light spot on each scale and a broad black spot on each side of the neck: southern Arizona.

S. occidentalis B. and G. (Fig. 105).   Length 200 mm.; tail 100 mm.; color greenish gray, with 2 rows of wavy cross bars on the back; legs very long: the Great Basin and mountain ranges of the Pacific region

FIG. 106.—*Sceloporus undulatus* (*from Fowler*).

from Oregon and Idaho to Nevada and southern California; common in rocky districts.

S. woodi Stejneger.   Length 103 mm.; tail 65 mm.; fourth toe extremely long: central and east-central Florida.

10. Phrynosoma Wiegmann. Horned toads; horned lizards. Body short, wide and flattened; tail short; hinder border of head armed with long, sharp, horn-like spines; long spines also often along the sides of the body and tail: about 17 species, in the desert regions of the southwest and of Mexico; terrestrial, living largely on insects; viviparous; harmless.

Key to the United States Species of Phrynosoma

a_1 Tympanum not covered with scales.
   b_1 Horns long and large (Fig. 107); 2 rows of enlarged marginal
      spines on the sides of the body.
      c_1 In the Great Plains region..............................*P. cornutum.*
      c_2 In California...*P. blainvillii.*
      c_3 In Arizona..*P. solare.*
   b_2 Horns small or rudimentary (Fig. 108); 1 row of marginal
      spines or none.
      c_1 No enlarged marginal spines present..................*P. modestum.*
      c_2 One row of enlarged marginal spines present............*P. douglassii.*
a_2 Tympanum covered with scales.
   b_1 Horns short; 6 to 12 femoral pores.......................*P. platyrhinos.*
   b_2 Horns long; 16 to 20 femoral pores.......................*P. m'callii.*

P. cornutum (Harlan). Common horned toad (Fig. 107; Fig. 109). Length 150 mm.; tail 45 mm.; width of body 60 mm.; color gray, spotted with brown and with a median yellow band; head spines very long: Kansas and Nebraska to Texas and Colorado; common.

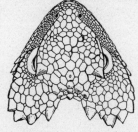

Fig. 107.—Head of *Phrynosoma cornutum (from Cope).*

Fig. 108.—Head of *Phrynosoma hernandesi (from Cope).*

P. blainvillii Gray. Length 150 mm.; tail 56 mm.; color light brown: California, southward and eastward of San Francisco; common.

Subspecies of P. blainvillii

P. b. blainvillii Gray. Southern California; Lower California.
P. b. frontale Van Denburgh. In the northern portion of the range.

P. solare Gray.   Length 140 mm.; tail 51 mm.; 4 equally long occipital horns form with the lateral horns an uninterrupted series: deserts of Arizona; westward to Tucson.

P. modestum Girard.   Length 95 mm.; color yellowish brown, sometimes pinkish, with a black patch on each side of the nape: Texas to Arizona; common.

Fig. 109.—*Phrynosoma cornutum (from Ditmars).*

P. douglassii (Bell).   Length 100 mm.; tail 26 mm.; color brown, with 2 rows of large dark blotches on the back; horns rudimentary; abdominal scales smooth: Oregon and Washington; Rocky Mountains and Great Basin; common.

Subspecies of P. douglassii

P. d. douglassii (Bell).   In Washington and Oregon.

P. d. ornatum Girard.   In the Salt Lake Basin.

P. d. hernandesi (Girard) (Fig. 108).   Length 94 mm.; tail 30 mm.; color yellowish or brown, with a row of large, obscure middorsal spots: in the Rocky Mountains; common.

P. d. ornatissimum (Girard).   Length 124 mm.; color yellowish, sometimes pinkish, with 2 rows of large dark brown spots on the back: in the Great Basin and the Grand Canyon region.

P. d. brevirostre (Girard).   Length 94 mm.; color similar to *P. d. orna-tissimum:* on the northern Great Plains.

P. platyrhinos Girard.   Length 120 mm.; tail 40 mm.; color pinkish gray or brown, with dark cross bands on the back; a large dark patch on each side of the nape; scales small and smooth; tympanum covered: eastern California and the Great Basin from Idaho to Arizona; common.

P. m'callii (Hallowell).   Length 100 mm.; tail 34 mm.; color gray with a narrow middorsal line with 2 rows of round spots on each side: deserts of the lower Colorado; rare.

Family 3. Anguidæ.—Elongated, often more or less snake-like lizards with weak legs or without any; tongue bifid and extensile; teeth pleurodont; body with a conspicuous lateral fold: about 44 species, in the New and Old Worlds, many in Mexico and Central America, 7 in the United States.

Key to the United States Genera of Anguidæ

a_1 Four legs present...1. *Gerrhonotus.*
a_2 Legs wanting..2. *Ophisaurus.*

1. Gerrhonotus Wiegmann.   Slender lizards with 2 pairs of weak legs; ears distinct; no femoral pores; tail long and brittle: 19 species, 6 in the United States.

Key to the United States Species of Gerrhonotus

a_1 In the Pacific States.
  b_1 Dark ventral lines between the longitudinal rows of scales
      present or absent.
    c_1 Dorsal scales strongly keeled, in 16 longitudinal rows.
      d_1 Temporal scales smooth........................*G. cœruleus.*
      d_2 Lower temporal scales keeled....................*G. palmeri.*
    c_2 Dorsal scales weakly keeled, in 14 rows..............*G. principis.*
  b_2 Dark ventral lines on the middle of the longitudinal rows
      of scales; dorsals strongly keeled, in 14 rows...........*G. multicorinatus.*
a_2 In the southwestern States; scales obscurely keeled.
  b_1 Back with alternating black and white bars.............*G. kingii.*
  b_2 Back with a few obscure cross bars....................*G. infernalis.*

G. cœruleus Wieg.   Length 290 mm.; tail 180 mm.; color brown or olive with numerous dark cross bands, spotted with white; dorsal scales strongly keeled and in about 16 regular rows: coast region of California, chiefly north of San Francisco.

G. palmeri Stejneger.   Similar to *P. cœruleus* but much less elongated and with a different coloration, being either uniform dark olive brown dotted with black and white on the sides or pale bluish drab clouded with irregular blotches: central California, on the slopes of the Sierra Nevada.

G. principis (Baird & Girard). Length 300 mm.; tail 190 mm.; color light brown, with a middorsal series of irregular dark blotches; dorsal scales obscurely keeled and in 14 rows: western Washington, Oregon and Vancouver Island.

G. multicorinatus (Blainville). Length 270 mm.; tail 160 mm.; color brown or gray with 10 to 14 dark rings across the back, and spotted with white; dorsal scales strongly keeled and in 14 longitudinal rows: California; common.

G. kingii Gray. Body very small and slender; color light yellowish olive; back with 10 broad black bars, each with a whitish bar behind; tail with 30 half rings; sides with narrow black bars: New Mexico and Arizona.

G. infernalis Baird. Body very small, depressed; tail twice the length of the head and body; color light olive with 7 or 8 obscure dark bars; dorsal scales keeled, lateral scales smooth: southern Texas.

2. Ophisaurus Daudin. Body snake-like, without legs; eyelids well developed; ear distinct, but small; tail longer than the body: 1 species.

O. ventralis (L.). Glass snake. Length 670 mm.; tail 400 mm.; color brown or greenish with a median and 2 lateral stripes; tail very brittle, whence the name of glass snake; to be distinguished from a snake by the eyelids, the ears and the scaly belly: southern and central States; northward into Virginia, Indiana and Wisconsin; westward to Nebraska and Texas and Mexico; common in dry meadows, where it feeds on insects and worms.

Family 4. Anniellidæ.—Elongate, legless lizards with a cylindrical body and no external ear-opening; eye a narrow slit: 1 genus and 2 species.

Anniella Gray. With the characters of the family: 2 species.

A. pulchra Gray. Length 180 mm.; tail 6 mm.; color gray or brown with 3 dark lines; abdomen yellowish: coastal region of southern California.

Family 5. Helodermatidæ.—Large, thick-bodied lizards with brightly colored bodies, covered with small bead-like tubercles; tail short; poison fangs in the lower jaw: 1 genus.

Heloderma Wiegmann. With the characters of the family: 2 species.

H. suspectum Cope. Gila monster. Length 470 mm.; tail 150 mm.; color black or purplish, with large, more or less transverse pink or yellowish blotches: deserts of Arizona and New Mexico; the only poisonous lizard in the country or the world.

Family 6. Xantusiidæ.—Diminutive, cylindrical lizards with very short legs, and granular scales on the sides and back; belly covered with plates; 3 folds of skin on the throat; eye usually very large and without eyelids; pupil vertical: about 5 species; in desert regions.

Xantusia Baird. With the characters of the family: 4 species in the United States.

X. henshawi Stejneger. Length 140 mm.; tail 85 mm.; color blackish brown, irregularly marbled with cream-colored lines: southern California.

Fig. 110.—*Cnemidophorus sexlineatus (from Ditmars).*

X. riversiana Cope. Length 175 mm.; tail 87 mm.; color gray or brown, spotted with brown or black: San Nicholas, San Barbara and San Clemente Islands.

X. vigilis Baird. Length 85 mm.; tail 45 mm.; color gray, yellow or brown, speckled with brown: southeastern California; southern Nevada; common in and beneath fallen yucca trees.

Family 7. Teiidæ.—Elongated lizards with a deeply bifid tongue and sometimes rudimentary legs: 1 genus in the United States.

Cnemidophorus Wagler. Race runners. Body slender; tail long and tapering; scales granular above, plated beneath: 4 species in the United States.

C. sexlineatus (L.) (Fig. 110). Swift. Length 250 mm.; tail 175 mm.; color dark brown, with 6 yellow stripes on the body; belly bluish or greenish: Maryland to Florida; westward to Colorado; up the Mississippi Valley to Lake Michigan and South Dakota; common towards the south; remarkable for its swiftness.

C. sackii Wiegmann (*C. gularis* Baird & Girard). Similar to *C. sexlineatus*, but with a row of pale dots between each two stripes: Oklahoma and Texas to Arizona and Utah.

Subspecies of C. sackii

C. s. sackii Wieg.   Six stripes present: in Texas and Oklahoma.

C. s. perplexus Wieg.   Seven stripes present: in New Mexico, Arizona, Colorado and Utah.

C. tessellatus (Say).   Length 450 mm.; tail 300 mm.; color dark olive, with 4 to 7 yellow stripes in the young animal; back marbled or blotched: in the adult western Texas to California; northward into Colorado and central California; common in dry sandy places.

C. hyperythrus Cope.   Length 200 mm.; only one fronto-parietal plate; 4 lateral stripes: southern California.

Family 8.   Scincidæ.—Skinks.   Small, active lizards with smooth scales underlaid with bony plates; head covered with symmetrical plates; tongue free, notched in front; eyelids well developed; pupil round; legs present or absent: about 200 species; cosmopolitan; ovoviviparous; about 14 species in the United States.

Key to the Genera of Scincidæ

a_1 Legs and digits normal.
    b_1 Paired scales above the nasals (supranasals); lower eyelid scaly...1. *Eumeces.*
    b_2 No supranasal scales; lower eyelid with transparent disk......2. *Leiolopisma.*
a_2 Legs diminutive; toes reduced in number....................3. *Neoseps.*

1. Eumeces Wiegmann.   Body small, with glossy, shining scales; lower eyelid scaly; palate with teeth: 30 species, in America, Africa and Asia; 14 species in the United States; diurnal; terrestrial.

Key to the Species of Eumeces

a_1 In the eastern States.
    b_1 Scales on body in 28 or more rows; color uniform or with 5 white stripes......................................*E. fasciatus.*
    b_2 Scales on body in 22 or 24 rows; not more than 4 white stripes.
        c_1 Scales in 24 rows; legs meeting on sides: in the Appalachian Mountains...............................*E. anthracinus.*
        c_2 Scales in 22 rows; legs short, not meeting; in Florida...*E. egregius.*
a_2 In the central States.
    b_1 Body with 7 or more light stripes; legs short.............*E. multivirgatus.*
    b_2 Body with 5 light stripes, or uniform; legs longer.
        c_1 Lateral scale rows horizontal; color uniform brown or with 5 light stripes; scales in 28 or more rows.......*E. fasciatus.*

c_2 Lateral scale rows oblique; color grayish black or with
      5 faint stripes; scales in 26 to 28 rows.............*E. obsoletus*
b_3 Body with 4 light stripes.
    c_1 Scales in 26 rows...............................*E. pluvialis.*
    c_2 Scales in 28 rows...............................*E. septentrionalis.*
a_3 In the far West.
    b_1 Color blackish without stripes or with 5 faint stripes.....*E. obsoletus.*
    b_2 With 4 stripes......................................*E. skiltonianus.*

E. septentrionalis Baird. Body stout; tail seven-fourths the length of the body; color light green with 4 dorsal black stripes and a lateral black stripe on each side between 2 white ones: Minnesota, Iowa, Oklahoma, Nebraska and Kansas.

E. fasciatus (L.) (*E. quinquelineatus* L.). Blue-tailed skink; scorpion (Figs. 99, 111). Length 240 mm.; tail 130 mm.; color black in youth

FIG. 111.—*Eumeces fasciatus (from Fowler).*

(100 mm.) with 5 dorsal yellow stripes on body and a blue tail, brown or olive in adult males with the stripes faint or absent and the head red: Massachusetts to Florida; westward to Arizona; up the Mississippi Valley to Canada; rare and small (150 mm.) towards the north; common in the south.

E. obsoletus Baird and Girard. Body large, 300 mm. long; color light olive; young black with 5 faint stripes: Kansas to Colorado, Arizona and Texas; southward into Mexico.

E. anthracinus Baird. Length 157 mm.; tail 101 mm.; color dark olive green, with 2 light lines on each side between which is a black band; tail bluish: Appalachian region, New York to North Carolina; common.

E. multivirgatus Hallowell. Body cylindrical; legs far apart; tail three-halves the length of the body; color pale olive with 4 or 5 stripes on each side: Nebraska to northern Texas, Colorado and New Mexico.

E. pluvialis (Cope).   Body small and rather stout with 4 green stripes; belly green: Alabama, Missouri, Arkansas, Kansas and Texas.

E. egregius Baird.   Body very small and vermiform; legs small and weak; length 100 mm.; color reddish or greenish, with 4 white stripes southern Florida and the Keys.

E. skiltonianus B. & G.   Length 150 mm.; tail 90 mm.; color olive green, with a dark band bordered by a white line above and below on each side; body with 26 rows of scales: Washington to Lower California; Nevada and Utah; common.

2. Leiolopisma Duméril & Bibron.   Body elongate, small, cylindrical ear-opening very large, exposed; legs very small; lower eyelid with a transparent disk; palate toothless: 28 species, cosmopolitan, 1 in America.

FIG. 112.—*Leiolopisma unicolor (from Ditmars).*

L. unicolor (Harlan) (*L. laterale* Say) (Fig. 112).   Length 80 mm.; tail 40 mm.; color olive brown, sometimes irregularly spotted, with a black band edged with white on each side; abdomen yellow; tail blue below: southern New Jersey to Florida, westward to Kansas and Texas; rare in the north, abundant in the south; terrestrial.

3. Neoseps Stejneger.   Body vermiform; fore leg rudimentary, with a single digit; hind leg very weak, with 2 digits; ear hidden: 1 species.

N. reynoldsi Stej.   Length 85 mm.; tail 27 mm.; color drab, each scale with a brown spot, these spots forming 4 dark stripes on the back and a broad lateral stripe on each side: Lake County, Florida, burrowing in the ground.

Family 9.   Amphisbænidæ.—Vermiform lizards without legs, scales or external ear-opening; teeth pleurodont; eyes concealed; body ringed: 60 species, 1 in the United States.

Rhineura Cope.   With the characters of the family: 1 species.

R. floridana (Baird).   Length 220 mm.; tail 170 mm.; color lavender: Florida; burrowing in soft soil and with the appearance of a large earthworm.

Order 3.   Serpentes.—Snakes.   Very elongate reptiles, covered with horny imbricate scales, and without limbs, tympanum or external ear-opening, or functional eyelids.   The bones of the jaws are very loosely articulated with one another and with the cranium, so that the mouth can be stretched to a remarkable degree. The vertebræ are procœlous, giving the body great flexibility, those in front of the anus, except the atlas, all bearing ribs, those back of the anus being without ribs but bearing long transverse processes. Acrodont teeth are always present; in poisonous snakes usually a single pair of maxillary teeth are much elongated and form the poison fangs, of which 3 types are observed in American snakes: 1. Those of the opisthoglyph snakes, belonging to the family *Colubridæ*, in which there are one or more pairs of elongate and grooved but not perforated fangs at the rear of the upper jaw; (2) those of the elapine snakes, belonging to the family *Elapidæ*, in which there is a pair of short rigid fangs in the front of the upper jaw, which are perforated by a poison canal and also grooved on the outer surface; and (3) those of the viperine snakes, belonging to the family *Crotalidæ*, in which there is a pair of very long perforated fangs in the front of the upper jaw, which lie against the roof of the mouth when not in action. The tongue is long and forked and protractile; it can be thrust out of the closed mouth, and is an important tactile organ.

The scales are arranged in a definite number of rows, and are either keeled (i.e., with a median longitudinal ridge called the *keel*) or not keeled. The scales on the ventral surface differ in most snakes from those on the dorsal and lateral surfaces, forming a single row of transverse plates called the *ventrals* or *gastrosteges* where they occur in front of the anus, and either a single or a double row called the *subcaudals* or *urosteges* where they lie back of it. The ventrals bear a relation to the ribs and are of assistance in locomotion inasmuch as the animal can move them and thus advance the body over a roughened surface; the ventral immediately in front of the anus is either divided in two or not, and is called the *anal plate*.

Habits and Distribution.—Most snakes are oviparous, although many species are ovoviviparous. They feed almost exclusively on live animals or on animals they have recently killed; a few tropical snakes, however, are herbivorous. The poisonous snakes kill their prey with their poison and the constrictor snakes by crushing before swallowing it; other snakes do not stop to kill the prey but swallow it alive. Snakes live in a great variety of localities, some species being terrestrial, others arboreal; a large number are aquatic, some living in the open sea. Many species are brightly colored, especially in the tropics, but in none has metachrosis, so common among lizards, been observed.

On the Identification of Snakes.—The length in millimeters of an average adult specimen from the tip of the snout to the tip of the tail

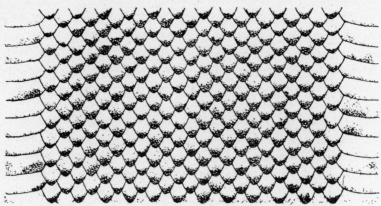

FIG. 113.—A portion of the skin of *Lampropeltis getulus*, showing 23 rows of scales (*from Blanchard*).

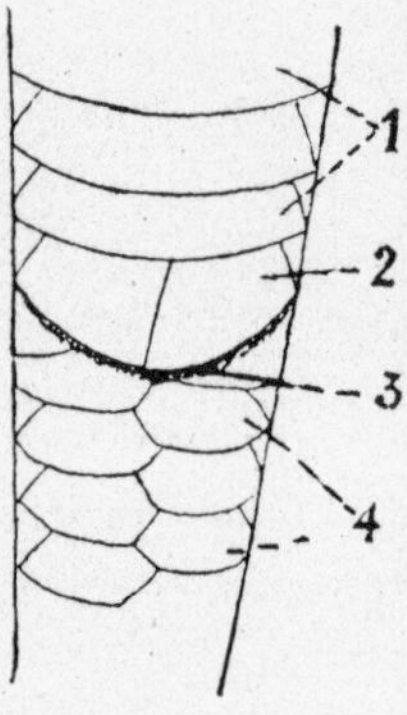

FIG. 114.—A portion of the ventral surface of *Abastor erythrogrammus*: 1, ventrals; 2, anal plate (which is here divided); 3, anus; 4, subcaudals (*from Cope*).

and also the length of the tail alone, are first given, followed by a description of its coloration. Those scales which lack the keel are said to be *smooth*, and these are usually much more glistening than keeled scales, which are dull in appearance. In some snakes only the dorsal scales are keeled, while those of the sides are smooth. The number of rows of scales (Fig. 113) is always important in the description; the number of ventrals is also often important; also the number of subcaudals, and whether a single or a double row is present. Whether the anal plate is single or divided is a very important character (Fig. 114).

In most species both dorsal and ventral surfaces of the head are covered with symmetrical plates, which are often important in descriptions (Fig. 115).

About 2,400 species of snakes are known, of which 126 species occur in the United States, grouped in 5 families.

Key to the Families of Serpentes

a₁ No ventrals present, the belly covered with scales; eyes
covered with scales...................................1. *Leptotyphlopidæ*.
a₂ Ventrals present; eyes not covered with scales.
  b₁ No elongate poison fangs in front part of mouth.

c_1 Subcaudals undivided, forming a single row; scales on
　chin all small...................................2. *Boidæ.*
c_2 Subcaudals divided, forming 2 rows (except in *Rhino-
　cheilus*); one or two pairs of enlarged elongate shields
　on the middle line of the chin...................3. *Colubridæ.*
b_2 Elongate poison fangs present in front part of mouth.
　c_1 Head not distinct from neck; no pit between eye and
　　nostril.......................................4. *Elapidæ.*
　c_2 Head very distinct; a pit between eye and nostril (Fig.
　　127)...5. *Crotalidæ.*

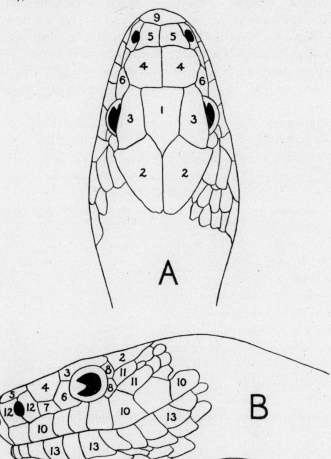

FIG. 115.—Head of snake (*Coluber constrictor*) showing the plates: 1, frontal; 2, parietals
3, supraoculars; 4, prefrontals; 5, internasals; 6, preoculars; 7, loreal; 8, postocular; 9, rostral; 10, upper labials; 11, temporals; 12, nasals; 13, lower labials (*from Hay*).

Family 1. Leptotyphlopidæ.—Small, blind, worm-like snakes
with rudiments (not visible) of hind legs and a pelvic girdle: 1 genus
and 3 species in the United States.

1. **Leptotyphlops** Fitzinger. Several species; 3 in the United States.

L. dulcis (Baird and Girard). Supraocular plates present; length 200 mm.; tail 10 mm.; color pale brown above; white beneath; scales in 14 rows: Texas, Oklahoma and New Mexico; burrowing in soft soil, often in ant-hills.

L. humilis (Baird and Girard). Body like preceding; supraocular plates absent: Arizona and southern California.

Family 2. Boidæ.—The Boas. Mostly large, arboreal constrictor snakes in which rudiments of hind legs and a pelvic girdle are present in form of a pair of spurs near the anus; scales smooth: many species, cosmopolitan; 2 species in the United States, both small. The family includes the boa-constrictors of South America and the pythons of Africa, Asia and the East Indies, which are the largest snakes, reaching a length of 35 feet.

1. **Lichanura** Cope. Form stout; tail obtuse; head covered with scales: several species.

L. roseofusca Cope. Length 788 mm.; tail 115 mm.; rows of scales 33 to 42; ventrals 229; subcaudals 49; color bluish gray or brown; abdomen red: southern California and Arizona.

2. **Charina** Gray. Small snakes with very small scales; head covered with plates: 2 species.

C. bottæ (Blainville). Rubber snake; ball snake. Length 600 mm.; tail 70 mm.; color brown or gray, yellow beneath; tail very blunt; rows or scales 42 to 47; upper labials 9 to 11; ventrals 200: California, Washington, Nevada, Utah, Wyoming and Montana; common in humid regions, feeding on mice, etc.

Family 3. Colubridæ.—Snakes with many conical teeth in both jaws; without poison fangs in the front part of the mouth, but certain genera, the opisthoglyph snakes,* are poisonous, one or more pairs of teeth at the rear of the upper jaw being elongate and grooved and forming the poison fangs, (however, no cases of injury to man by these snakes in the United States have yet been reported; *Tantilla* and *Sonora* are so small that they are probably harmless); top of head covered with symmetrical plates; a single row of ventrals and usually a double row of subcaudals present; no rudimentary hind limbs; eyes well developed: 1,300 species, in all the tropical and temperate regions of the world; over 100 species in the United States.

---

*The opisthoglyph genera in the United States are the following: *Oxybelis, Sonora, Tantilla, Coniophanes, Leptodeira, Trimorphodon.*

Key to Genera of Colubridae

(Several genera appear more than once in this key)

a_1 Some or all of scales on body keeled.

  b_1 Anal double.

    c_1 Rostral pointed, upturned, and keeled above........... *Heterodon.*

    c_2 Rostral normal.

      d_1 Loreal, preoculars and two internasals present; head scales normal.

        e_1 Scale rows 17.

          f_1 Uniform green above.......................... *Opheodrys.*

          f_2 Not uniform green.

            g_1 Brown stripes........................... *Seminatrix.*

            g_2 Dark with a light dot on each scale......... *Drymobius.*

        e_2 Scale rows more than 17.

          f_1 Scales heavily keeled; 3 postoculars (if 2, scales 19–23).................................... *Natrix.*

          f_2 Scales weakly keeled; 2 postoculars; scales 25–33 *Elaphe.*

      d_2 Some of head scales absent.

        e_1 Loreal absent................................. *Storeria.*

        e_2 Loreal present.

          f_1 A single internasal.

            g_1 Scales 17............................... *Potamophis.*

            g_2 Scales 19–21.

              h_1 A preocular.......................... *Liodytes.*

              h_2 No preocular......................... *Farancia.*

          f_2 Two internasals, no preocular.

            g_1 7 Upper labials........................... *Abastor.*

            g_2 6 Upper labials........................... *Virginia.*

            g_3 5 Upper labials.......................... *Potamophis.*

  b_2 Anal single.

    c_1 Scales 29–35; 4 prefrontals........................... *Pituophis.*

    c_2 Scales less than 29; 2 prefrontals.

      d_1 Eye in contact with labials; rostral normal.

        e_1 Upper labials more than 5; striped.............. *Thamnophis.*

        e_2 Upper labials 5; not striped.................... *Potamophis.*

      d_2 Eye cut off from labials by small scales; rostral very large and patch-like............................. *Phyllorhynchus.*

a_2 Scales smooth (not keeled).

  b_1 Anal single.

    c_1 Eye cut off from labials by small scales; rostral very large and patch-like.................................... *Phyllorhynchus.*

    c_2 Eye in contact with labials; rostral normal.

      d_1 Scale rows on body more numerous in the middle.

        e_1 Subcaudal plates mostly single.................. *Rhinocheilus.*

        e_2 Subcaudal plates all double.

          f_1 Belly immaculate; rostral prominent........... *Arizona.*

          f_2 Belly with some markings; rostral not prominent *Lampropeltis.*

      d_2 Scale rows on body same number throughout.

        e_1 Scales 17..................................... *Drymarchon.*

e_2 Scales 19.

    f_1 Two internasals.

        g_1 Loreal present; parietal not in contact with labials.................................. *Cemophora.*

        g_2 Loreal absent; parietal in contact with labials *Stilosoma.*

    f_2 One internasal.............................. *Liodytes.*

b_2 Anal double.

    c_1 Scales 19 or more.

        d_1 Two internasals.

            e_1 Preocular present.

                f_1 Pupil round; one preocular................... *Coniophanes.*

                f_2 Pupil vertically elliptic; 2–3 preoculars.

                    g_1 One loreal.

                        h_1 Several rows of spots................... *Hypsiglena.*

                        h_2 Crossbars........................... *Leptodeira.*

                    g_2 Two loreals.............................. *Trimorphodon.*

            e_2 No preocular................................. *Abastor.*

        d_2 One internasal.

            e_1 Preocular present............................. *Liodytes.*

            e_2 No preocular................................. *Farancia.*

    c_2 Scales 17 or less.

        d_1 Loreal present.

            e_1 2–3 preoculars.

                f_1 Rostral enlarged, patch-like.................... *Salvadora.*

                f_2 Rostral normal.

                    g_1 2–3 anterior temporals; lower preocular very small, wedged between labials............ *Coluber.*

                    g_2 One anterior temporal; lower preocular like upper.

                        h_1 Uniform grass green.................... *Liopeltis.*

                        h_2 Black with a yellow neck ring........... *Diadophis.*

            e_2 One preocular.

                f_1 Scales 17.

                    g_1 Upper labials 7.......................... *Rhadinæa.*

                    g_2 Upper labials 8.......................... *Seminatrix.*

                f_2 Scales less than 17.

                    g_1 Grass green............................. *Liopeltis.*

                    g_2 Not grass green.

                        h_1 Belly with black cross lines.............. *Contia.*

                        h_2 Belly immaculate or with bands that encircle body....................... *Sonora.*

            e_3 No preocular.

                f_1 Scales 15–17............................. *Virginia.*

                f_2 Scales 13................................. *Chilomeniscus.*

        d_2 No loreal.

            e_1 13 scale rows; southwestern states.............. *Chilomeniscus.*

            eastern states .... *Carphophis*

            e_2 15 scale rows................................. *Tantilla.*

            e_3 17 scale rows.

f₁ Small stout snakes with rostral upturned to a
    hook...................................... *Ficimia.*
f₂ Large, extremely slim snakes, with very pointed
    head and rostral tapered to an acute point... *Oxybelis.*

1. **Carphophis** Gervais. Small, non-poisonous snakes without a
distinct neck and with a pointed snout; no preocular; colors uniform:
2 species; terrestrial and burrowing.

C. amœnus (Say). Ground snake (Fig. 116). Length 260 mm.;
tail 45 mm.; color brown above, pink below; eyes very
small; ventrals about 128: Connecticut to Florida; westward to Illinois; often common, but secretive and rarely
seen.

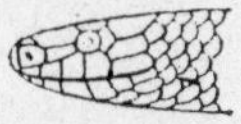

FIG. 116.—
*Carphophis
amœnus (from
Cope).*

2. **Abastor** Gray. Large, brightly colored snakes
with head not distinct from body; no preocular; ventrals
about 180; upper labials 7: 1 species.

A. erythrogrammus (Daudin). Rainbow snake (Fig. 114). Length
1,200 mm.; tail 160 mm.; color blue-black, with 3 longitudinal red
stripes; abdomen red, with 2 rows of black blotches: Virginia to the
Gulf, in the coastal plain, in swampy, wooded places; burrowing;
common.

3. **Farancia** Gray. Large, brightly colored snakes with indistinct
head; no preocular; upper labials 7; ventrals about 172: 1 species.

F. abacura (Holbrook). Horn snake; mud snake. Length 1,250
mm.; tail 160 mm.; color blue-black, with a series of large red spots on
each side; abdomen red, blotched with black; a horny spine at the end
of the tail: Atlantic and Gulf States from Virginia to Louisiana, and
up the Mississippi Valley into Indiana; in wet woods, burrowing under
logs and in the sand; common in the south.

4. **Diadophis** Baird & Girard. Ring-neck snakes. Small snakes
with a flattened head and a yellow ring around the neck: 4 species;
terrestrial, burrowing, feeding on earthworms, etc.

Key to the Species of Diadophis

a₁ Ventral color not covering any of the dorsal scale rows..........*D. punctatus.*
a₂ Ventral color encroaching on the lower dorsal scale rows.
  b₁ In Texas to Arizona.......................................*D. regalis.*
  b₂ On the Pacific slope.......................................*D. amabilis.*

D. punctatus (L.). Length 330 mm.; tail 70 mm.; color dark gray or
black, with a yellow collar; belly orange, sometimes with black
spots; ventrals about 155: United States east of the Great Plains;
common.

D. amabilis B. and G.   Length 430 mm.; tail 90 mm.; color bluish or greenish-black with a reddish collar; belly reddish: Oregon to Lower California; common.

D. regalis B. and G.   Length 600 mm.; color dark bluish-gray above; belly yellow or reddish, with many small black spots; coloration sometimes faint or absent: Texas to Arizona.

5. Heterodon Latreille.   Hog-nosed snakes (Fig. 117).   Moderate sized snakes with a broad, upturned snout (rostral plate) and an extra plate (the azygous) back of the rostral; scales in 23 to 25 rows; ventrals

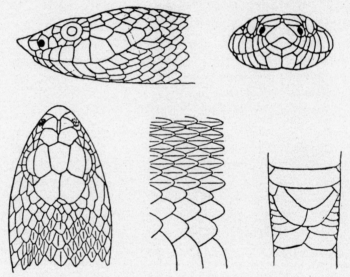

FIG. 117.—*Heterodon contortrix (from Cope).*

about 140; upper labials 8: 4 species, all in the eastern and central States; terrestrial, feeding on toads and insects and burrowing with the peculiar snout; when alarmed they dilate and flatten the neck and head while hissing loudly, and often throwing themselves into contortions or feigning death; they are harmless.

Key to the Species of Heterodon

a_1 No accessory scales around the azygous plate; scales in 25 rows. .*H. contortrix.*
a_2 Accessory scales around the axygous plate.
   b_1 Scales in 25 rows...*H. simus.*
   b_2 Scales in 23 rows...*H. nasicus.*

H. contortrix (L.) (*H. platyrhinus* Latreille) (Fig. 117).   Puffing or spreading adder; blowing viper.   Length 700 mm.; color brown or reddish, with about 28 dark or black dorsal patches between the head and tail, and a series of similar patches on each side alternating irregu-

larly with them; on the tail the blotches tend to form rings around
the body; belly yellowish, blotched on the edges with black; a melanistic
variety occurs which is plain black: Massachusetts to Montana, Florida
and Texas; common, especially in dry, sandy places.

H. nasicus Baird & Girard.   Length 660 mm.; tail 70 mm.; color
gray or light brown, with a dorsal and 2 lateral series on each side of
small darker spots, which on the tail tend to form rings; center of
abdomen black: western States from Dakota and Montana into Mexico;
common in Texas and the south.

H. simus (L.) (Fig. 118).   Length 470 mm.; tail 80 mm.; color gray
or brownish with about 35 dark brown dorsal patches
alternating with smaller ones on each side; belly yellowish: southeastern States, from North Carolina to the
Mississippi, and northward in its valley into Indiana;
less common than *H. contortrix*.

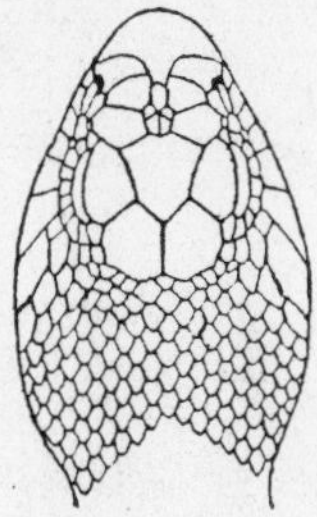

6. Liopeltis Fitzinger.   Small, green snakes with
smooth scales in 15 rows; upper labials 7; ventrals 135:
several species in eastern Asia, 1 in America.

L. vernalis (Harlan).   Green snake; grass snake.
Length 400 mm.; tail 130 mm.; color uniform green,
lighter underneath: eastern, western and central States;
westward to New Mexico; common towards the north; terrestrial,
living in the grass and in shrubbery, and feeding on insects.

FIG. 118.—
Heterodon simus
(from Cope).

7. Opheodrys Fitzinger (*Cyclophis* Gunther).   Small, green snakes
with keeled scales in 17 rows; upper labials 7; ventrals 155: several
species in Asia, 1 in America.

O. æstivus (L.)   Green snake.   Length 840 mm.; tail 320 mm.; color
uniform green; belly yellow: southern New Jersey to the Gulf; westward
to New Mexico and northward in the Mississippi Valley to Illinois and
Kansas; common; arboreal, feeding on insects.

8. Salvadora Baird and Girard.   Slender ground snakes with a snout
surmounted by a triangular rostral shield, giving it a truncated appearance in front; scales smooth and in 17 rows; upper labials 8: 2 species in
Mexico, 1 in the United States.

S. grahamiæ B. and G.   Patch-nose snake.   Length 700 mm.; tail
100 mm.; back with a broad yellow middorsal stripe, bordered on each
side by a dark brown stripe of equal width, beneath which is a light
brown band; belly yellow; ventrals about 180: western Texas to
California and Utah; common, especially in rocky places.

9. Phyllorhynchus Stejneger.   Small slender snakes with a large
triangular rostral shield giving the snout a truncated appearance; anal

plate single; scales in 19 rows and imperfectly keeled; upper labials 6: 2 species.

P. browni Stej. Length 325 mm.; tail 42 mm.; color whitish, with 15 brown blotches on the back; belly white; scales keeled on the hinder two-thirds of the body and very faintly keeled on the forward third: southern Arizona.

10. Coluber L. (*Zamenis* Wagler). Blacksnakes; racers. Large, non-venomous snakes with head distinct from the neck; scales smooth, in 15 or 17 rows; upper labials 7 or 8: many species in the New and Old Worlds, 4 in the United States; active snakes which live on the ground but can also climb bushes and trees, feeding on small mammals, reptiles and frogs; they do not constrict their prey but may kill it by pressing it against the ground.

Key to the Species of Coluber

a_1 Body never striped.
  b_1 Color black, bluish or green............................*C. constrictor.*
  b_2 Color brown, at least posteriorly.........................*C. flagellum.*
a_2 Body striped.
  b_1 A yellow stripe on each side...............................*C. lateralis.*
  b_2 Four or five stripes on each side...........................*C. tæniatus.*

C. constrictor L. Blacksnake; blue racer; hoop snake (Fig. 115). Body slender; length 1,700 mm.; tail 449 mm.; greatest length 2,200 mm.; color slaty or blue-black above, greenish black to yellow beneath; chin and throat white; ventrals about 180; young animals (500 mm. long) gray in color with dorsal transverse bars and lateral spots: entire country.

Subspecies of C. constrictor

C. c. constrictor L. Belly black: eastern forested States; common.

C. c. flaviventris Say. Belly yellow: in the plains and prairie States, north and west of the Ohio and Mississippi to the Rockies; common.

C. c. mormon (Baird and Girard). Size small; color green: west of the Rockies.

C. flagellum Shaw. Whip snake. Body very slender, 2,000 mm. long; tail 500 mm.; color yellowish brown to dark brown, being darker anteriorly; abdomen white or yellow, more or less blotched with brown anteriorly; ventrals about 190; young animals with dorsal blotches: southern States from Virginia to California; common.

Subspecies of C. flagellum

C. f. flagellum Shaw. Body black anteriorly: North Carolina to Oklahoma and Texas.

C. f. frenatus (Stejneger). In Arizona, Utah, Nevada and California.

C. f. flavi-gularis (Hallowell). In Oklahoma and Texas to New Mexico.

C. lateralis (Hallowell). Length 665 mm.; tail 250 mm.; color brown above with a yellow stripe on each side, yellow below; head somewhat spotted; ventrals about 200: in western California and southern Arizona.

C. tæniatus (Hallowell). Body very slender, 1,280 mm. long; tail 400 mm.; color black with many yellow lines on the sides; belly white, but pink on the tail; throat spotted with black: Idaho to Texas, Arizona and eastern California; often common.

11. Elaphe Wagler (*Coluber* Auct.). Large, non-venomous snakes with a flat, blunt head; dorsal scales with slight keels; lateral scales smooth; scales in 25 to 29 rows: about 20 species in North America and Europe and Asia; 9 species in the United States.

Key to the Species of Elaphe

a_1 Few dorsal scale rows keeled; 2 bands from the neck cross the
    parietals and meet on the frontal.
    b_1 Spots bright red; belly checkered black and white; south
        western; in the southeast............................*E. guttata.*
    b_2 Spots brown; belly white and gray; western.............*E læta.*
a_2 Most of the scale rows keeled.
    b_1 Body spotted in color.
        c_1 Dorsal blotches squarish...........................*E. vulpina.*
        c_2 Dorsal blotches H-shaped..........................*E. o. confinis.*
    b_2 Body not spotted.
        c_1 Color black.......................................*E. o. obsoleta.*
        c_2 Color yellowish, with 4 dark stripes.
            d_1 Neck spots H-shaped...........................*E. o. confinis.*
            d_2 Neck spots not H-shaped.......................*E. vulpina.*
            d_3 No neck spots................................*E. quadrivittata*

E. quadrivittata (Holbrook). Chicken snake. Length 2,000 mm.; tail 300 mm.; color yellow or light brown, with 4 dark brown or black stripes; scales in 27 rows: southeastern and Gulf States, from North Carolina to the Mississippi River; arboreal; often around chicken houses, where they feed on rats, young chickens and eggs.

E. læta (Baird and Girard) (*Coluber emoryi* B. & G.). Length 800 mm.; tail 160 mm.; color gray, with a dorsal series of large rectangular brown blotches alternating with 2 more or less distinct smaller series on each side: Missouri and Kansas to Mexico; common towards the south.

E. guttata (L.).   Corn-snake.   Length 1,000 mm.; tail 160 mm.; greatest length 1,750 mm.; color reddish or yellowish brown, with a dorsal series of about 54 large red, black-bordered blotches; belly white, with black spots: south Atlantic and Gulf States from New Jersey to Louisiana; common.

E. obsoleta (Say) (Fig. 119).   Length 1,800 mm.; tail 300 mm.; greatest length 2,400 mm.; color black to gray, with the edges of the scales often yellow, and often a series of large dark dorsal blotches; throat white; belly dark, more or less blotched: Massachusetts to the Gulf; westward to Michigan and Texas; one of the largest American snakes.

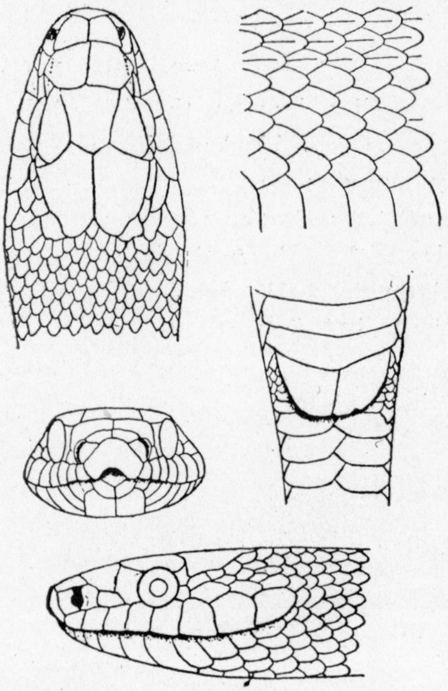

FIG. 119.—*Elaphe obsoleta (from Cope)*.

Subspecies of E. obsoleta

E. o. obsoleta (Say).   Pilot blacksnake.   Color uniform black: northern States.

E. o. confinis (B. and G.). Color gray, with large, irregular dark dorsal spots and smaller lateral spots: south Atlantic and Gulf States; Missouri.

E. vulpina (B. and G.).   Fox-snake.   Length 1,150 mm.; tail 200 mm.; color brown or yellowish, with a series of dark brown blotches which alternate with a lateral series on each side; belly yellow, with dark spots; head often reddish: Ohio to Minnesota; southward to the Missouri; often common, feeding on rats round barns; they often emit a fox-like odor.

12. Drymobius Fitzinger.   Medium sized tropical snakes allied to our racers (*Coluber*); scales keeled, in 17 rows; anal plate divided; upper labials 9, 3 entering the orbit; a single preocular present: 4 species in tropical America, 1 reaching Texas.

D. margaritiferus (Schlegel).   Length about 1,000 mm.; color black, with a green spot on each scale: Brownsville, Texas.

13. Drymarchon Fitzinger (*Spilotes* Wagler).   Large tropical, non-poisonous snakes with a simple anal plate and smooth scales; upper labials 8; color shining black, above and below: 1 species.

D. corais couperi (Holbrook). Indigo snake; gopher snake. Length 2,300 mm.; tail 330 mm.; scales in 17 rows: Gulf States; northward into South Carolina; westward to Texas; the largest American snake; often round barns and houses, looking for rats and mice.

14. Pituophis Holbrook. Bull-snakes. Large, non-poisonous, constrictor snakes with a long pointed head; scales in 25 to 35 rows; dorsal scales keeled, lateral scales smooth; ventrals about 215; upper labials

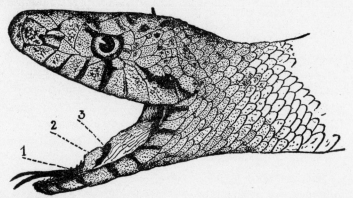

FIG. 120.—*Pituophis sayi:* 1, sheath of tongue; 2, epiglottis; 3, glottis (*from Cope*).

8 or 9; a peculiar epiglottis-like membrane (Fig. 120) in front of the glottis vibrates when the animal is alarmed, producing a loud hiss: 4 species, all American; the largest American, harmless snakes; terrestrial and arboreal, feeding on small mammals, birds and eggs, and living usually in dry woods.

Key to the Species of Pituophis

a₁ In the eastern forested region............................*P. melanoleucus.*
a₂ In the prairie States and Great Plains......................*P. sayi.*
a₃ On the Pacific slope and in the Great Basin................*P. catenifer.*

P. melanoleucus (Daudin). Pine snake. Length 1,500 mm.; tail 220 mm.; greatest length 2,400 mm.; color whitish, with a series of from 27 to 33 large, black or brown, irregular dorsal blotches and 2 series of smaller lateral blotches on each side; belly white: southern New York to Florida and Louisiana; often abundant in pine woods.

P. sayi (Schlegel) (Fig. 120). Length 1,550 mm.; tail 200 mm.; greatest length 2,600 mm.; color reddish yellow, with a series of large, square brown or black dorsal blotches, and a series of smaller blotches on each side; abdomen yellow, with a row of black spots on each side: western Indiana and Alberta, Canada, to Arizona and Texas and the

Rockies; very common towards the south; one of the largest American snakes.

P. catenifer (Blainville). Length 1,400 mm.; tail 240 mm.; color yellowish brown, with a series of about 100 small square, reddish brown or black dorsal spots and a series of more or less obscure spots on each side; belly yellowish white with 2 series of spots: British Columbia to California, Idaho, Utah and Nevada; common.

15. Arizona Kennicott. Large snakes with a rostral plate recurved and extending between the internasals; scales smooth; anal plate single: 2 species.

A. elegans Kenn. Length 918 mm.; tail 145 mm.; color grayish brown, crossed by 55 to 65 transverse brown spots in front of the anus; belly whitish, unspotted; scales in 29 to 31 rows: along the Mexican border; northward into Oklahoma and Arkansas.

16. Rhadinæa Fitzinger. Small snakes with smooth scales in 17 rows; ventrals 125; upper labials 7: many species in Mexico and Central America, 1 in the United States.

R. flavilata (Cope). Length 300 mm.; tail 90 mm.; color golden brown; abdomen yellowish white: North Carolina to Florida; terrestrial.

17. Lampropeltis Fitzinger. King-snakes. Non-poisonous, constrictor snakes with smooth scales in 19 to 27 rows; colors often bright, arranged usually in transverse bands: about 12 species, all American, 9 in the United States; terrestrial, feeding on rodents and other small animals, including snakes, being immune to the bites of poisonous ones.

Key to the Species of Lampropeltis

a_1 Ground color black, with usually narrow transverse color
bands..*L. getulus.*
a_2 Ground color pale, with large, red or brown blotches.
  b_1 Blotches wide and long, making up most of the color
    pattern..*L. triangulum.*
  b_2 Blotches small, oblong.
    c_1 Scales in 23 rows...............................*L. rhombomaculata.*
    c_2 Scales in 25 rows...................................*L. calligaster.*
a_3 Color pattern contains color rings encircling body.
  b_1 Ground color red; rings black........................*L. elapsoides.*
  b_2 Ground color red; rings whitish.......................*L. pyrhomelana.*
  b_3 Ground color white; rings black......................*L. multicincta.*

L. getulus (L.). Chain-snake (Fig. 113). Length 1,500 mm.; tail 200 mm.; greatest length 1,800 mm.; color black, with usually narrow yellow or white dorsal bands which may fork on the sides and join one another, giving the effect of a chain; belly black, blotched with white or yellow; scales in 21 to 25 rows; superior labials 7: entire country south of latitude 40; common.

Subspecies of L. getulus

L. g. getulus (L.). Color bands narrow, forking on the sides; scales in 21 rows: New Jersey to the Gulf.

L. g. holbrooki Stejneger. Scales in 21 rows; a yellow spot on each dorsal scale; no bands: Louisiana to Texas; northward to Illinois and Wyoming.

L. g. nigra (Yarrow). Scales in 21 rows; scales without light centers or with very small ones: eastern Illinois to Ohio; southward into Alabama.

L. g. floridana Blanchard. Scales in 23 rows; cross bands more than 50, or not distinguishable: Florida.

L. g. boylii (Baird and Girard). Scales in 23 rows; color bands broad and forming rings: western Arizona and Utah to California.

L. g. californiæ (Blainville). Scales in 23 rows; a dorsal longitudinal stripe either complete or interrupted: southern California.

L. triangulum (Lacépède) (*L. doliata* L.). Length 860 mm.; tail 130 mm.; ground color gray or yellow, with a series of broad, black-bordered red or brown bands or saddles occupying the dorsal and lateral sides of the body; abdomen yellowish or red, with black spots alternating irregularly with the bands; scales in 21 rows: eastern and central States; westward into Texas, Kansas and Iowa; often common.

Subspecies of L. triangulum

L. t. syspila (Cope). Dorsal saddles 23 to 35 in number: Ohio and Tennessee to Iowa and Oklahoma.

L. t. triangulum Lac. Milk-snake. Ground color gray, bands much broken and brown or reddish: northern States; southward into North Carolina; westward into Iowa.

L. t. amaura Cope. Scarlet king-snake. Ground color yellow; bands bright red, nearly encircling the body and about 20 in number: Mississippi to Texas.

L. t. gentilis (B. and G.). Bands dull red with black borders and 25 to 40 in number: Texas to Dakota.

L. rhombomaculata (Holbrook). Length 830 mm.; tail 111 mm.; color light brown, with a series of about 55 chestnut lenticular dorsal blotches, alternating with a series of smaller blotches on each side;

belly yellowish, more or less blotched; scales in 21 rows: Maryland to northern Florida.

L. calligaster (Say). Length 1,150 mm.; tail 160 mm.; color gray or light brown, with a series of about 60 squarish, brown black-bordered blotches and 2 series of smaller blotches on each side; scales in 25 rows: Indiana to Minnesota; southward to Texas.

L. elapsoides (Holbrook). Scarlet snake. Length 430 mm.; tail 67 mm.; color bright red, with about 18 pairs of black rings encircling the body, each pair enclosing a white ring; scales in 19 rows: southeastern and Gulf States, from Maryland to Louisiana.

L. pyromelana (Cope). Length 725 mm.; tail 102 mm.; color yellowish or red, forming about 38 broad bands encircling the body which are separated by as many narrow yellowish bands each bordered with black; scales in 23 rows; labials 7: southern New Mexico to California.

L. multicincta (Yarrow). Coral king-snake. Length 850 mm.; tail 147 mm.; color pattern formed of about 45 black rings encircling the body, each ring enclosing some red, and separated by narrower whitish rings; head black; scales usually in 23 rows: California, except in deserts.

18. Stilosoma Brown. Slender snakes with smooth scales in 19 rows; head not distinct from the body; no loreals: 1 species.

S. extenuatum Brown. Length 532 mm.; tail 50 mm.; color silver-gray, with 61 dorsal dark brown spots on the body and 11 on the tail; belly gray, blotched with black: north-central Florida.

19. Contia Baird & Girard. Small snakes with smooth scales in 15 rows; ventrals about 150; upper labials 7: several species, 1 in the United States.

C. tenuis (B. and G.). Length 290 mm.; tail 60 mm.; color deep chestnut brown, with 2 light longitudinal bands; yellow below with dark bars: Puget Sound to southern California; rare.

20. Sonora Baird and Girard. Small poisonous snakes with smooth scales in 13 to 15 rows; rear maxillary teeth elongate and grooved; ventrals about 160; upper labials 7: 4 species.

Key to the Species of Sonora

a_1 Scales in 13 rows...*S. taylori.*
a_2 Scales in 15 rows
    b_1 Ventrals 145 to 153; subcaudals 35 to 57.................*S. semiannulata.*
    b_2 Ventrals 158; subcaudals 34............................*S. occipitalis.*

S. taylori (Boulenger). Length 270 mm.; tail 55 mm.; color pale brown above, white beneath: southern Texas.

S. semiannulata B. & G.   Length 230 mm.; tail 40 mm.; color ashen or pink, crossed by about 20 black half rings, or uniform; belly white: Idaho to southeastern California, Kansas and Texas.

S. occipitalis (Hollowell).   Length 323 mm.; tail 53 mm.; color milk white above, with 34 transverse black bands; belly white: Colorado to southeastern California.

21. Cemophora Cope.   Small, harmless snakes with smooth scales in 19 rows; ventrals about 170; upper labials 6: 1 species.

C. coccinea (Blumenbach).   Length 410 mm.; tail 60 mm.; color scarlet, with about 20 pairs of black cross bands, each pair enclosing a yellow band; belly white or yellow; top of head red or orange: southern and Gulf States from Maryland to the Mississippi; common in Florida; very similar in appearance to the poisonous coral snakes, but differing from them in having a plain, unblotched belly; similar also to the scarlet king-snake which differs from it in that its rings nearly encircle the body.

22. Rhinocheilus Baird & Girard.   Small snakes with smooth scales in 23 rows and undivided subcaudals: 1 species.

R. lecontei B. and G.   Length 600 mm.; tail 85 mm.; color black and red, there being 33 large square black blotches alternating with red bands; belly white: Kansas and Idaho to California.

23. Hypsiglena Cope.   Small snakes with smooth scales in 21 rows; rear teeth in upper jaw enlarged; pupil vertical: 1 species.

H. ochrorhynchus Cope.   Length 675 mm.; tail 75 mm.; color gray with about 48 large brown spots on the body and 2 alternating series on the tail; 2 lateral series; ventrals 167; subcaudals 55: western Texas to Idaho and southeastern California.

24. Ficimia Gray.   Small, stout snakes with an acute rostral plate, the anterior end of which is turned up; no loreal plate; scales smooth, in 17 rows; anal plate divided; pupil round: 2 species.

F. cana (Cope).   Length 188 mm.; tail 23 mm.; color brownish yellow, with 30 cross bands; belly whitish, unspotted; upper labials 7: western Texas to Arizona.

25. Chilomeniscus Cope.   Small, stout burrowing snakes with a prominent rounded, flattened snout; scales smooth, in 13 rows; anal plate divided; no loreal plate: 1 species.

C. cinctus Cope.   Length 120 mm.; tail 16 mm.; color red or orange, with 21 black cross bars in front of the anus; belly white: southern Arizona and California.

26. Natrix Laurenti (*Tropidonotus* Kuhl).   Water snakes.   Thick-bodied non-poisonous snakes with a distinct head and with keeled scales in from 19 to 33 rows; ventrals about 140; colors brown or black: many species in North America and Eurasia, all viviparous and semi-aquatic, living along the borders of streams or ponds and feeding on frogs, fish and other cold blooded animals.

Key to the United States Species of Natrix

a_1 Body striped longitudinally.
   b_1 Scales in 19 rows; upper labials 7.
      c_1 Abdomen with 2 broken stripes.
         d_1 Ventrolateral light stripes; eastern States.........*N. septemvittata.*
         d_2 No ventrolateral light stripes; southeastern States.*N. rigida.*
      c_2 Abdomen plain or with a central black stripe........*N. grahamii.*
   b_2 Scales in 21 rows; Gulf States.......................*N. clarkii.*
a_2 Body with transverse bands or spots.
   b_1 Scales in 19 rows; central States.....................*N. kirtlandii.*
   b_2 Scales in 21 rows; Florida...........................*N. compressicauda.*
   b_3 Scales in 23 to 25 rows.
      c_1 A light line from eye to angle of mouth; ventrals 123
         to 135..*N. fasciata.*
      c_2 No such light line.
         d_1 Half-moon shaped spot on belly; ventrals 135 to
            145; pattern of bands anteriorly and alternating
            blotches posteriorly...........................*N. sipedon.*
         d_2 Belly uniform yellow or red; adults uniform brown
            above; young with alternating blotches above;
            ventrals 145 to 155...........................*N. erythrogaster.*
   b_4 Scales in 27 to 33 rows.
      c_1 Two anterior temporals; dorsal and lateral alternating
         rows of isolated large square spots.................*N. taxispilota.*
      c_2 One anterior temporal; narrow dorsal and lateral spots.
         d_1 Eye in contact with labials; pattern conspicuous,
            forming diamonds on back....................*N. rhombifera.*
         d_2 Eye separated by subocular from labials; pattern
            indistinct, not forming diamonds.............*N. cyclopion.*

N. septemvittata (Say). Moon-snake; queen-snake. Length 600 mm.; tail 120 mm.; color dark brown, with 3 narrow, black dorsal stripes, often indistinct, and a bright yellow lateral band; belly yellow, with 2 brown bands: United States east of the Mississippi, except New England and New York; common.

N. rigida (Say). Length 560 mm.; tail 120 mm.; color brown, with 2 narrow black stripes; belly yellow, with 2 stripes or rows of black spots: South Carolina to Louisiana.

N. grahamii (Baird and Girard). Length 640 mm.; tail 120 mm.; color brown with a pale middorsal band and a broad pale or yellow lateral band bordered beneath with black; belly plain yellowish: Mississippi Valley, from the Great Lakes to Texas; common.

N. clarkii (B. and G.). Length 790 mm.; tail 178 mm.; color brown, with 4 bands of deep brown; belly yellow, with 2 brown bands dotted with black: coastal regions from Florida to Texas.

N. kirtlandii (Kennicott). Length 400 mm.; tail 100 mm.; color light brown or reddish, with 2 series of rather indistinct round spots on the back alternating with a series of large black blotches on each side; belly red in the middle portions, with a row of dark spots on each side; upper labials 6: north-central States, from Wisconsin to New Jersey; common in the west; rare in the east.

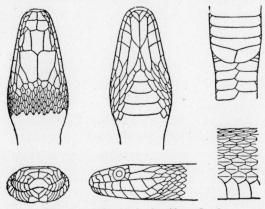

FIG. 121.—*Natrix sipedon (from Cope).*

N. compressicauda (Kennicott). Length 560 mm.; tail 130 mm.; color gray, with irregular, obscure darker bands; belly gray or brown, with a central series of yellow spots; tail flattened at base: southwestern Florida.

N. sipedon (L.) (*N. fasciata* L.). Common water snake (Fig. 121). Length 960 mm.; tail 200 mm.; color brown, with 30 or 40 yellowish or reddish, often indistinct transverse bars which may widen on the sides; belly yellowish or white, with many brown or red spots; scales in 23 or 25 rows: eastern and central States; westward into Colorado.

N. fasciata (L.). A series of cross bands; belly yellowish or reddish, more or less spotted: Atlantic coast from North Carolina southward; westward to Louisiana and up the Mississippi Valley to Nebraska and Indiana.

N. erythrogaster Foster. Dorsal bands broken into blotches the entire length of body; in young individuals belly uniform, unspotted; in adult (in the east also save new-born) uniform above: New York to

Georgia, Michigan and Texas; very rare and local in northeast; common in south and west.

N. rhombifera (Hallowell).   Length 1,000 mm.; tail 240 mm.; color brownish, with a series of about 50 dorsal rhomboidal blotches; scales in 27 rows: southern Indiana and Illinois to Louisiana and Texas.

N. cyclopion (Duméril & Bibron).   Length 1,000 mm.; tail 260 mm.; color dark greenish with many dorsal transverse black bands; eye surrounded by a ring of scales; scales in 29 rows: Florida to Louisiana and up the Mississippi Valley to southern Illinois.

N. taxispilota (Holbrook) Water-pilot.   Length 1,300 mm.; tail 300 mm.; color rusty brown, with a series dark blotches on the back alternating with a similar series on each side; scales in 29 to 33 rows: Atlantic and Gulf States; northward to North Carolina; the largest American water snake.

27. Seminatrix Cope.   Small snakes living in or near the water, with smooth scales in 17 rows; scales on the tail weakly keeled; upper-labials usually 8: 1 species.

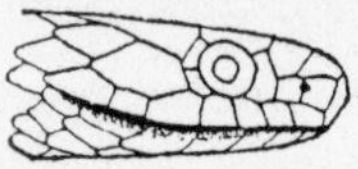

S. pygæa (Cope).   Length 420 mm.; tail 70 mm.;

FIG. 122.—*Storeria dekayi (from Cope).* color black, with a faint pale line running along the center of each scale; belly red, crossed on the body with narrow black bars; and plate divided: South Carolina to Florida.

28. Storeria Baird and Girard.   Small snakes with head distinct from the neck and with scales in 15 to 17 rows; ventrals about 135; loreal plate absent: 4 species, all American and viviparous; 3 species in the United States.

S. dekayi (Holbrook).   Dekay's snake; brown snake (Fig. 122). Length 300 mm.; tail 60 mm.; color chestnut or grayish brown, with a lighter middorsal stripe bordered with black dots; belly whitish; upper labials 7; scales in 17 rows: eastern and central States; westward to Kansas; southward into Mexico; terrestrial, secretive, living under stones and logs, often in towns, feeding on insects, worms, etc.; common.

S. occipito-maculata (Storer).   Red-bellied snake.   Length 250 mm.; tail 60 mm.; color chestnut brown or grayish with a lighter middorsal stripe bordered with dark dots; belly red; upper labials 5 or 6; scales in 15 rows: eastern and central States; westward to Kansas; southward into Mexico.

29. Potamophis Fitzinger (*Haldea* Baird & Girard).   Small snakes with keeled scales in 17 rows; head distinct from the neck and very narrow and pointed: 1 species.

P. striatulus (L.)   Length 280 mm.; tail 40 mm.; color grayish or reddish brown; belly red; ventrals 119 to 130; upper labials 5: southern and central States; northward into Virginia east of the mountains and into Minnesota west of them; southwestward into Texas; common in damp woods, under the bark of fallen trees and stones; viviparous.

30. Virginia Baird & Girard. Small snakes with smooth scales in 15 to 17 rows; upper labials 6, ventrals 125: 2 species.

V. valeriæ B and G. Length 180 mm.; tail 30 mm.; color grayish brown or chestnut, with minute black dots; belly yellowish white; scales in 15 rows: southern and central States; northward into New Jersey; westward to Tennessee; common; secretive.

V. v. elegans Kennicott. Similar to *V. valeriæ*, but differing in having scales in 17 rows: Indiana and Illinois to Texas.

31. Thamnophis Fitzinger. (*Eutænia* Baird & Girard). Garter snakes. Rather small, slender snakes, with a distinct head and keeled scales in 17 to 23 rows; upper labials usually 7 or 8; 3 longitudinal, more or less yellowish stripes; also several series of spots usually present; ventrals 130 to 180: about 24 species, all North American; 11 species in the United States, all viviparous; terrestrial and often aquatic, feeding on frogs, toads, worms and other cold blooded animals.

Key to the United States Species of Thamnophis

a_1 Lateral stripes anteriorly on third and fourth scale rows.
   b_1 Tail long; snake slim; stripes narrow and bright.............*T. sauritus.*
   b_2 Tail shorter; snake stout; stripes broader and vaguer........*T. radix.*
a_2 Lateral stripes on third scale row..............................*T. marcianus.*
a_3 Lateral stripes on second and third scale rows.
   b_1 Upper labials normally 8.................................*T. ordinoides.*
   b_2 Upper labials normally 7.
      c_1 Eye small; scales usually 17; posterior and anterior chin
        shields equal..*T. ordinoides.*
      c_2 Eye large; scales 19; posterior chin shield much the larger...*T. sirtalis.*
   b_3 Upper labials 5 or 6....................................*T. lineatus.*

T. sirtalis (L.) Common garter snake (Fig. 123). Length 750 mm.; tail 130 mm.; color very variable, varying from greenish to blackish, with 3 yellowish, longitudinal stripes and 2 or 3 series of black spots on each side, both stripes and spots being indistinct in some cases; belly greenish: entire country; our commonest snake.

Subspecies of T. sirtalis

T. s. sirtalis (L.) Typical form: eastern and central States; westward to Minnesota and Missouri.

T. s. concinnus (Hallowell). A series of reddish, vertically elongated spots on each side; ground color black; throat and lips red; belly black: coast region of Oregon, Washington and British Columbia.

T. s. infernalis (Blainville).   In western Nevada and California.

T. s. parietalis (Say).   Ground color light brown; belly slate color; a series of vertical red bars on each side: Missouri to the Sierra Nevadas and Cascades.

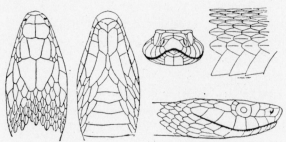

FIG. 123.—*Thamnophis sirtalis (from Cope).*

T. sauritus (L.)   Ribbon snake.   Length 660 mm.; tail 230 mm.; body very slender; stripes bright yellow: eastern States; westward to Texas and Nebraska.

Subspecies of *T. sauritus*

T. s. sauritus (L.).   East of the Mississippi and north of Florida.

T. s. sackenii (Kennicott).   Usually without dorsal stripe: Florida.

T. s. proximus (Say).   West of the Mississippi.

T. radix (B. and G.).   Length 800 mm.; tail 170 mm.; stripes yellow; lateral stripes on the third and fourth rows of scales: from the Rockies to western New York and south to Kansas and Missouri.

Subspecies of *T. radix*

T. r. radix (B and G.).   Larger; scales 21: west of Indiana.

T. r. butleri (Cope).   Smaller; scales 19: Indiana to New York.

T. ordinoides (B. and G.) (*T. elegans* B. & G.).   Length 700 mm.; tail 140 mm.; ground color dark brown or black; dorsal stripe bright yellow; lateral stripe faint, and on second and third rows of scales, or absent; back often with regular rows of large black blotches: coastal region of Pacific States; eastward to New Mexico and Wyoming.

T. lineatus (Hallowell).   Small snakes; length 360 mm.; tail 40 mm.; lateral stripe on scale rows 2 and 3; 19 scale rows; 5 to 6 upper labials: Ohio to Iowa and Tennessee.

T. marcianus (B. and G.).   Length 510 mm.; tail 160 mm.; color light yellow, with numerous square, black spots arranged like a checker board; belly white: Oklahoma and Texas to southeastern California.

32. Liodytes Cope.   Stout snakes with a distinct head and smooth scales in 19 rows; caudal scales keeled; body tapering abruptly at both ends: 1 species.

L. allenii (Garman).   Length 600 mm.; tail 135 mm.; color of back dark brown; sides with a broad olive band and a darker band beneath it; belly yellow, unspotted: Florida and southern Georgia.

33. Tantilla Baird & Girard.   Very small, somewhat poisonous snakes with smooth scales in 15 rows; ventrals about 150; upper labials 6 or 7; one or more pairs of grooved teeth at the rear of the upper jaw through which poison is injected; closely resembling *Sonora*, but without a loreal plate: many species in the southern States and Mexico.

T. coronata B. and G.   Length 230 mm.; tail 40 mm.; color reddish brown; lighter beneath; head black or dark brown, with a light neck band followed by a dark one; upper labials 7: Virginia to Mississippi.

T. gracilis B. & G.   Length 140 mm.; tail 30 mm.; color uniform greenish brown; upper labials 6: Missouri to Texas.

T. nigriceps Kennicott.   Body brown; head and nape black; upper labials 6: Texas to Arizona.

34. Coniophanes Cope.   Medium sized and poisonous snakes with smooth scales and double anal plates, closely resembling *Rhadinæa*, but with hinder maxillary teeth grooved: several species in Mexico and Central America, 1 reaching Texas.

C. imperialis (Baird).   Length 350 mm.; tail 150 mm.; 19 scale rows; color pale brown, with a black band on the back and one on each side from snout to temple: near Brownsville, Texas.

35. Leptodeira Fitzinger.   Medium sized poisonous snakes; hinder maxillary teeth elongate and grooved; scales smooth; and plate double; pupil of eye vertically elliptic; resembling Hypsiglena, but with grooved fangs: 7 species in the American tropics, 1 entering Texas.

L. septentrionalis (Kennicott).   Length 750 mm.; tail 150 mm.; color light brown, with broad rings of black; head black: near Brownsville, Texas; nocturnal.

36. Oxybelis Wegler.   Extremely slender tree-snakes, with a very long, pointed snout; scales smooth, in oblique rows on the sides; enlarged fangs on the hinder part of the maxilla which are poisonous: 35 species in Central America, 1 in Arizona.

O. micropthalmus Barbour and Amaral.   Length 1350 mm.; tail 550 mm.; color reddish above and below, with a white line along the sides of the belly; 17 scale rows; snout four times as long as the eye: southern Arizona.

37. Trimorphodon Cope. Medium sized, poisonous snakes with a flat broad and very distinct head, resembling *Leptodeira;* but with 2 loreals on each side; hinder maxillary teeth elongate and grooved; scales smooth; anal plate single or divided: about 10 species in Mexico; 3 in the United States.

Key to the Species of Trimorphodon

a₁ Dorsal spots divided by a white line; head dark above, with a
    light lyre-shaped pattern.
  b₁ Anal usually single; color darker; body with 30 to 42 spots.*T. vandenburghi.*
  b₂ Anal usually double; color paler; body with 21 to 33 spots.*T. lyrophanes.*
a₂ Dorsal spots solid; head pale above, with 3 round black spots...*T. vilkinsonii.*

T. vandenburghi Klauber. Similar to *T. lyrophanes*, differing as in key: southwestern California.

T. vilkinsonii Cope. Similar to *T. lyrophanes*: El Paso, Texas.

T. lyrophanes (Cope). Length 1,750 mm.; tail 150 mm.; color gray, with 21 to 33 brown blotches on the back in front of the anus; tail and sides also blotched; scales in 23 rows: southern Arizona.

Family 4. Elapidæ.—Elapine snakes. Poisonous snakes with usually many teeth in both jaws, the front pair of teeth in the upper jaw forming a pair of short rigid fangs which are perforated each by a poison canal opening at the tip; subcaudals in two rows; head covered with plates and not scales: about 140 species in India, Africa, America and Australia, including many very poisonous ones; 1 genus in the United States. The largest of these snakes is the Indian cobra, which may attain a length of 10 or 12 feet and is, perhaps, the most deadly serpent known.

Micrurus Wagler (*Elaps* Auct., not Schneider). Body slender and cylindrical; head small; no loreal; scales smooth and in 15 rows; anal plate divided: many species in tropical America; 2 in the United States.

M. fulvius (L.). Coral snake; harlequin snake. Length 930 mm.; tail 70 mm.; color red, black and yellow, arranged in bands encircling the body, there being about 14 broad red bands separated from as many broad black bands by narrow yellow rings; head and tail with only black and yellow; upper labials 7: south Atlantic and Gulf States from North Carolina to Texas; a burrowing snake which feeds on lizards and snakes, with a bite that may be very dangerous; the most deadly American snake; three-quarter of those bitten die.

M. euryxanthus (Kennicott). Similar to *M. fulvius*, but differing from it in that the first broad band back of the head is red instead of black: southern New Mexico and Arizona.

Family 5. Crotalidæ.—Rattlesnakes and copperheads; viperine snakes. Poisonous snakes with a thick body, a slender neck and a flat, triangular head; upper jaw without solid maxillary teeth, but with a pair of long poison fangs which are perforated each with a canal opening at the tip and lie against the roof of the mouth when not in use, but are erected or directed forward when the animal strikes; a deep pit present between the eye and the nostril; pupil vertical; subcaudals mostly undivided; anal plate undivided; the end of the tail in most species composed of horny rings (the rattle); scales keeled: 3 genera and about 18 species in the United States; about 6 genera in the Neotropic region and 4 genera in the old world; viviparous, but few young produced at a birth, at most a dozen or fifteen.

Key to the United States Genera of Crotalidæ

a₁ No rattle present..1. *Agkistrodon.*
a₂ Rattle present.
  b₁ Top of head covered with plates (Fig. 126)................2. *Sistrurus.*
  b₂ Top of head covered with scales (Fig. 127)................3. *Crotalus.*

1. Agkistrodon Beauvois. Head covered with 9 symmetrical plates; no rattle present; scales in 23 or 25 rows; upper labials 8; ventrals 130 to 150; anterior subcaudals undivided, posterior ones divided: 10 species, 7 in Asia, 2 in the United States.

Key to the Species of Agkistrodon

a₁ Scales in 23 rows; loreal plate present.........................*A. mokasen.*
a₂ Scales in 25 rows; loreal plate absent.........................*A. piscivorus·*

A. mokasen Beauvois (*A. contortrix* L.). Copperhead; moccasin (Fig. 124). Length 830 mm.; tail 120 mm.; color light brown, with about 15 transverse bands of darker brown which are narrow on top and very broad at the sides; head copper color; belly whitish, with a series of large dark spots on each side: Massachusetts to

FIG. 124.—*Agkistrodon mokanse (from Cope).*

northern Florida; westward to Illinois and Texas; sometimes abundant in swampy or rocky places, feeding on frogs, rodents, birds and snakes; bite very dangerous.

Subspecies of A. mokasen

A. m. mokasen Beauvois. Cross band narrow: eastern States.
A. m. laticinctus Gloyd and Conant. Cross bands wider: Texas and Oklahoma.

A. *piscivorus* (Lacépède). Water moccasion; cottonmouth (Fig. 125). Length 1,000 mm.; tail 190 mm.; color olive brown, crossed by 20 to 30 obscure darker bands; head purplish black; belly yellow, with

black blotches: Atlantic and Gulf drainage from Virginia to eastern Texas; semiaquatic, often common along streams, feeding on frogs, fish, rodents and birds, for which the snakes will often lie in wait, perched

FIG. 125.—*Agkistrodon piscivorus (from Cope)*.

in bushes overhanging the water; bite very dangerous.

2. Sistrurus Garman. Rather small snakes, with head covered with 9 symmetrical plates, and with a small rattle composed of not more than 8 rings; scales in 21 to 25 rows; upper labials 10 to 12; ventrals 125 to 145; subcaudals, except a few of the terminal ones, undivided: 3 species, 1 in Mexico.

S. *catenatus* (Rafinesque). Massasauga (Fig. 126). Length 800 mm.; tail 100 mm.; color light brown, with a middorsal series of 30 to 36 irregular dark brown blotches, each one edged with white, and 3 similar laterals series; belly mottled brown; melanistic coloring not uncommon; scales in 23 or 25 rows; upper labials 11 or 12: western New York to Nebraska; southward into Texas and Mexico; in wet fields and swamps, feeding on frogs and other small animals; bite very dangerous.

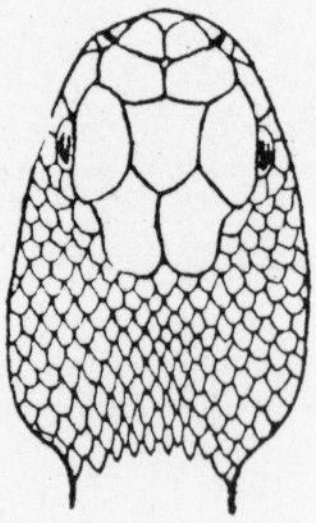

Subspecies of S. catenatus

S. *c. catenatus* (Raf.). Scales in 25 rows; colors darker; blotches larger: eastern and central parts of range.

S. *c. edwardsii* (Baird and Girard). Scales in 23 rows; colors paler; blotches smaller: Oklahoma and western Texas.

FIG. 126.—*Sistrurus catenatus (from Cope)*.

S. *miliarius* (L.). Ground rattler. Length 430 mm.; tail 60 mm.; color gray, yellowish or brown, with a middorsal series of about 40 irregular spots or cross bars and 1 or 2 lateral series of smaller spots on each side; belly white, with numerous dark blotches; scales in 21 to 23 rows; upper labials 10 or 11: Atlantic and Gulf drainage from central North Carolina to Texas, and up the Mississippi Valley to Arkansas and Oklahoma; in wet places; the least dangerous of the rattlesnakes.

3. Crotalus L. Rattlesnakes. Head covered with scales, most species having also small plates between and in front of the eyes; rattle large and composed of at most 14 rings; scales in 23 to 31 rows; upper labials 12 to 16; ventrals about 175; subcaudals undivided: 15 species, in North and South America, 12 in the United States, all very dangerous snakes. The young rattler has no rattle, but a soft horny button at the end of its tail. During its first season it adds one horny ring to the button. In the succeeding seasons it usually adds 3 rings a year, the terminal rings usually becoming lost as the snake gets older.

Key to the United States Species of Crotalus

a_1 Supraocular horned..*C. cerastes.*
a_2 Supraocular not horned.
  b_1 Eye separated from labials by 1 row of scales..............*C. triseriatus.*
  b_2 Eye separated from labials by 2 to 5 rows of scales.
    c_1 Upper preocular small, higher than wide...............*C. lepidus.*
    c_2 Upper preocular large, much wider than high
      d_1 Pattern of short cross bands of white...............*C. willardi.*
      d_2 Pattern not of white cross bands.
        e_1 Dorsal bands enclosing paired light spots; tail black..*C. molossus.*
        e_2 Dorsal bands not enclosing paired light spots.
          f_1 Dorsal pattern of dark chevrons; tail usually black.....................................*C. horridus.*
          f_2 Dorsal pattern of more or less squarish spots or straight cross bands.
            g_1 Large snakes with dorsal diamond markings; a light line from back of eye reaches scale row above labials at least 2 scales anterior to angle of jaw.
              h_1 North Carolina to Louisiana.............*C. adamanteus.*
              h_2 Texas and Oklahoma to southeastern California............................*C. atrox.*
              h_3 Southwestern California.................*C. ruber.*
            g_2 A light line from back of eye (if present) reaches scale above labials only at angle of mouth, or not at all; pattern of squarish blotches or cross bands.
              h_1 Squarish blotches present, at least anteriorly.
                i_1 Two scales on snout between nasals; 2 scales between supraoculars..........*C. scutulatus.*
                i_2 Four scales on snout between nasals; 4 to 6 scales between supraoculars.....*C. confluentus.*
              h_2 Many narrow cross bars present..........*C. tigris.*

C. horridus L. Common rattlesnake (Fig. 127). Length 1,000 mm.; tail 130 mm.; greatest length 1,750 mm.; color yellowish brown, with about 22 wide, dark brown, more or less irregular cross bands, each of which is often broken into 3 separate irregular blotches; abdomen yellowish, with black spots; melanistic coloring not uncommon; tail of adult black; scales in 23 to 25 rows; upper labials 13 or 14: entire country east of the Great Plains; northward to Maine; southward to northern Florida; in rocky regions, feeding on rodents and birds; bite very dangerous.

C. adamanteus Beauvois. Diamond-back rattlesnake. Length 1,800 mm.; tail 220 mm.; diameter of body 100 mm.; greatest length 2,500 mm.; color olive or brown, with a dorsal series of about 20 more or less irregular diamond-shaped markings, each diamond enclosing the ground color; tail ringed with black; belly yellow; scales in 27 to 29 rows; upper labials 15: Atlantic and Gulf coastal regions, from North Carolina to Louisiana, in swamps and wet woods; the largest American poisonous snake.

C. atrox Baird & Girard. Length 1,300 mm.; tail 150 mm.; color gray with a dorsal series of brown, diamond-shaped spots, each bordered with

FIG. 127.—*Crotalus horridus (from Cope).*

white; scales in 27 rows; upper labials 15 or 16: Arkansas to southeastern California, in arid regions; a feral colony exists in Wood County, Wisconsin: common.

C. molossus B. & G.   Length 1,000 mm.; tail 80 mm.; color sulphur yellow, with a dorsal series of brown rhombs open at the side; tail black; scales in 29 rows: southern Texas to southern Arizona.

C. ruber Cope.   A large rattler very like *C. atrox*, but reddish, with indistinct marking: extreme southwestern California.

C. cerastes Hollowell.   Sidewinder.   Length 480 mm.; tail 50 mm.; a pair of conspicuous horn-like projections between the eyes; color light brown, with a middorsal series of about 40 brown square spots and a lateral series of small spots on each side; scales in 21 rows; upper labials 12: deserts of southern Utah and Nevada, Arizona and eastern California; the popular name applies to a curious sidewise method of locomotion.

C. confluentus Say.   Prairie rattler.   Length 960 mm.; tail 100 mm.; body rather slender; color yellowish brown or green, with a middorsal series of about 40 irregularly rounded white-bordered brown blotches; a pale band passes from beneath the center of the eye to the angle of the mouth; scales in 25 to 27 rows; upper labials 14 or 15: the Great Plains from Canada to Texas and the entire country west to the Pacific; common, being frequently seen in prairie dog burrows, on the young of which they feed.

Subspecies of C. confluentus

C. c. confluentus Say. Body brightly marked with blotches: the Great Plains.

C. c. lutosus Klauber. Body brightly marked with small blotches anteriorly and with narrow bars posteriorly: the Great Basin region.

C. c. oregonus Holbrook. Body brightly marked with blotches: the Pacific Coast States.

C. scutulatus (Kennicott). Body marked with diamonds like *C. atrox;* light line back of eye as in *C. confluentus;* large scales on top of snout: desert regions of southern Arizona and California.

C. willardi Meck. A small rattler, with brightly marked head; body dull, with white cross lines: southern Arizona.

C. lepidus (Kennicott). Length 555 mm.; tail 50 mm.; color greenish with black rings at wide intervals; scales in 23 rows; upper labials 12: along the Mexican border of Texas, New Mexico and Arizona.

C. triseriatus Wagler. Length 525 mm.; tail 60 mm.; color grayish brown, with 2 series of small brown blotches on the back; scales in 21 rows: southern Arizona.

C. tigris Kenn. Length 650 mm.; tail 50 mm.; color yellowish gray, with indistinct cross bands; scales in 23 or 25 rows; upper labials 13: southern Arizona.

Order 4. Testudinata.—Turtles. Reptiles in which the body is wide and short, and is enclosed in a shell composed of a dorsal shield, called the *carapace*, and a ventral shield, the *plastron*. The shell, in most cases, is formed of large external, epidermal, horny plates (tortoise shell), which overlie internal bony plates. These latter consist, in the carapace, of the flattened ribs and the flattened trunk vertebræ which coalesce with overlying dermal bony plates, and are surrounded on the circumference of the shell by a series of marginal dermal bony plates; in the plastron they consist of exclusively dermal plates, there being no sternum. The carapace and the plastron are more or less firmly united by a wide bridge on each side.

The head is a very solid and compact structure, and is often covered with scales. The jaws are toothless and are covered by a horny sheath which forms a cutting edge. The *Trionychidæ* are the only turtles which have fleshy lips. The eye has an upper and a lower lid and also a nictitating membrane.   The tympanum is at the surface of the body, but in some species is hidden.   The neck is long and flexible and has 8 vertebræ, and together with the head can usually be retracted within the shell.   Two pairs of stout, pentadactyle limbs are generally present, the toes of which are more or less webbed in the aquatic turtles.   In the marine turtles the limbs are flippers, with a reduced number of toes. The tail is usually short and thick, and in many species ends with a claw.   The skin covering the soft portion of the body is usually provided with scales.

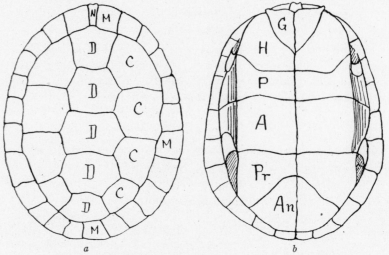

FIG. 128.—Carapace (*a*) and plastron (*b*) of *Chrysemys picta marginata*, to show the plates: *A*, abdominal; *An*, anal; *C*, costal or lateral; *D*, dorsal or vertebral; *G*, gular; *H*, humeral; *M*, marginal; *N*, nuchal; *P*, pectoral; *Pr*, preanal (*from Hurter*).

Habits and Distribution.—Most species of turtles are more or less aquatic in their habits.   The land turtles, however, live exclusively on the land, and will often drown if thrown into the water; and all of them, even the giant marine turtles whose limbs are flippers, come on to land to lay their eggs.

Turtles are noted for their tenacity of life.   Many species can remain submerged in the water several hours without drowning.   Some species have true water respiration.   Species of the *Trionychidæ*, for instance, take water into the mouth and expel it regularly, when submerged, and a number of species have rectal respiration.

Turtles feed on vegital and animal food.   The land turtles feed principally on the former, but also eat grubs, worms and other small animals they can catch.   The aquatic turtles usually feed mainly on animal food, which they devour under the water.   The snappers and soft-shells are fierce beasts of prey, which eat large numbers of fish, water birds and other animals which frequent the water.

Turtles usually breed in the late spring or early summer. All are oviviparous; the eggs are buried by the female in the sand or earth and are incubated by the heat of the sun.

About 245 species of turtles are known, of which about 50 species are found in the United States; these are grouped in 6 families.

On the Identification of Turtles.—The epidermal, horny plates forming the outer covering of the carapace fall into three groups, the *dorsal* or *vertebral*, the *lateral* or *costal* and the *marginal plates* (Fig. 128). The dorsal plates, in most turtles, form a median row of 5 plates; the lateral plates are paired and consist of a row of 4 or 5 plates on each side of the median row; the marginal plates form the margin of the carapace and number usually 12 pairs. The median anterior marginal is called the *nuchal plate*. The epidermal plates of the plastron are usually 11 or 12 in number (Fig. 128). In some turtles the epidermal plates are absent, the shell being covered with a leathery skin.

The measurements used in the identification of turtles are those of the carapace, and in certain cases of the plastron also, and are always made in a straight line and not to follow the curve of the shell.

Key to the Families of Testudinata

a_1 Limbs not in the form of flippers; land and pond turtles.
  b_1 Shell covered with horny plates.
    c_1 Tail short and without dorsal tubercles; plastron large and oval.
      d_1 Plastron with 9 to 11 horny plates; a single anterior median plate; margin of carapace not flaring, but turned downwards (Fig. 130)....................1. *Kinosternidæ.*
      d_2 Plastron with 12 horny plates; an anterior pair of plates; margin of carapace flaring outwards (Fig. 131)...3. *Testudinidæ.*
    c_2 Tail very long, with a dorsal row of tubercles (Fig. 129); plastron small, cross-shaped; snappers..............2. *Chelydridæ.*
  b_2 Shell not covered with horny plates, but with a leathery skin...4. *Trionychidæ.*
a_2 Limbs in the form of flippers; size very large; sea turtles.
  b_1 Shell covered with horny plates.........................5. *Cheloniidæ.*
  b_2 Shell not covered with horny plates, but with a leathery skin...6. *Dermochelidæ.*

Family 1. Kinosternidæ.—Mud and musk turtles. Rather small, aquatic turtles with an elongate body; carapace elliptical, with 23 marginal plates, usually smooth, without a flaring edge (Fig. 130);

plastron well developed, with movable anterior and posterior lobes, covered with 9 to 11 plates and joined with the carapace by narrow bridges; toes 5-5; claws 5-4; feet webbed; head pointed; jaws strong: 14 species, all American, 7 in the United States, inhabiting slow streams

FIG. 129.—Tail of *Chelydra serpentina* (*from Surface*).

and muddy ponds, and eating animal food; eggs elliptical; all the species emit a musky odor.

Key to the Genera of the Kinosternidæ

a₁ Plastron narrow, not capable of closing the shell.............1. *Sternotherus.*
a₂ Plastron broad, capable of closing the shell.................2. *Kinosternon.*

1. Sternotherus Gray. Musk turtles. Plastron reduced, scarcely movable: 3 species.

S. odoratus (Latreille). Musk turtle. Carapace 90 mm. long and 60 mm. wide; color brownish, often striped or blotched with a darker color; plastron yellowish or brown; head large, with strong jaws; plastron 68 mm. long and 31 mm. wide; side of head with 2 narrow yellow stripes, one passing above and the other beneath the eye: eastern and central States, from Canada to the Gulf; westward into Missouri and Texas; common; odor of musk strong.

S. carinatus (Gray). Similar to *S. odoratus* but with a prominent middorsal keel and with imbricated plates; head spotted with black, without stripes: Mississippi, Louisiana and Texas.

2. Kinosternon Spix. Mud turtles. Plastron with central plate and 2 movable lobes, capable of closing the shell: 10 species, 5 in the United States, North and Central America, barely entering South America.

Key to the United States Species

a₁ Bridge very short, about a third the length of fore lobe of
   plastron...*K. steindachneri.*
a₂ Bridge longer, about half the length of fore lobe of plastron.
   b₁ Fore lobe shorter than hind; carapace with 3 yellow stripes..*K. baurii.*
   b₂ Fore lobe as long or longer than hind.
      c₁ Head spotted with yellow...........................*K. subrubrum.*
      c₂ Sides of head bright yellow.........................*K. flavescens.*
      c₃ No yellow on head or body..........................*K. sonoriense.*

K. baurii Garman.   Carapace 900 mm. long and 65 mm. wide; color brown or olive, with 3 yellow bands extending the length of the carapace: Florida and Georgia.

K. steindachneri Siebenrock.   Similar to *K. subrubrum*, but differs in having a very short bridge: central Florida.

K. subrubrum (Lacépède) (*K. pensilvanicum* Gmelin).   Common mud-turtle (Fig. 130).   Carapace 85 mm. long and 60 mm. wide; plastron 78 mm. long and 37 mm. wide; color dark brown, with black

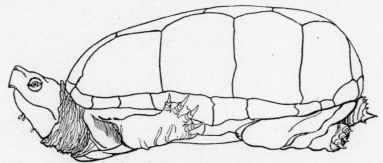

Fig. 130.—*Kinosternon subrubrum (from Surface).*

sutures; plastron yellow or brown, with distinct lines of growth; head dark, with yellowish spots: eastern and central States from New York south, exclusive of peninsular Florida; westward to Texas, Missouri and eastern Illinois; common.

Subspecies of K. subrubrum

K. s. hippocrepis (Gray).   Two orange bands on the side of the head: southern Alabama to Texas and northward in the Mississippi Valley to Missouri.

K. flavescens (Agassiz).   Carapace 110 mm. long and 80 mm. wide; color yellowish brown and yellowish green; plastron yellow; sides of head and neck bright yellow: Texas to Arizona; northward to Illinois, Kansas and Colorado.

K. sonoriense LeConte.   Carapace 110 mm. long, 67 mm. wide; color brown, with faint darker radiating lines on each plate; vertebral plates imbricating: western Texas into southeastern California.

Family 2.   Chelydridæ.—Snapping turtles.   Body large, high in front; carapace rough and tuberculate, and with 24 marginal plates; plastron small, cruciform and composed of 10 plates, besides the 2 narrow bridges; head, neck and tail very large; jaws powerful and hooked; toes 5-5, with small webs; claws 5-4: 3 species, 2 in the United States; the largest turtles in the country (except the marine turtles), noted for their ferocity and voracity; aquatic, living on fish, water-birds and other animals; flesh valued for food.

Key to the Genera of Cheiydridæ

a₁ Head covered with a soft skin............................1. *Chelydra.*
a₂ Head covered with symmetrical plates......................2. *Macrochelys.*

1. Chelydra Schweigger. Carapace with 3 blunt keels, more or less pronounced, growing less so with age; tail very long, with 2 rows of scales beneath; eyes superior in position: 1 species.

C. serpentina (L.). Common snapper. Length 700 mm. or more; length of carapace 300 mm.; width 260 mm.; weight 30 lbs. or more; 2 chin barbels; a row of large compressed tubercles on the upper surface of the tail (Fig. 129); eggs spherical, 25 mm. in diameter, about 25 in number: North America, east of the Rockies, from Canada to the Gulf; common.

2. Macrochelys Gray. Head very large and covered above with plates; tail with small scales beneath; eyes lateral in position: carapace with 3 very prominent tuberculated ridges: 1 species.

M. temmincki (Holbrook). Alligator snapper. Length 1,000 mm.; length of carapace 620 mm.; width 530 mm.; weight 120 lbs.; eggs 35 mm. in diameter: Gulf States; northward in the Mississippi Valley into northern Missouri.

Family 3. Testudinidæ.—Pond and land turtles. Carapace ovate and with flaring edges (Fig. 131) and either depressed or more or less strongly convex, and covered with 5 dorsals, 4 pairs of costals and 25 marginals; plastron covered with 12 plates, and of large size and firmly joined with the carapace by wide bridges, and in some species with a movable anterior lobe enabling the animal to close its shell; toes 5-4; egg elliptical: about 80 species in the United States; many species are used for food.

Key to the Genera of Testudinidæ

a₁ Digits spreading, not closely bound together.
  b₁ Plastron without hinge, immovably joined to carapace.
    c₁ Alveolar surfaces of jaws broad; hind feet largest, broadly webbed.
      d₁ Alveolar surfaces of jaws smooth; upper jaws not notched in front; carapace keeled.
        e₁ Lower jaw not spoon-shaped at tip; plates of cara-pace rugose...................................4. *Malaclemys.*
        e₂ Lower jaw spoon-shaped at tip; plates of carapace smooth..5. *Graptemys.*

    d_2 Alveolar surfaces of jaws with a longitudinal ridge;
        upper jaw notched in front; carapace not keeled.......7. *Pseudemys*.
   c_2 Alveolar surfaces of jaws narrow.
    d_1 Hind feet largest, broadly webbed.
      e_1 Marginal shields with red markings...............6. *Chrysemys*.
      e_2 Marginal shields without red markings............8. *Deirochelys*.
    d_2 Hind feet not larger, slightly webbed..............1. *Clemmys*.
  b_2 Plastron with hinge across the middle, enabling the animal to
    close its shell.
   c_1 Body depressed; plastron notched behind; upper jaw
      notched in front...................................2. *Emys*.
   c_2 Body arched; plastron rounded or truncate behind; upper
      jaw hooked in front...............................3. *Terrapene*.
a_2 Digits club-shaped, being closely bound together, only the last
  joint being free; southern States.........................9. *Gopherus*.

1. Clemmys Ritgen. Wood-tortoises. Small turtles with usually a depressed carapace with a more or less prominent keel; plastron joined with the carapace by a wide rigid bridge; feet more or less webbed: 4 United States species.

Key to the Species of Clemmys

a_1 In the eastern and central States.
  b_1 Carapace smooth with small yellow spots on a black back-
    ground..*C. guttata*.
  b_2 Carapace with deep concentric grooves in each plate and
    serrated behind; color uniform brown..................*C. insculpta*.
  b_3 Head with a large yellow or orange spot on each side.......*C. muhlenbergii*.
a_2 On the Pacific slope.......................................*C. marmorata*.

C. guttata (Schneider). Spotted turtle (Fig. 131). Body black above, with numerous small round orange or yellow spots; plastron

Fig. 131.—*Clemmys guttata (from Fowler).*

black, blotched with yellow or orange; carapace smooth, without keel, 100 mm. long and 75 mm. wide: eastern States; southward along the coast to northern Florida; westward to southern Michigan; very common.

C. *insculpta* (LeConte).   Wood-turtle.   Shell dark gray or brown in color and much roughened by deep concentric grooves and ridges on each plate; plastron yellow, with a large black blotch on each plate; carapace keeled; length 150 mm.; width 120 mm.; soft parts, except the

FIG. 132.—*Clemmys muhlenbergi* (*from Surface*).

top of the head and the limbs, red: northeastern States; southward to Virginia; westward to Wisconsin; terrestrial, in fields and woods; valued for food.

C. *marmorata* (Baird & Girard).   Carapace smooth, dark brown or black in color, with numerous yellow dots or dashes; plastron black and yellow; length of carapace 150 mm.: entire Pacific slope, in ponds and rivers; common.

C. *muhlenbergii* (Schœpff) (Fig. 132).   Carapace with fine concentric lines on the plates in young adults, and dark brown or black in color, with yellowish or reddish markings; head black, with a large orange or yellow spot on each side; length of carapace 100 mm.; width 65 mm.: New Jersey and southeastern Pennsylvania to Rhode Island, central New York and mountains of western North Carolina; in marshes and ponds and small streams; often common.

2. Emys Duméril.   Shell moderately high, with narrow bridges, plastron notched behind, movable and joined with the carapace by a ligament on each side; a transverse hinge in front of the bridges divides the plastron into 2 lobes, both of which are movable, although the shell cannot be completely closed; digits webbed: 1 species.

E. blandingii (Holbrook) (Fig. 133).   Carapace black, with numerous small yellow spots; plastron yellow in the center, with large irregular black blotches along the two sides; length of carapace 200 mm.; width

FIG. 133.—*Emys blandingi* (*from Fowler*).

120 mm.: north-central States and New England; westward to Minnesota; not common.

3. Terrapene Merrem (*Cistudo* Fleming).   Box-turtles.   Shell high and very convex; plastron large, united with the carapace by a ligament on each side, rounded at both ends, and with a transverse hinge which divides it into two movable lobes so that the shell can be completely closed; upper jaw with a beak; digits with a small web or with none: 6 species.

Key to the Species of Terrapene

a_1 Carapace keeled.
  b_1 Carapace irregularly marked with yellow.....................*T. carolina.*
  b_2 Carapace with yellow radiating lines.........................*T. major*
a_2 Carapace not keeled..*T. ornata.*

T. carolina (L.).   Common box-turtle.   Shell more or less globular, with a blunt keel; color yellow and blackish, but very variable; male usually with red eyes, female usually with yellow; length of carapace

130 mm.; width 115 mm.; height 70 mm.: eastern and southern States; terrestrial; common.

Subspecies of T. carolina

T. c. carolina (L.).   Eastern States; southward to Georgia; westward to Tennessee and western Illinois; northward to central Michigan and Maine.

T. c. triunguis (Agassiz).   Hind foot with but 3 claws; yellow markings usually obscure: Gulf slope; westward into Texas; northward into Missouri.

FIG. 134.—*Malaclemys centrata (from Fowler).*

T. major (Agassiz).   Similar to *T. carolina;* size large; carapace 180 mm. long, and with yellow radiating lines: Gulf States from Florida to Texas.

T. ornata (Agassiz).   Similar to *T. carolina*, but without a keel; fore legs usually red: Indiana to the Rocky Mountains; southward to the gulf of Mexico and Arizona; often common.

4. Malaclemys Gray.   Salt marsh turtles.   Carapace depressed and with a keel; plastron without a hinge and immovably joined with the carapace; feet large and webbed; head covered with a soft skin: 2 species.

Key to the Species of Malaclemys

a₁ On the Atlantic slope...*M. centrata.*
a₂ On the Gulf slope...*M. pileata.*

M. centrata (Latreille).   Diamond-back terrapin (Fig. 134).   Shell rough, each plate having concentric lines of growth; carapace dark olive or grayish in color and 180 mm. long and 130 mm. wide; weight

2 lbs.; legs and head spotted; plastron yellow; young individuals whitish, with black concentric lines; head without stripes: salt marshes from Massachusetts to Florida, where it feeds on crustaceans and mollusks; highly prized for food.

Subspecies of M. centrata

M. c. centrata (Lat.).   Cape Hatteras to Florida.

M. c. concentrica (Shaw).   Size smaller; concentric lines on each plate very distinct: Massachusetts to Cape Hatteras.

M. pileata (Wied).   Similar to *M. centrata;* carapace with a more or less tuberculate keel and black or brown in color, with distinct concentric lines on each plate: Gulf coast.

Subspecies of M. pileata

M. p. pileata (Wied).   Color black or very dark brown; top of head dark: Gulf coast, from Florida to the Mississippi River.

FIG. 135.—*Graptemys geographica (from Fowler)*.

M. p. littoralis (W. P. Hay).   Color light brown; top of head white: coast of Texas.

M. p. macrospilota (W. P. Hay).   Each plate of carapace with a large central yellow or orange blotch: west coast of Florida.

5. Graptemys Agassiz.   Map turtles.   Carapace depressed and with a keel; plastron without a hinge and immovably joined with the carapace; head covered with a soft skin; lower jaw with a dilatation at the tip: 2 species.

Key to the Species of Graptemys

a_1 A triangular yellowish spot back of eye; keel not serrate....*G. geographica*.
a_2 A transverse cresent back of eye; keel serrate..........*G. pseudogeographica*.

G. geographica (LeSueur) (Fig. 135).   Body dark brown and marked with a network of greenish and yellowish lines; plastron yellow; length of carapace 240 mm.; width 180 mm.; carapace circular, notched at the sutures of the marginal plates: central States; eastward into New York and Pennsylvania in the Susquehanna River; westward into Missouri and Arkansas; northward to Michigan and Lake Champlain; common.

G. pseudogeographica (Gray). Similar to *G. geographica* but with a more distinct keel; median row of plates imbricated and each with a high tubercle; no yellowish net-work on carapace; head, neck and legs with bright yellow stripes: Mississippi Valley and Gulf slope.

Subspecies of G. pseudogeographica

G. p. pseudogeographica (Gray). Each dorsal plate with a large dark blotch: eastward to Alabama and Ohio; northward to Wisconsin; westward to Kansas and Oklahoma.

G. p. kohni (Baur). A large yellow spot behind the eye: Pensacola to eastern Texas.

G. p. oculifera (Baur). A yellow spot behind the eye, and 2 yellow stripes on the neck: southern Louisiana.

6. Chrysemys Gray. Painted turtles. Carapace smooth, depressed, without keel, and with wide bridges which join it immovably with the plastron; feet webbed, with long claws; no concentric lines on the plates of the carapace: 1 species.

C. picta (Schneider). Carapace smooth, dark olive or brown in color, the plates margined with yellow; throat striped with yellow; marginal plates above and beneath blotched with crimson, which may disappear on the dorsal marginal plates in old specimens; plastron yellow, with a broad blackish patch in the center; length of the carapace 125 mm.; width 90 mm.: eastern, central and western States; very common.

Subspecies of C. picta

C. p. marginata Agassiz (Fig. 128). Vertebral row of plates alternating with those of the costal rows: northern New York to Wisconsin; southward to Missouri.

C. p. bellii (Gray). Yellow margins of dorsal plates absent; plastron with a pair of wide black bands joined at the ends: Great Plains; westward to Vancouver Island; northeastward to northern Michigan.

C. p. dorsalis Agassiz. Carapace with a yellow dorsal stripe: lower Mississippi Valley; northward to Missouri.

C. p. picta (Schneider) (Fig. 136). Plastron yellow; vertebrals nearly in same transverse line as costals: eastern States from New Brunswick to Georgia; very common.

FIG. 136.—*Chrysemys p. picta (from Fowler).*

7. Pseudemys Gray. Sliders; cooters. Carapace moderately depressed, with a serrate hinder margin; plastron notched behind; upper jaw notched in front; head covered with a hard skin: 10 species.

Key to the Species of Pseudemys

a_1 Edges of jaws smooth, a black spot on each plastral scute.
  b_1 A yellow patch back of eye; Atlantic States................*P. scripta.*
  b_2 A red line back of eye, or no marking; Mississippi drainage....*P. troostii.*
a_2 Edge of lower jaw serrate; no black spot on each plastral plate.
  b_1 Upper jaw smooth.......................................*P. concinna.*
  b_2 Upper jaw serrate, at least with central notch and lateral cusp.
    c_1 Plastron red; Atlantic coastal plain....................*P. rubriventris.*
    c_2 Plastron yellow; Gulf States and lower Mississippi Valley.
      d_1 In central Florida................................*P. floridana.*
      d_2 In Gulf coast region.............................*P. mobilensis.*
      d_3 From Missouri to Mexico.........................*P. texana.*

P. troostii (Holbrook) (*P. elegans* Wied). Carapace greenish black, with darker blotches; under surface of marginals and plastron yellow, with black blotches; adult males (*P. troostii*) without markings; females and young (*P. elegans*) with a red mark back of eye, yellow lines on head and neck and yellow marks on carapace; edges of both jaws smooth; length of carapace 250 mm.; width 180 mm.: Mississippi Valley; northward to Iowa and Ohio; south to Texas; common; used for food.

P. scripta (Schœpff). Carapace dark brown in color, with dull yellow transverse stripes; plastron yellow; length of carapace 250 mm.;

width 170 mm.; head with a broad yellow spot just back of the eye: Georgia to North Carolina.

P. concinna (LeConte).   Shell broad and flat; carapace wrinkled on the sides, olive or brownish in color with yellow or brownish markings; plastron yellow; head black, striped with yellow; length of carapace 300 mm.; width 210 mm.: rivers of the southeast, above tide water, Maryland to Georgia and west to Mississippi.

FIG. 137.—*Pseudemys rubriventris (from Fowler).*

P. rubriventris (LeConte).   Red-bellied terrapin (Fig. 137).   Carapace brownish, streaked or blotched with red; plastron red; length of carapace 300 mm.; width 180 mm.; height 110 mm.; extreme length of carapace 450 mm.: eastern States from Cape Cod to Florida, in coastal plain rivers; the largest turtle in this territory except the snapper; used for food.

P. floridana (LeConte).   Carapace circular and very high; head black, very small; carapace dark brown, with wavy yellow cross bars, 325 mm. long and 225 mm. wide; plastron yellow; lower jaw nearly smooth: Florida and southern Georgia.

P. mobilensis (Holbrook).   Carapace high and 300 mm. long; plastron yellow; color similar to *P. rubriventris:* Gulf coast from Florida to Louisiana.

P. texana Baur.   Carapace brown, with yellow concentric lines; plastron yellow; head streaked with yellow; length of carapace 230 mm.; width 170 mm.: southwestern Missouri to Texas and Mexico.

8. Deirochelys Agassiz.   Similar to *Chrysemys;* upper jaw notched in front; lower jaw arched upwards and terminating in a sharp point; neck long: 1 species.

D. reticularia (Latreille). Chicken turtle. Carapace narrow, rather high, and olive or brown in color with a net-work of fine yellow lines, each upper marginal with a yellow bar and each under marginal with a black blotch on a yellow field; plastron yellow; length of carapace 125 mm.; width 80 mm.; neck very long: Atlantic and Gulf coastal plain from central North Carolina to Texas and Oklahoma; southward to central Florida.

9. Gopherus Rafinesque. Land tortoises. Shell high and dome-like; plastron large and often with a hinged front lobe; feet not webbed: 3 species in the United States, all herbivorous and strictly terrestrial; they are allied to the giant land tortoises of the Galapagos Islands, the largest of which has a carapace a meter and a third in length and weighs over 225 kilos.

Key to the United States Species of Gopherus

a_1 In the southern and south-central States......................*G. polyphemus.*
a_2 In Texas..*G. berlandieri.*
a_3 In the extreme southwest...................................*G. agassizii.*

G. polyphemus (Daudin). Gopher turtle. Carapace with concentric lines on each scale, brownish in color; plastron dull yellow, notched behind, extending beyond the carapace in front; length of carapace 280 mm.; width 200 mm.; inner surface of fore arm with enlarged scales: south Atlantic and Gulf States; northward to South Carolina and Arkansas; gregarious, living in dry, sandy regions and burrowing in the ground. The burrow runs obliquely in the ground to a depth of 4 or more feet, and is enlarged at the end, where a single pair lives.

G. agassizii (Cooper). Similar to *G. polyphemus;* no enlarged scales on the inner surface of the fore arm: southwestern Arizona and southeastern California into Nevada and Utah.

G. berlandieri (Agassiz). Shell globular, being very broad and high; carapace brown and 150 mm. long, 136 mm. wide and 80 mm. high; plastron yellow: southwest Texas into Mexico.

Family 4. Trionychidæ.—The soft-shell turtles. Large turtles with a flat, circular shell which is covered with a leathery skin and not with horny plates or scales; ossification of the carapace not complete; neck very long; head pointed, ending in a flexible proboscis-like snout; jaws powerful, with fleshy lips; feet webbed; toes 5-5; claws 3-3: about 30 species, in both hemispheres, 4 in the United States; savage, active turtles, aquatic and carnivorous, valued for food; eggs spherical. It has been demonstrated that these turtles can remain under water several hours at a time, and that they have true water respiration when submerged, taking in water into the mouth and expelling it regularly about 16 times a minute.

Amyda Oken.   With the characters of the family: 4 United States species.

Key to the Species of Amyda

a_1 Fore part of carapace smooth.................................*A. mutica.*
a_2 Fore part of carapace with conical tubercles.
   b_1 Light stripes on head unite between the eyes.................*A. emoryi.*
   b_2 Light stripes on head unite at end of the snout..............*A. spinifera.*
   b_3 Light stripes on head unite in front of the orbits.............*A. ferox.*

A. mutica (LeSueur).   Body brown in color, irregularly blotched, being spotted in the young; whitish below; length of carapace 170

FIG. 138.—*Amyda spinifera (from Fowler).*

mm.; width 160 mm.: central and northern tributaries of the Mississippi, Brazos and Colorado rivers; not so common as *A. spinifera.*

A. emoryi (Agassiz).   Similar to *A. spinifera:* Texas and into southern Oklahoma and Arkansas.

A. spinifera (LeSueur).   Soft-shell turtle (Fig. 138).   Body olive brown in color, with numerous round dark spots, each margined with black in young animals; head and neck olive, with stripes; tubercles on forward edge of carapace larger in the female than in the male; plastron white; length of carapace 350 mm.; width 300 mm.: Mississippi and St. Lawrence rivers and Great Lakes and their tributaries; common.

A. ferox (Schneider).   Large turtles similar to *A. spinifera*, but plain brown in color in the adult; young spotted or blotched; length of carapace 450 mm.; width 370 mm.; weight 13 kilos: southern States from South Carolina to Louisiana; common.

Family 5. Cheloniidæ.—Marine turtles of large size, in which the shell is covered with large horny plates; carapace depressed, highest in front; head large, covered with plates and incompletely retractile; limbs in form of flippers, with 1 or 2 claws on each; eggs spherical: 7 species, which live in the open ocean in the warmer parts of the earth, coming to the shore on tropical and subtropical beaches to bury their eggs.

a₁ Four costal plates on each side.
   b₁ Plates of carapace imbricated.............................1. *Eretmochelys.*
   b₂ Plates of carapace not imbricated......................2. *Chelonia.*
ʿa₂ Five costal plates on each side...............................3. *Caretta.*

1. **Eretmochelys** Fitzinger. Head broad, with a large median plate surrounded by 7 smaller ones; costal plates 4 on a side; 7 to 10 plates on each cheek: 2 species.

E. imbricata (L.). Tortoise shell turtle; hawk-bill. Body brown or blackish above and yellow beneath; upper jaw with a hooked tip; each foot with 2 claws; length of carapace 750 mm.: tropical seas; the Florida and Gulf coasts; occasionally as far north as Massachusetts; valued for the tortoise shell of commerce, this turtle being the only one which furnishes it.

2. **Chelonia** Latreille. Top of head with a large median plate surrounded by 7 smaller ones; costal plates 4 on a side; 15 to 20 plates on each cheek; head narrow: 2 species.

C. mydas (L.). Green turtle. Body olive or brown above, marked with yellow, and yellow beneath; length of carapace 1,200 mm. or less; weight up to 500 lbs.; 1 claw on each foot: tropical seas; Atlantic Ocean as far north as Massachusetts; valued for food, the fat being green; common.

3. **Caretta** Rafinesque. Top of head with a large median plate surrounded by 13 to 20 smaller ones; costal plates 5 on a side; 15 to 20 plates on each cheek; head broad: 3 species.

C. caretta (L.). Loggerhead turtle. Body brown above, yellowish below; feet with 2 claws each; 3 inframarginal scutes; horny ridges on roof of mouth low; length of carapace 1 m. and more; weight 350 lbs. and more: tropical seas; northward as far as Massachusetts; common on the West India and Florida coasts; flesh and eggs used for food.

C. kempi (Garman). Bastard turtle. Similar to *C. caretta*, but with ridges on the roof of mouth high anteriorly and separated by a notch; 4 in framarginal scutes: south Atlantic; as far north as New Jersey.

Family 6. Dermochelidæ.—Sea turtles with the body covered with a smooth leathery skin; carapace with 7 longitudinal ridges; toes without claws: 1 genus.

Dermochelys Blainville. With the characters of the family: 1 species.

D. coriacea (L.). Leather-turtle; trunk-back. Color dark brown; length of carapace 1,500 mm.; width 900 mm.; weight 700 lbs. and more: tropical seas; northward as far as Maine.

CLASS 5. MAMMALS (Mammalia)

Warm-blooded, air-breathing vertebrates which have a hairy integument. With the exception of the Australian monotremes all mammals are viviparous, and all possess mammary glands on the ventral body surface with which they suckle their young, in the marsupials these glands being located in an integumental pouch. The teeth are adapted to the grasping and chewing of food, there being four different forms, the *incisors* or front teeth, the *canines*, and the *premolars* and *molars* which are the back teeth or grinders. The heart is composed of four chambers, two ventricles and two auricles; there is a single (left) aortic arch and the blood contains non-nucleated red blood-corpuscles. The head articulates with the neck by two occipital condyles and there are, with rare exceptions (the Florida manatee alone of American mammals), seven cervical vertebræ. The lower jaw consists of a single bone on each side and articulates directly with the cranium and not by means of the quadrate bones. An external ear in form of a large integumental fold is, with the exception of certain aquatic mammals, present. The cochlea is spirally coiled, and the tympanum is joined with the inner ear by means of the three ear-ossicles. The abdominal cavity is separated from the thoracic by means of a muscular diaphragm.

On the Identification of Mammals.—The *measurements* of a species of mammals are given in millimeters and include (1) the length of the body from the tip of the snout to the hinder end of the vertebræ of the tail, (2) the length of the tail measured from its base to the hinder end of its vertebræ and (3) the length of the hind foot measured from the bend of the ankle to the tip of the longest toe. An average large male specimen is probably generally used in making the measurements, but it must be remembered that individual differences always exist between individuals of a species, due to differences in age, sex, locality and environmental conditions, and that a considerable margin must be allowed for these differences. The color of a species is also to a certain extent variable, and is much more so in some species of mammals than in others.

The general form of the body and that of its various parts are usually noted, and also any peculiarities of form or color which would tend to mark a species or larger group. The *dentition*, or number of teeth, is a constant and very important character, and is given in this book in the following manner, the figures referring to the number of incisor, canine, premolar and molar teeth on each side of the jaws: "dentition 3/3, 1/1, 4/4, 2/3," the meaning of which is that on each side of the mouth there are 3 upper and 3 lower incisors, 1 upper and 1 lower canine, 4 upper and 4 lower premolars and 2 upper and 3 lower molars.

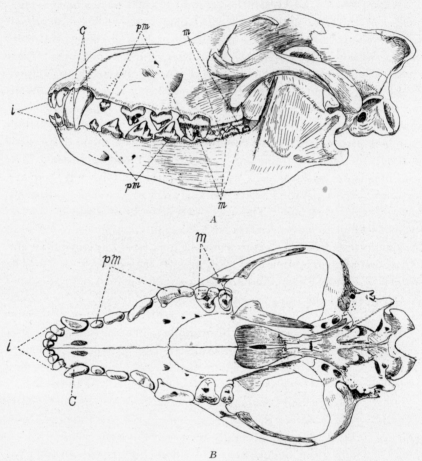

Fig. 139.—Skull of dog, showing dentition, the formula of which is 3/3, 1/1, 4/4, 2/3: *A* side view; *B*, upper jaw; *c*, canines; *i*, incisors; *m*, molars; *pm*, premolars.

This is the dentition of the dog (Fig. 139), which has thus 10 teeth in the upper jaw on each side and 11 teeth in the lower jaw on each side or 20 teeth in the upper jaw on both sides and 22 teeth in the lower jaw on both sides, and 42 teeth altogether. The dentition of the pocket gopher is 1/1, 0/0, 1/1, 3/3, the meaning of which is that this animal has 1 upper and 1 lower incisor on each side or 2 upper and 2 lower incisors altogether, no canines in either jaw, 1 upper and 1 lower premolar on each side and 3 upper and 3 lower molars on each side, or 10 teeth in the upper jaw on both sides and 10 teeth in the lower jaw on both sides, or 20 teeth altogether.

The friction pads of the feet are called the *plantar tubercles* (Fig. 163) and are employed in certain species of rodents for purposes of identifications.

In a country as large as the United States, in which the conditions of climate, rain-fall, moisture and altitude are so very varied, and where forests, plains and deserts, large and small rivers, lakes and marshes form an endless succession of localities which harbor mammalian life, any species which inhabits any considerable area is sure to be divided into a number of geographical races or subspecies. Often the best means of identifying a mammal is to tell where and under what conditions it lives, and the descriptions in this book usually give such details.

History.—The *Mammalia* as a definite scientific group of animals has existed in the literature since the time of Aristotle. Linnæus made it one of the six classes into which he divided the Animal Kingdom, and Lamarck one of the classes of *Vertebrata*.

About 10,000 species and subspecies of mammals are known, grouped in about 15 orders, of which 9 are represented in the United States.

Key to the Orders of Mammals in the United States

a_1 A marsupial pouch present; opossums . . . . 1. *Marsupialia* (p. 245).
a_2 No parsupial pouch present.
    b_1 Hind limbs wanting; manatees . . . . 3. *Sirenia* (p. 247).
    b_2 Hind limbs present.
        c_1 Body covered with a bony shell; armadillos . . . . . . 2. *Edentata* (p. 247).
        c_2 Body not so covered.
            d_1 Flying mammals; bats . . . . 5. *Chiroptera* (p. 257).
            d_2 Non-flying mammals.
                e_1 Feet with claws and not with hoofs.
                    f_1 Canine teeth present.
                        g_1 Limbs used mainly for walking and running.
                            h_1 Canines small; moles and shrews . . . 4. *Insectivora* (p. 247).
                            h_2 Canines prominent . . . . 6. *Carnivora* (p. 264).
                        g_2 Limbs used mainly for swimming; seals . 7. *Pinnipedia* (p. 288).
                    f_1 Canines absent . . . . 8. *Rodentia* (p. 289).
                e_2 Feet with hoofs . . . . 9. *Ungulata* (p. 352).

Order 1. Marsupialia.—Aplacental mammals in which the young are born in a very immature condition and are maintained by the mother in an abdominal pouch called the *marsupium*, in which the nipples of the milk-glands are situated. The marsupium is supported on each side by the marsupial bone which projects forward from the pelvis and is present in both sexes. The uterus and vagina are double and paired.

The marsupials vary much in their general form and in the form of their teeth, and the different groups are fitted to maintain themselves in very diverse environments. About 150 species are known, grouped in 2 suborders, all of which, with the exception of about two dozen American species, inhabit Australia and the neighboring islands.

Key to the Suborders of Marsupialia

a₁ Prominent eye-teeth present; carnivorous species...........1. *Polyprotodontia.*
a₂ Eye-teeth small or wanting; herbivorous species (not present
    in America)...2. *Diprotodontia.*

Suborder Polyprotodontia.—Carnivorous marsupials with 4 or 5 upper and 3 or 4 lower incisors, prominent canines and cuspidate molars: 4 families, in the American and Australian regions, 1 in America.

Family Didelphiidæ.—Opossums. Body rather slender, tail long and prehensile and scaly; legs of about equal length; feet pentadactylous; first digit of hind foot nailless and opposable; dentition 5/4, 1/1, 3/3, 4/4: 10 genera, all American, mostly tropical; arboreal or aquatic; 5 genera and 22 species in North and Central America; 1 genus in the United States.

Didelphis L. Marsupial pouch well developed; fur a mixture of soft hairs and bristles: about 4 species, 1 in the United States.

D. virginiana Kerr. Common opossum. Length 700 mm.; tail 300 mm.; color dirty white on the sides, gray on the back: eastern and central States, from Long Island and the Great Lakes to the Gulf; westward to Louisiana, Oklahoma and Nebraska; arboreal animals which feed on birds, insects and reptiles, as well as on nuts, corn and fruit. The young are often carried on the mother's back when they are big enough to leave her pouch, clinging to her fur or holding on by entwining their tails around hers as she holds it over her back. The nest is usually in a hollow tree; the young number from 5 to 14 and two or three litters are raised in a season. A new-born oppossum is about 12 mm. long.

Subspecies of D. virginiana

D. v. texensis Allen. Color black or gray: southwestern Texas; northward to San Antonio.

D. v. pigra Bangs. Smaller and with a much longer and slenderer tail and smaller feet: Florida and the Gulf coast; westward to western Louisiana.

Order 2. Edentata.—Mammals either without teeth or with primitive, conical teeth which lack enamel and roots and never form a complete series, canines and incisors being generally absent: about 100 species, which include armadillos, anteaters and sloths, most of which live in South and Central America; two genera in Africa and Asia; 1 species in the United States.

Family Dasypodidæ.—Head narrow; snout long; body almost hairless and covered with a bony carapace in which are 6 to 12 movable rings in the middle region; tail long; toes 4-5, all with strong, curved claws: 2 genera; nocturnal, burrowing animals, feeding mainly on insects which they lick up with the sticky surface of their extensile tongues.

Dasypus L. With the characters of the family; toes on the fore feet nearly symmetrical: 1 species.

D. novemcinctus L. The nine-banded armadillo. Carapace with 9 transverse rings in the middle and on the sides; tail very long and covered with rings; top of head and legs covered with shields and scales; color of head pale brown, of back black, of sides yellowish white; length 800 mm.; tail 375 mm.; hind foot 100 mm.; dentition o/o, o/o, o/o, 8/8: southern Texas and New Mexico, and southward to Argentina; 4 or 8 young at a birth in respectively either one or two monozygotic groups of quadruplets. The armor is largely a protection against cactus and other spiny plants.

Order 3. Sirenia.—Aquatic, herbivorous mammals of large size without hind limbs or external ears; cervical vertebræ 6; fore limbs oval flippers; tail rounded and flattened; 1 pair of thoracic mammæ; body naked: 2 families, 1 American.

Family Trichechidæ.—With the characters of the order; dentition 2/2, o/o, o/o, 6/6 to 11/11: 1 genus.

Trichechus L. With the characters of the order: 2 species, one (*T. inunguis*) in the Amazon and Orinoco.

T. latirostris (Harlan). Manatee. Color uniform grayish black; extreme length 4000 mm.; extreme weight 2000 lbs; upper lip divided and very broad; eyes very small: east coast of Florida to Yucatan and the West Indias, in estuaries of broad rivers and coastal lagoons, where they feed on water plants; 1 or 2 young at a birth.

Order 4. Insectivora.—Moles and shrews. Small, mostly nocturnal mammals which live in or on the ground; feet plantigrade and usually pentadactylous; canine teeth small; skull elongate; snout often prolonged to form a proboscis: about 9 families, 2 North American; widely distributed, one of the largest species being the European hedgehog.

Key to the North American Families of Insectivora

a_1 Fore feet very large and modified for digging; moles..............1. *Talpidæ.*
a_2 Fore feet not so modified; shrews................................2. *Soricidæ.*

Family 1. Talpidæ.—Moles. Body stout and cylindrical, covered by very soft fur; external ears absent; eyes very small and concealed in the fur; fore feet enormously enlarged and held vertically; neck not apparent; snout proboscis-like: about 36 species and subspecies; about 10 in the United States.   Moles inhabit the Palearctic and Nearctic regions, living in burrows underground where they feed principally on earthworms and insect grubs.   The nest is from 10 to 18 inches beneath the surface, and from it deep tunnels radiate.   A second series of tunnels is made just beneath the surface, which appear as the familiar surface ridges which often disfigure lawns; they are made in search of food. A single litter of about 4 young is born in the spring time.

Key to the United States Genera of Talpidæ

a_1 In the eastern and central States.
  b_1 Tail very short.
    c_1 Tail slender and nearly naked; the common mole (Fig.
      140)...1. *Scalopus.*
    c_2 Tail thick and very hairy (Fig. 140)..................2. *Parascalops.*
  b_2 Tail long; snout with a star-shaped disc...................3. *Condylura.*
a_2 In the Pacific coast States.
  b_1 Large moles, over 150 mm. long........................4. *Scapanus.*
  b_2 Small moles, under 125 mm. long.......................5. *Neurotrichus.*

1. Scalopus Geoffroy.   Adult dentition 3/2, 1/0, 3/3, 3/3; youthful dentition 3/3, 1/1, 3/3, 3/3; nostrils superior in position, being at the end of the snout, which is obliquely truncated; digits webbed: 12 species and subspecies.

S. aquaticus (L.).   Common mole (Fig. 140; Fig. 141).   Body dark slate color, often tinged with brown; length 160 mm.; tail 27 mm.; hind foot 20 mm.: eastern and central States from Massachusetts and central Minnesota to Texas; westward to northeastern Colorado; very common; of considerable importance as a fur-bearing animal.

Subspecies of S. aquaticus

S. a. aquaticus (L.).   Atlantic States from southern Massachusetts and southeastern New York to North Carolina and eastern Tennessee.

S. a. howelli Jackson. Color dark drab; length 152 mm.: eastern and central North Carolina and South Carolina southwesterly to the Mississippi and the Gulf coast.

S. a. australis Chapman. Color clove-brown; length (male) 145 mm.: eastern Georgia and eastern Florida.

S. a. anastasæ (Bangs). Color sepia; length (male) 137 mm.: Anastasia Island, Florida.

S. a. parvus (Rhoads). Color dark sepia; length (male) 134 mm.: Tampa Bay, Florida.

S. a. machrinus (Rafinesque). Color sepia or brown; length 200 mm.: eastern Ohio to central Iowa and southern Minnesota; central Michigan to Tennessee.

S. a. machrinoides Jackson. Color brown; length 172 mm.: central Minnesota to Arkansas and eastern Kansas.

S. a. pulcher Jack. Color dark fuscous or brown; length (male) 155 mm.: central Arkansas to southern Louisiana and eastern Texas.

S. a. caryi Jack. Color light drab; length (male) 159 mm.: western Nebraska and north-western Kansas.

a b

FIG. 140.—The tail of (*a*) *Scalopus aquaticus* and (*b*) *Parascalops breweri.*

S. a. intermedius (Elliot). Color light drab; length 164 mm.: central and western Oklahoma.

S. a. texanus (Allen). Color brown; length 138 mm.: coast region of western Texas; northward to central Texas.

2. Parascalops True. Dentition 3/3, 1/1, 4/4, 3/3; nostrils lateral, on the outer side of the snout; digits not webbed; tail hairy: 1 species.

P. breweri (Bachman). Hairy-tailed mole (Fig. 140; Fig. 142). Body blackish, often with a brownish gloss; length 150 mm.; tail

FIG. 141.—Lower jaw and fore foot of *Scalopus aquaticus* (*from Jackson*).

30 mm.; hind foot 19: eastern States from New Brunswick to North Carolina, in higher altitudes; westward to Ohio; in dry sandy soil; not common.

3. Condylura Illiger.   Dentition 3/3, 1/1, 4/4, 3/3; snout terminating with a disc bearing on its margin a fringe of 22 long processes, 11 on each side; nostrils in the anterior surface of the disc; tail long, covered with coarse hair; digits not webbed: 1 species.

FIG. 142.—Fore foot of *Parascalops breweri (from Jackson).*   FIG. 143.—Snout of *Condylura cristata (from Jackson).*

C. cristata (L.).   Star-nosed mole (Fig. 143).   Body blackish; length 185 mm.; tail 65 mm.; hind foot 28: southern Labrador to southeastern Manitoba; southward to central Ohio and Indiana west of the Alleghenies and to Georgia on the Atlantic slope; in wet meadows and marshes, frequently leaving its burrows and running on the surface; not common; annual litter of 5 young.

4. Scapanus Pomel.   Dentition 3/3, 1/1, 4/4, 3/3; nostrils crescentic in shape, superior in position; tail short, thick, scantily haired; digits not webbed: several species, all on the Pacific slope, where they take the place of *Scalopus* in the eastern States and have similar habits.

Key to the Species of Scapanus

a_1 Unicuspid teeth evenly spaced and not crowded (Fig. 144); color
very dark.
   b_1 Length more than 200 mm...............................*S. townsendi.*
   b_2 Length less than 200 mm..................................*S. orarius.*
a_2 Unicuspid teeth unevenly spaced and crowded (Fig. 144); color
   usually brown or gray, seldom black.........................*S. latimanus.*

a   b

FIG. 144.—Lower jaw of (*a*) *Scapanus townsendi* and (*b*) *S. latimanus (from Jackson).*

S. townsendi (Bachman) (Fig. 144).   Body of large size and blackish in color; length 225 mm.; tail 41 mm.; hind foot 26 mm.: northwestern

California, Oregon and Washington, between the Cascades and the Coast Range; common; annual litter of 1 to 4 young.

S. orarius True. Body blackish or grayish in color; length 167 mm.; tail 33 mm.; hind foot 20 mm.: Washington, Oregon and northern California.

Subspecies of S. orarius

S. o. orarius True. Color fuscous black: coast region of Washington, Oregon and northern California.

S. o. schefferi Jackson. Color gray: north-central Oregon to British Columbia.

S. latimanus (Bach.) (Fig. 144). Body usually fuscous black, gray or drab in color; length 173 mm.; tail 35 mm.; hind foot 23 mm.: southern Oregon and California; annual litter of 2 or 3 each.

Subspecies of S. latimanus

S. l. latimanus (Bach.). Color black in winter, brown in summer; length 170 mm.: western California from Santa Maria River to Oregon.

S. l. occultus Grinnell & Swarth. Color lighter: southern California, west of the deserts and south of Olancha.

S. l. grinnelli Jack. Color black; length 156 mm.: Inyo County, California.

S. l. sericatus Jack. Color black; length 170 mm.: Yosemite region.

S. l. minusculus Bangs. Color in summer, brown; length 160 mm.: El Dorado County, California.

S. l. dilatus True. Color gray or drab; length 175 mm.: south-central Oregon and northeastern California.

S. l. alpinus Merriam. Color in summer, gray; length 188 mm.: Crater Lake, Oregon.

5. Neurotrichus Günther. Size very small; dentition 2/1, 1/1, 3/4, 3/3; snout terminating in a small disc in which are the laterally situated nostrils; digits not webbed: 1 species.

N. gibbsii (Baird). Body dark gray in color; length 113 mm.; tail 37 mm.; hind foot 15 mm.: British Columbia to Eureka, California, west of the Cascades and Sierra Nevada; in wet woods or meadows, often on the surface or under logs.

Subspecies of N. gibbsii

N. g. hyacinthinus Bangs. Size larger; color darker: coast region of California from Monterey to Eureka.

Family 2. Soricidæ.—Shrews. Body rather slender; neck distinct; snout elongate and proboscis-like; eyes and external ears normal, but small; feet pentadactylous, the fore feet not modified; fur soft and silky; zygomatic arch of skull wanting: many species, which are found throughout the world, except in the Australian and South American regions; about 36 species and 6 genera in the United States. The shrews are among the smallest mammals. They live in shallow tunnels, in run-ways in moss and mold and under logs and brush, feeding on worms, grubs, snails, mice and other small animals, including one another, and are noted for their fierceness and voracity. They raise two or more litters of 6 to 10 each during the summer and fall, and do not hibernate.

Key to the United States Genera of Soricidæ

a_1 Tail long, being much longer than the head (Fig. 146).
   b_1 Body 100 mm. to 130 mm. long..........................1. *Sorex.*
   b_2 Body about 150 mm. long................................2. *Neosorex.*
   b_3 Body about 85 mm. long................................3. *Microsorex.*
a_2 Tail short, being usually shorter than the head (Fig. 147).
   b_1 Teeth 32; size large..4. *Blarina.*
   b_2 Teeth 30; size small..5. *Cryptotis.*
   b_3 Teeth 28; size small..6. *Notiosorex.*

1. Sorex L. Long-tailed shrews. External ears well developed, generally appearing above the fur and directed backwards; tail about as

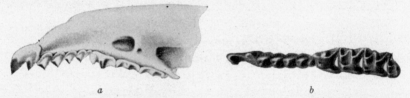

a   *b*

Fig. 145.—Upper jaw of *Sorex personatus: a,* lateral view; *b,* lower surface (*from Merriam*).

long as the body; dentition 4/2, 1/0, 2/1, 3/3: over 50 species and subspecies in the United States and Canada.

S. personatus Geoffroy. Common shrew (Fig. 145). Body brown above, gray beneath; length 100 mm.; tail 38 mm.; hind foot 12 mm.: New England to Alaska; southward to southern Pennsylvania, Tennessee and Northern Nebraska, and in the higher Alleghenies into North Carolina; not in the southern Rockies and the Cascade-Sierra systems; Boreal and Transition zones; the commonest species.

S. fontinalis Hollister. Like *S. personatus,* but with a much shorter tail: District of Columbia and its neighborhood.

S. dispar Batchelder. Size large; body stout, slate-color; length 130 mm.; tail 60 mm.; hind foot 15 mm.: Adirondack and Catskill Mountains; West Virginia.

S. richardsoni Bachman. Color blackish, indistinctly tricolor; length 112 mm.; tail 40 mm.; hind foot 13 mm.: northern Wisconsin and Minnesota to the lower Mackensie Valley.

S. fumeus Miller. Smoky shrew. Body slate-color; length 115 mm.; tail 45 mm.; hind foot 14 mm.: northeastern States and Canada; westward to the Great Lakes; southward into the mountains of North Carolina.

S. vagrans Baird. Body dark chestnut brown in color; length 103 mm.; tail 43 mm.; hind foot 12 mm.: Rocky Mountain region from British Columbia into Arizona, and the Pacific slope southward to Monterey; very common.

Subspecies of S. vagrans

S. v. vagrans Baird. Western Washington, Oregon and northern California; northern Rockies.

S. v. dobsoni Merriam. Color grayish brown: Idaho, western Montana, Wyoming and Utah.

S. v. monticola Merr. Color sepia brown: Arizona.

S. amœnus Merr. Color sooty brown; length 103 mm.; tail 37 mm.; hind foot 12 mm.: Sierra Nevada Mountains, California.

S. nevadensis Merr. Color slate black, mixed with hoary; length 96 mm.; tail 39 mm.; hind foot 12 mm.: interior of the Great Basin.

S. obscurus Merr. Body dull sepia brown in color; length 108 mm.; tail 46 mm.; hind foot 12 mm.; mountain regions from British Columbia to Colorado, Utah and central California; common.

S. longicaudus Merr. Size large; tail long; color dark chestnut-brown above; length 131 mm.; tail 62 mm.; hind foot 15 mm.: Puget Sound to Alaska.

S. bairdi Merr. Color dull chestnut; length 129 mm.; tail 57 mm.; hind foot 15 mm.: Oregon coast, mouth of the Columbia.

S. trowbridgii Baird. Color blackish, slate or plumbeous; tail sharply bicolor; length 121 mm.; tail 51 mm.; hind foot 13 mm.: western Washington and Oregon.

S. montereyensis Merr. Color slate black; tail sharply bicolor; length 120 mm.; tail 52 mm.; hind foot 14 mm.: south-central California.

S. ornatus Merr. Color ash gray, indistinctly bicolor; length 108 mm.; tail 43 mm.; hind foot 13 mm.: mountains of southern California.

S. californicus Merr.   Color ash gray, with a pepper and salt appearance; length 93 mm.; tail 34 mm.; hind foot 11 mm.; brain case very flat; central California.

S. tenellus Merr.   Body pale ash gray; white beneath; tail bicolor; length 103 mm.; tail 42 mm.; hind foot 12 mm.; skull very narrow: central California and southward.

Subspecies of S. tenellus

S. t. tenellus Merr.   Southeastern California.

S. t. lyelli Merr.   Browner; tail darker: Tuolumne county, California.

S. t. myops Merr.   Smaller; ears larger; color paler: White Mountains, California.

S. t. nanus Merr.   Smaller; color darker: Larimer County, Colorado.

S. longirostris Bach.   Body brown above; length 85 mm.; tail 28 mm.; hind foot 10 mm.: Washington, D. C. to Georgia; westward to southern Illinois; in swamps and wet places.

S. fisheri Merr.   Color chestnut brown; length 108 mm.; tail 33 mm.; hind foot 12 mm.: Dismal Swamp, Virginia.

S. pacificus Coues.   Color cinnamon rufous; length 150 mm.; tail 63 mm.; hind foot 17 mm.: coastal region of northern California and southern Oregon.

S. leucogenys Osgood.   Color brownish drab; length 107 mm.; tail 38 mm.; hind foot 12 mm.: Beaver County, Utah.

2. Neosorex Baird.   Similar to *Sorex;* hind feet adapted to swimming, being very long and broad and fringed with bristles; toes also fringed, the third and fourth united at base and slightly webbed: 10 species, and subspecies in the United States.

Key to the Species of Neosorex

a_1 In the north-central States....................................*N. palustris.*
a_2 In the northeastern States....................................*N. albibarbis.*
a_3 In the Rocky Mountain and Pacific States.
    b_1 In the Rockies and the Sierra Nevadas....................*N. navigator.*
    b_2 In western Oregon and Washington........................*N. bendirii.*

N. palustris (Richardson).   Color seal brown; gray beneath; length 157 mm.; tail 68 mm.; hind foot 20 mm.: central Minnesota to the Rockies; northward to Hudson Bay; in marshy places.

N. albibarbis Cope.   Marsh shrew (Fig. 146).   Body blackish slate in color, sparingly mixed with white tipped hairs, and dusky beneath; length 154 mm.; tail 70 mm.; hind foot 19 mm.: eastern North America from the Pennsylvania mountains to Labrador; not common; in swamps and wet fields and woods; Hudsonian and Canadian zones.

N. navigator Baird. Body plumbeous above, whitish beneath; length 150 mm.; tail 72 mm.; hind foot 20 mm.: Rocky Mountains from British Columbia to southern Colorado and the Sierra Nevadas; southward to Sequoia Park.

N. bendirii (Merriam). Color blackish brown above and below; length 150 mm.; tail 68 mm.; hind foot 20 mm.: western Oregon and Washington.

Subspecies of N. bendirii

N. b. bendirii (Merr.). Klamath Basin, Oregon, to Puget Sound.

N. b. palmeri (Merr.). Color glossy black; size larger: western Oregon.

N. b. albiventer (Merr.). Size larger; beneath whitish: Olympic Mountains.

3. Microsorex Coues. Similar to *Sorex;* body very small; inner side of canines and second and third incisors with a distinct secondary cusp; fourth upper incisor very small and nearly hidden: 7 species and subspecies in the United States.

M. hoyi (Baird). Body brown in color; length 90 mm.; tail 32 mm.; hind foot 10 mm.: northern America from New England to British Columbia; southward to Wisconsin and northern New York; rare.

M. winnemana Preble. Color grayish brown; tail bicolor; length 78 mm.; tail 28 mm.; hind foot 9 mm.: northern Virginia; the smallest American mammal.

4. Blarina Gray. Short-tailed shrews. Body rather stout, somewhat mole-like; ears hidden in the fur; teeth tipped with chestnut; tail about as long as the head; dentition 4/2, 1/0, 2/1, 3/3: 3 species, 2 in the United States.

Fig. 146.—*Neosorex albibarbis (from Rhoads)*.

B. brevicauda (Say). Mole shrew (Fig. 147). Body dark brown in color; length 127 mm.; tail 26 mm.; hind foot 16 mm.: eastern and central America; westward to western Nebraska; common in woods and fields, bogs and swamps; emits a fetid odor.

Subspecies of B. brevicauda

B. b. brevicauda (Say).   Western Nebraska to Manitoba; eastward to the Mississippi River.

B. b. aloga Bangs.   Smaller and paler; color brownish drab: Marthas Vineyard.

B. b. compacta Bangs.   Color slaty gray; tail unicolor: Nantucket.

B. b. carolinensis (Bachman).   Size smaller: southern States from Indiana and Maryland to Arkansas and Florida.

B. b. hulophaga Elliot.   Smaller, lighter in color and with an extremely short tail: Oklahoma.

B. b. peninsulæ Merriam.   Color more slaty; hind feet longer: Florida south of latitude 28.

B. b. talpoides (Gapper).   Northeastern and central States; westward to the Mississippi; southward to Georgia and Tennessee.

B. telmalestes Merr.   Similar to *B. brevicauda* but more plumbeous in color; length 118 mm.; tail 28 mm.; hind foot 16 mm.: Dismal Swamp, Virginia.

5. Cryptotis Pomel.   Similar to *Blarina*, but much smaller; tail very short; dentition 3/2, 1/0, 2/1, 3/3: 18 species, all tropical but two.

C. parva (Say).   Body brownish in color; length 79 mm.; tail 16 mm.; hind foot 10 mm.: eastern and central States, south of New York; westward to Nebraska and Texas; in meadows and fields; often rare.

C. floridana (Merriam).   Color iron gray; length 89 mm.; tail 22 mm.; hind foot 22 mm.; similar to C. *parva*, but larger: Florida, south of latitude 29.

FIG. 147.—*Blarina bre-vicauda (from Rhoads).*

C. berlandieri (Baird).   Color ash brown; length 83 mm.; tail 19 mm.; hind foot 12 mm.: coast of southern Texas and valley of the lower Rio Grande.

6. Notiosorex Baird.   Body very small; tail short; dentition 3/2, 1/0, 1/1, 3/3: 1 species.

N. crawfordi (Baird).   Color olive gray; beneath whitish; length 82 mm.; tail 26 mm.; hind foot 10 mm.: eastern Texas to southern Caifornia.

Order 5. Chiroptera.—Bats. Small, flying mammals in which the greatly elongated fore limbs form the supports of the wings. These consist of a paired integumental membrane which extends between the arms and the four fingers and the body, and includes the hind legs and the tail. The knee bends backwards. The portion of the membrane between the hind legs which incloses the tail is called the *interfemoral membrane*. The thumb is not included in the wing membrane. The foot has 5 digits; a long spur extends from the heel along the base of the interfemoral membrane. The ear is large and bears an elongated lobe in its concavity called the *tragus* (Fig. 148). In many families, at the end of the snout and surrounding the nostrils is a series of more or less complicated membranes called the *nose-leaf* (Fig. 148). The mammæ are thoracic in position and number 1 or 2 pairs. The sternum bears a keel.

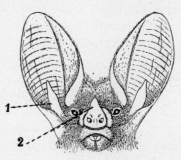

FIG. 148.—Head of *Microtus californicus:* 1, tragus; 2, nose-leaf (*from Allen*).

The order contains about 900 species, grouped in 2 suborders, one of which, the *Megachiroptera*, or the frugivorous flying foxes of India and Australia, is not represented in this country.

Suborder Microchiroptera.—Bats with a short snout, large ears and multicuspid molar teeth: 16 families and about 600 species, 3 families and about 30 species occurring in the United States. Bats are nocturnal animals, which feed mostly on beetles, mosquitoes and other night-flying insects, which they chew before swallowing. Some species are, however, frugivorous and some sanguivorous. The female of most species bears one or two at a birth, which she may carry about with her, clinging to her body until they are old enough to be left in some safe place. Bats spend the day in caves and other dark places, hanging head downward by the hind feet. In the winter they hibernate or migrate.

Key to the United States Families of the Microchiroptera

a_1 Third finger with 3 phalanges; nose-leaf present; only in the
extreme south...1. *Phyllostomidæ.*
a_2 Third finger with 2 phalanges; nose-leaf absent.
  b_1 Ear with tragus; all United States bats, with a few exceptions..2. *Vespertilionidæ.*
  b_2 Ear without tragus; in the extreme southwest...........3. *Molossidæ.*

Family 1. Phyllostomidæ.—American leaf-nosed or vampire bats. Nose usually with a nose-leaf; tragus present; wing membrane reaching to the ankle; tail usually long, extending beyond the interfemoral membrane; lower lip cleft: about 50 genera, all South and Central American, 3 species occurring along the southern border of the United States. The family includes the large fruit-eating vampire of South America (*Vampyrus spectrum*), whose horrid aspect has given it the undeserved reputation of being a blood-sucker. The true bloodsucking bats of South America are of small size and belong to the genera *Desmodus* and *Diphylla* of this family.

1. Mormoops Leach.   Crown of head greatly elevated above face; dentition 2/2, 1/1, 2/3, 3/3; nose-leaf absent: 2 species, 1 in the United States.

M. megalophylla senicula Rehn.   Body brown in color; length 90 mm.; tail 28 mm.; forearm 56 mm.: southern Texas to Ecuador.

2. Macrotus Gray.   Dentition 2/2, 1/1, 2/3, 3/3; head elongate; nose-leaf simple: 4 species, 1 in the United States.

M. californicus Baird (Fig. 148).   Body pale brownish gray in color; length 88 mm.; tail 33 mm.; ears very large: arid regions of southwestern United States and of Mexico.

3. Artibeus Leach.   Dentition 2/2, 1/1, 2/2, 2/3 or 3/3; nose-leaf well developed; no external tail: 9 species, 1 in the United States.

A. jamaicensis parvipes Rehn.   Body brown or gray in color; length 70 mm.; forearm 52 mm.: West Indies and Central America, occasionally in Florida.

Family 2. Vespertilionidæ.—Mostly small bats with a large tragus and a long tail which is either entirely or mostly enclosed in the interfemoral membrane; no nose-leaf; molars with distinct W-shaped cusps; bony palate defective: 260 species, of cosmopolitan distribution, including, with a few exceptions, all of the bats occurring in the United States; 2 subfamilies.

Key to the United States Subfamilies of Vespertilionidæ

a_1 Lower incisors 6; snout without ridge....................1. *Vespertilioninæ.*
a_2 Lower incisors 4; horseshoe-shaped ridge on snout.........2. *Nyctophilinæ.*

Subfamily 1. Vespertilioninæ. Bats with a simple snout and nostrils, with 6 lower incisors and ears usually not joined in front: over 20 American species.

Key to the United States Genera of Vespertilioninæ

a_1 Ears not united in front.
  b_1 Upper incisors 4 (both sides) (Fig. 149).

    c_1 Upper premolars 3 (on each side) (Fig. 149)...........1. *Myotis.*
    c_2 Upper premolars 2.
        d_1 Lower premolars 3.............................2. *Lasionycteris.*
        d_2 Lower premolars 2.............................3. *Pipistrellus.*
    c_3 Upper premolars 1...............................4. *Eptesicus.*
  b_2 Upper incisors 2 (both sides).
    c_1 Upper premolars 2 (on each side)...................5. *Nycteris.*
    c_2 Upper premolars 1.
        d_1 Mandibular tooth-row more than 8 mm. long.......6. *Dasypterus.*
        d_2 Mandibular tooth-row less than 7 mm. long.........7. *Nycticeius.*
a_2 Ears very large and united at base in front.
  b_1 Nostrils simple..8. *Euderma.*
  b_2 Nostrils with a high ridge behind each..................9. *Corynorhinus.*

1. Myotis Kaup. Small, slender bats with a long tail, a hairy face and narrow ears; dentition 2/3, 1/1, 3/3, 3/3: 80 species, cosmopolitan; about 30 species and subspecies in the United States and Canada.

FIG. 149.—Teeth of *Myotis lucifugus*: *A*, left side of upper jaw; *B*, left side of lower jaw (*from Miller*).

M. lucifugus (LeConte). Little brown bat (Fig. 149). Body brown in color; length 87 mm.; tail 38 mm.; fore arm 38 mm.; ears short and broad and when laid foreward reach about to the nostrils: entire United States, except the coastal regions of the Pacific slope north of Puget Sound; common, especially towards the south.

Subspecies of M. lucifugus

M. l. lucifugus (LeC.). Entire country, except the Rocky Mountains and the Pacific coast.

M. l. altipetens (Grinnell). Color yellowish; size smaller: the central Sierras near Mount Shasta.

M. longicrus (True). Upper parts bister; under parts buff; length 100 mm.; tail 45 mm.: Pacific Slope; Boreal and Transition Zones.

Subspecies of M. longicrus

M. l. longicrus (True). Body larger: Puget Sound region and eastward to Wyoming and southward to Arizona and southern California.

M. l. interior Miller. Color tawny olive: Idaho and Wyoming south into Arizona and New Mexico.

M. subulatus (Say). Color light brown; length 85 mm.; tail 38 mm.; fore arm 35 mm.; ears slender and when laid forward reaching considerably beyond tip of nose: North America, east of the Rockies; common; number of young at a birth 2.

M. velifer (J. A. Allen). Color dull sepia; length 95 mm.; tail 44 mm.; forearm 41 mm.; ears short, reaching to the nostril when laid forward: the Mexican border.

M. incautus (J. A. A.). Like *M. velifer* but with a more pallid coloration: New Mexico and Texas.

M. baileyi Hollister. Like *M. velifer* but smaller: White Mountains, New Mexico.

M. grisescens Howell. Like *M. velifer* but darker: Indiana, Missouri, and Tennessee.

M. occultus Holl. Color glossy brown; length 96 mm.; tail 40 mm.: San Bernardino County, California.

M. carissima Thomas. Color blackish; length 81 mm.; tail 36 mm.: Yellowstone Lake, Wyoming, Montana.

M. californicus (Audubon & Bachman). Body slender and very small, with a long tail and legs; color yellowish gray; wings, ears and snout blackish; fur very long; length 78 mm.; tail 38 mm.; forearm 31 mm.; western United States; eastward to Texas and Kansas: common.

Subspecies of M. californicus

M. c. californicus (Aud. and Bach.). Western United States; eastward to Wyoming and Texas.

M. c. caurinus Miller. Very much darker in color: coast district, northern California to British Columbia.

M. c. ciliolabrum (Merriam). Very much paler in color: Kansas to central South Dakota.

M. c. pallidus Stephens. Smaller and paler: Mohave and Colorado deserts, California.

M. c. quercinus Grinnell. Upper parts cinnamon; under parts light buff: southern California and the Channel Islands.

M. yumanensis (H. Allen). Body small, whitish gray or brown in color; length 80 mm.; tail 36 mm.; forearm 34 mm.; feet very large: western United States.

Subspecies of M. yumanensis

M. y. yumanensis (H. A.). Southwestern States from Utah to southern California.

M. y. saturatus. Miller. Color much darker: central Oregon to British Columbia.

M. evotis (H. Allen). Long-eared bat. Color light yellowish brown; length 90 mm.; tail 42 mm.; forearm 37; ears very long, reaching 7 to 10 mm. beyond the tip of the nose when laid forward: western States; eastward to the eastern edge of the Rocky Mountains.

2. Lasionycteris Peters. Medium sized bats with short, broad ears and a broad tragus; dentition 2/3, 1/1, 2/3, 3/3: 1 species.

L. noctivagans (LeConte). Silver-haired bat (Fig. 150). Color deep brown-black, the back with a silvery sheen; length 100 mm.; tail 41 mm.; forearm 42 mm.: North America, north of Mexico; common.

FIG. 150.—Teeth of *Lasionycteris noctivagans,* the upper jaw at the left (*from Miller*).

3. Pipistrellus Kaup. Small bats, similar to *Myotis;* dentition 2/3, 1/1, 2/2, 3/3: 40 species, 2 in the United States.

Key to the United States Species of Pipistrellus

a_1 Tragus blunt, with tip bent forward.............................*P. hesperus.*
a_2 Tragus tapering and straight..................................*P. subflavus.*

P. hesperus (H. Allen) (Fig. 151). Color light yellowish gray; length 75 mm.; tail 32 mm.; forearm 30 mm.: southern and western Texas to the Pacific.

FIG. 151.—Teeth of *Pipistrellus hesperus* (above) and *P. subflavus* (below), the upper jaw at the left (*from Miller*).

P. subflavus (F. Cuvier) (Fig. 151). Color light yellowish brown; length 85 mm.; tail 40 mm.; forearm 34 mm.: eastern United States; westward to Iowa and Texas; Austral zone.

Subspecies of P. subflavus

P. s. subflavus (F. Cuv.). Eastern United States.

P. s. obscurus Miller. Color duller and less yellow: eastern and central New York (Lake George).

4. Eptesicus Rafinesque. Dentition 2/3, 1/1, 1/2, 3/3; inter-femoral portion of membrane naked: 5 species, 1 in the United States.

E. fuscus (Beauvois). Big brown bat; house-bat (Fig. 152). Color sepia brown; length 110 mm.; tail 45 mm.; forearm 45 mm.: United States and Mexico; common.

Subspecies of E. fuscus

E. f. fuscus (Beauv.).   Size large: United States.

E. f. osceola Rhoads.   Color deeper and darker: southern and central Florida.

FIG. 152.—Teeth of *Eptesicus fuscus*, the upper jaw at the left (*from Miller*).

E. f. bernardinus Rhoads.   Size large; wings and ears very dark: San Bernardino, California.

E. f. melanopterus Stone.   Color more reddish: Eldorado County, California.

5. **Nycteris** Borkhausen (*Lasiurus* Gray).   Dentition 1/3, 1/1, 2/2, 3/3; interfemoral portion of membrane densely furred; ears short and round: 12 species, 2 in the United States; these are unusually tolerant of sunlight, often roosting in trees during the day in the full glare of the sun and beginning to feed in the afternoon; number of young 2 to 4.

FIG. 153.—Teeth of *Nycteris borealis:* a, *N. b. teliotis*; b, *N. b. borealis*, the upper jaw at the left (*from Miller*).

N. borealis (Müller).   Red bat (Fig. 153).   Body varying from rufous red to yellowish gray in color, with a white spot on each shoulder, the two spots connected by a white chest band; length 110 mm.; tail 50 mm.; forearm 40 mm.: eastern and central North America; common.

Subspecies of N. borealis

N. b. borealis (Müller).   West to Oklahoma and Colorado.

N. b. seminola (Rhoads).   Color mahogany brown, slightly grayish: South Carolina to south Texas.

N. b. teliotis (H. Allen).   Size smaller; color redder: central and southern California.

N. cinerea (Beauvois).   Hoary bat.   Body gray in color; length 135 mm.; tail 50 mm.; forearm 40 mm.; wings long and pointed: northern North America; southward to central New York, migrating in winter into the southern States.

6. **Dasypterus** Peters. Dentition 1/3, 1/1, 1/2, 3/3; dorsal portion of interfemoral membrane furred on basal half only; ears higher than broad: 3 species in Mexico and the United States.

D. intermedius (H. Allen) (Fig. 154). Color light yellowish brown: length 145 mm.; tail 65 mm.; forearm 55 mm.: Gulf States and northern Mexico.

D. floridanus Miller. Color light yellowish brown; length 129 mm.; tail 52 mm.; forearm 49 mm.: Gulf coast from Florida to Louisiana.

7. Nycticeius Rafinesque. Dentition 1/3, 1/1, 1/2, 3/3; interfemoral portion of membrane furred at the base only; ears short: 2 species, 1 in Cuba.

FIG. 154.—Teeth of *Dasypterus intermedius*, the upper jaw at the left (*from Miller*).

N. humeralis (Raf.). Body dull brown in color; length 90 mm.; tail 36 mm.; forearm 36 mm.; ear small, with a short, blunt tragus: southeastern and central States; northward to Pennsylvania; westward to Arkansas; Austral zone.

8. Euderma H. Allen. Dentition 2/3, 1/1, 2/2, 3/3; ears joined across the forehead: 1 species.

E. maculatum (J. A. Allen). Color dark sepia, almost black above; length 110 mm.; tail 50 mm.; forearm 50 mm.: southern California, Arizona and New Mexico; rare.

9. Corynorhinus H. Allen. Dentition 2/3, 1/1, 2/3, 3/3; a pair of large glandular masses on the snout, rising high above the nostrils; ears very large and united at their anterior base: 4 species and subspecies.

C. rafinesquii (Lesson). Big-eared bat. Body large, yellowish brown in color, distinctly bicolor; length 105 mm.; tail 52 mm.; forearm 43 mm.; ear 33 mm.: southern United States, from one coast to the other; also in the extreme northwest.

Subspecies of C. rafinesquii

C. r. rafinesquii (Les.). Eastern central States; Lower Austral zone.

C. r. pallescens (Miller). Color much paler, nowhere distinctly bicolor: southwestern States from southern California to western Texas and Colorado.

C. r. townsendii (Cooper). Color much darker, nowhere distinctly bicolor: coast district of Oregon and Washington.

Subfamily 2. Nyctophilinæ.—Bats with a horshoe-shaped ridge around the nostrils and with 4 lower incisors: 1 genus.

Antrozous H. Allen. Dentition 1/2, 1/1, 1/2, 3/3; mammæ 2: 2 species, 1 in Lower California.

A. pallidus (LeConte). Body pale drab in color; length 105 mm.; tail 45 mm.; forearm 53 mm.; ears very large, extending 20 mm. beyond the nose when laid forwards: southwestern States from western Texas to the Pacific.

Family 3. Molossidæ.—Wings long and narrow, thick and leathery; no tragus; legs short and stout; nostrils usually on a special

FIG. 155.—Head of *Tadarida cynocephala (from Allen)*.

pad: about 80 species, in the warmer parts of the earth.

Tadarida (LeConte). Head and body flattened; dentition 1/2 or 1/3, 1/1, 2/2, 3/3; ears large, rounded, extending beyond the snout when laid forwards, nearly united on the top of the head: 40 species, 16 American, 2 in the United States.

T. cynocephala (LeConte). Mexican bat (Fig. 155). Body plumbeous or dusky brown in color; length 100 mm.; tail 30 mm.; forearm 40 mm.; sides of snout with a series of deep wrinkles; half of tail in interfemoral membrane: southern States; common.

Order 6. Carnivora.—The flesh-eaters. Carnivorous, sometimes omnivorous mammals with large projecting canine teeth, cutting premolars and tuberculate molars; the last upper premolar and the first lower molar being carnassial (flesh-cutting) teeth (Fig. 139); digits unguiculate and never less than 4: 250 species, 120 in the United States, grouped in 5 families; predatory mammals distributed throughout the world.

Key to the Families of Carnivora

a_1 Claws not retractile.
   b_1 Tail rudimentary; bears.................................1. *Ursidæ.*
   b_2 Tail well developed and long.
      c_1 Feet digitigrade; hind foot with 4 toes; wolves; foxes....2. *Canidæ.*
      c_2 Feet plantigrade; hind foot with 5 toes.
         d_1 Toes not webbed; raccoons........................3. *Procyonidæ.*
         d_2 Toes webbed; cacomistles........................4. *Bassariscidæ.*
a_2 Claws more or less retractile.
   b_1 Hind foot with 5 toes; weasels; skunks...................5. *Mustelidæ.*
   b_2 Hind foot with 4 toes; cats...........................6. *Felidæ.*

Family 1. Ursidæ.—Bears. Body of large size, thick and heavy; feet plantigrade; toes 5-5; claws not retractile: in all geographical regions except the Ethiopean and Australian; 3 genera, one of which, *Thalarctos* Gray, includes the Polar bear, *T. maritimus* (Phipps).

1. Euarctos Gray. American black bears. Color black or dark brown; facial contour straight; head short and broad; snout depressed; dentition 3/3, 1/1, 4/4, 2/3; molars very broad and tuberculate: North America; about 10 species and subspecies, 6 in the United States, omnivorous, mainly nocturnal animals which hibernate in the winter in the cold portion of their range, but not in the warmer portions. The young, from 1 to 3 in number, are born in midwinter.

E. amercanus (Pallas). Black bear; cinnamon bear. Body black, with a brown muzzle, or entirely brown, there being two color phases, the cinnamon bear of the northern Rockies being the brown phase; length 1,540 mm.; tail 120 mm.; weight up to 500 lbs.: forest lands of North America north of the Gulf States and the Sierra Madre in Mexico; Hudsonian, Canadian, Transition and Upper Austral zones; climbs trees readily.

Subspecies of E. americanus

E. a. americanus (Pal.). North America.

E. a. amblyceps (Baird). Color brown: southern Texas. New Mexico and Arizona.

E. floridanus (Merriam). Head very long, high and narrow: Florida, northwards into Georgia.

E. luteolus (Griffith). Color yellowish brown, darker on the nape; similar to *E. americanus*, but with a long, flattened skull: Louisiana and eastern Texas.

E. altifrontalis (Elliot). Color black; nose tan: forehead broad, high and bulging: Clallam County, Washington.

2. Ursus L. Grizzlies and Big Brown Bears. Color light brown or yellowish brown, often with scattered white-tipped hairs; facial contour concave; size large or very large: numerous species in the nearctic and palearctic regions; North American species numerous (Merriam lists 86 species and subspecies), which fall into two general groups which grade into each other, (1) the *Grizzlies*, ranging in the southerly and northerly Rockies, the Central Platteau and Great Plains regions, and (2) the *Big Brown Bears*, ranging in Alaska and the Alaskan Islands; of the latter *U. middendorffi* Merriam and *U. gigas* (Merriam) are the largest and heaviest of all the *Carnivora*.

U. horribilis Ord. Grizzly bear. Color brownish yellow, being darker on the back and legs; fur long and shaggy; length up to 2,500 mm.; weight up to 1,000 lbs.: western America from Mexico, New

Mexico and Arizona to Alaska and Hudson Bay; does not climb trees, except when a cub.

U. horriæus (Baird).   Size smaller; the frontal bones flattened and concave between the postorbital process: New Mexico and Arizona to Utah and Colorado.

U. californicus Merr.   Size large; ears longer: central and southern California.

Family 2.   Canidæ.—Dogs, wolves and foxes.   Body slender, with long legs; feet digitigrade; toes 5-4; claws blunt and non-retractile; head elongate; dentition 3/3, 1/1, 4/4, 2/3 (Fig. 139): cosmopolitan; about 50 species in North America.

Key to the United States Genera

a_1 Pupil round; dogs and wolves..................................1. *Canis.*
a_2 Pupil elliptical; tail bushy; foxes.
   b_1 Tail with soft under-fur...................................2. *Vulpes.*
   b_2 Tail with coarse fur......................................3. *Urocyon.*

1 Canis L.   Dogs and wolves.   Legs long; tail moderately bushy; upper incisors distinctly lobed: many species; cosmopolitan; about 24 in North America, and 15 in the United States.   The domestic dog, *C. familiaris*, is descended from a number of wild stocks.   The native wild dogs and wolves fall into 2 groups or subgenera, one of which is *Canis* L. and has for its characteristic representative the gray wolf, and the other is *Lyciscus* Hamilton Smith, which is represented by the coyote.   They are very prolific, wolves having sometimes as many as 12 young at a birth and coyotes as many as 14.

Key to the United States Species of Canis

a_1 Size large; wolves; length mostly over 1,400 mm.
   b_1 East of the Mississippi.
      c_1 In the northeastern States............................*C. lycaon.*
      c_2 In the southern States..............................*C. floridanus.*
   b_2 West of the Mississippi.
      c_1 On the Great Plains and in Rocky Mountains; tail short..*C. nubilus.*
      c_2 In the Puget Sound region............................*C. gigas.*
      c_3 In Texas..*C. frustror.*
                                      C. rufus.
a_2 Size smaller; coyotes; length under 1,200 mm.; muzzle sharp.
   b_1 On the northern prairies..............................*C. latrans.*
   b_2 On the Great Plains.................................*C. nebracensis.*
   b_3 In the mountains and the Great Basin...................*C. lestes.*
   b_4 In the southwest.
      c_1 In the lower Rio Grande Valley.......................*C. microdon.*
      c_2 In Arizona..*C. mearnsi.*

C. lycaon Schreber (*C. occidentalis* Richardson). Gray wolf. Color gray, mixed with blackish or tawny; length 1,465 mm.; tail 405 mm.; hind foot 225 mm.: eastern Canada and northeastern United States; exterminated, except towards the north.

C. floridanus Miller. Southern wolf. Similar to *C. lycaon*, but much darker; color black above, buffy gray faintly clouded on the sides and beneath; muzzle and legs yellowish: Florida.

C. nubilus Say. Gray wolf of the plains; lobo; timber wolf. Color gray, varying to blackish on the back and tawny on the belly; length males 1,600 mm.; tail 400 mm.; weight about 100 lbs. or more: the interior States and central Canada; southward to Nebraska and Colorado; exterminated in well settled districts, but common in many places in the Great Plains and Rocky Mountains.

C. frustror Woodhouse. American jackal. Color gray, clouded with black; length 1,143 mm.; tail 355 mm.; hind foot 180 mm.: Texas and Oklahoma.

C. gigas Townsend. Northwest timber wolf. Size large; tail very short; color black above, reddish brown on the sides, cinereous below: region of Puget Sound.

C. rufus Audubon and Bachman. Texas red wolf. Color reddish brown mixed with irregular patches of black; upper surface and end of tail black; length 1,200 mm.; tail 325 mm.; form slender; fur smooth: southwestern Texas.

C. latrans Say. Coyote; prairie wolf. Color fulvous or grayish, clouded with black; tail tipped with black; muzzle sharp; length 1,250 mm.; tail 394 mm.; hind foot 179 mm.; weight up to 35 lbs.: humid prairies and woodlands of northern Mississippi Valley, in Iowa and Minnesota and westward to the Rockies in Alberta.

C. nebracensis Merriam. Plains coyote. Similar to *C. latrans*, but a little smaller and paler; upper parts whitish, sparingly mixed with black hairs; under parts white: Great Plains from Canada to Texas.

Subspecies of *C. nebracensis*

C. n. nebracensis Merr. Nebraska and eastern Colorado to Montana and Canada.

C. n. texensis Bailey. Color darker and brighter: Texas and Oklahoma.

C. lestes Merr. Mountain coyote. Size large, but somewhat smaller than *C. latrans;* color similar but paler; ears and tail large: highlands and mountains of the Great Basin and Rockies and the Sierra Nevada from British Columbia to Mexico.

C. microdon Merr.   Color cinnamon rufous; length 1,070 mm.; tail 320 mm.; hind foot 186 mm.; teeth very small; hind foot whitish above: lower Rio Grande region.

C. mearnsi Merr.   Similar to *C. microdon* in size; color fulvous and very rich and bright: Arizona.

C. estor Merr.   Similar to *C. mearnsi* in size and color, but paler, being a pale desert form: eastern California, Nevada and Utah.

C. ochropus Eschscholtz.   Similar to *C. latrans*, but smaller and darker; ears large; head small: San Joaquin Valley, California.

2. Vulpes Oken.   Red foxes.   Upper incisors not lobed; legs rather short; tail bushy, with soft under-fur: about 20 species, all in the northern hemisphere, 10 in the United States, all valuable fur-bearing animals.   Their dens are holes in the ground dug by themselves, and they bear 4 to 9 at a birth.

Key to the United States Species of Vulpes

a_1 In the eastern and central States.
   b_1 In the States east of the Mississippi......................*V. fulva.*
   b_2 In Nova Scotia and Labrador...........................*V. rubricosa.*
   b_3 In Newfoundland..*V. deletrix.*
a_2 In the western States.
   b_1 On the Great Plains.
      c_1 In the northern States and Canada....................*V. regalis.*
      c_2 In the central Mountain States.......................*V. velox.*
      c_3 In the southwestern deserts...........................*V. macrotis.*
   b_2 In the mountains.
      c_1 In the central Rockies................................*V. macroura.*
      c_2 In the Sierras and Cascades.........................*V. cascadensis.*
      c_3 In the high Sierras..................................*V. necator.*
b_3 In central California....................................*V. mutica.*

V. fulva (Desmarest).   Red fox; black fox; cross fox; silver gray fox.   Color reddish gray; feet and ears black; tail darker than body; tip of tail and under parts white; melanic individuals sometimes occur, the black fox being entirely black, the cross fox having a black band along the back crossed by one on the shoulders, and the silver fox being silver gray; length 1,034 mm.; tail 394 mm.; hind foot 163 mm.: eastern America, southward to Georgia and Tennessee; northward to Maine; westward to the Great Plains; introduced into other regions.

V. rubricosa Bangs.   Size slightly larger and color deeper than *V. fulva;* tail very dark, with a basal ring of black: Nova Scotia and Labrador.

V. deletrix Bangs. Size slightly smaller than *V. fulva;* hind feet and claws very large; color very pale, being light straw: Newfoundland.

V. regalis Merriam. Size much larger than *V. fulva,* the length being 1,117 mm.; ears very broad and large; tail very long but thin; color golden yellow; legs abruptly reddish; feet black: northern plains from Minnesota to Montana and Alberta.

V. macroura Baird. Size and color of *V. fulva,* but tail much longer and hind feet larger: Nebraska to Oklahoma; mountains of Colorado, Utah and Wyoming.

V. necator Merr. Size and color of *V. fulva:* high Sierras, California.

V. cascadensis Merr. Color similar to *V. fulva;* black-cross color phase common; length 1,070 mm.; tail 412 mm.; hind foot 178 mm.: northern Sierras, Cascades and northward.

V. velox (Say). Swift fox; kit fox. Size small; length 645 mm.; tail 226 mm.; hind foot 95 mm.; color yellowish gray above and white underneath; tip of tail black: northern Texas through Nebraska and eastern Colorado into Alberta; not common.

V. mutica Merr. Similar to *V. macrotis;* top of head and middle of back reddish brown; outside of hind foot fulvous; tip of tail black; length 950 mm.; tail 350 mm.; hind foot 122 mm.: San Joaquin Valley, California.

V. macrotis Merr. Long eared fox; desert fox. Length 850 mm.; tail 290 mm.; hind foot 110 mm.; color grizzled gray above; sides fulvous; under parts white, mixed with buff; terminal quarter of tail black; ears well haired, very long and broad; tail long and slender: Mexican border from Texas to California.

3. Urocyon Baird. Gray foxes. Upper incisors not lobed; tail with concealed stiff hairs and no soft under-fur: 7 species, 5 in the United States and 2 in Central America, being most numerous in the semiarid regions of the southwest; they do not dig a den, as do the red foxes, but live in hollow logs or in cavities in the rocks; the young number from 3 to 9. Gray foxes often climb low trees.

Key to the Species of Urocyon

a_1 In the eastern and central States........................*U. cinereoargenteus.*
a_2 On the Pacific slope.
   b_1 On the main land......................................*U. californicus.*
   b_2 On the islands off the coast..........................*U. clementæ.*
                                                U. catalinæ.
                                                U. littoralis.

U. cinereoargenteus (Schreber). Gray fox. Color gray, darker on the back; sides of neck, collar and a band along belly tawny; feet and tip of tail black; under parts whitish; length 1,000 mm.; tail 300 mm.; hind foot 125 mm.: northern America south of southern New York and central New England, from the Atlantic to southern California.

Subspecies of U. cinereoargenteus

U. c. cinereoargenteus (Schreber). Eastern States; southward to Georgia; westward to the Mississippi Valley and Lake Michigan.

U. c. borealis Merriam. Size larger; fourth lower premolar very large: southern New Hampshire.

U. c. floridanus Rhoads. Size small; fur coarse; no white beneath: Florida and southern Georgia.

U. c. ocythous Bangs. Size large; tail long; color with more yellow: upper Mississippi Valley north of Tennessee; westward to the plains.

U. c. scotti Mearns. Tail and ears very long; color pale: Texas to southern California.

U. californicus Mearns. Similar to *U. cinereoargenteus*, but smaller and paler and with larger ears and a longer tail; length 950 mm.; tail 375 mm.; hind foot 120 mm.: southern California to Washington.

Subspecies of U. californicus

U. c. californicus Mearns. Southern California.

U. c. sequoiensis Dixon. Length 975 mm.; tail 400 mm.; hind foot 135 mm.: central California.

U. c. townsendi Merr. Tawny tints darker; ears smaller; length 1,100 mm.: northern California.

U. clementæ Merr. Length 688 mm.; tail 250 mm.; hind foot 100 mm.; under side of thigh and upper side of hind foot whitish: San Clemente Island, California.

U. catalinæ Merr. Length 795 mm.; tail 298 mm.; hind foot 112 mm.; white on under side of thigh greatly restricted: Catalina Island, California.

U. littoralis (Baird). Length 708 mm.; tail 260 mm.; hind foot 109 mm.: San Miguel and Santa Cruz Islands, California.

Family 3. Procyonidæ.—Raccoons. Body of small or medium size, stout and bear-like; feet plantigrade; claws not retractile; toes 5-5; tail well developed; teeth 3/3, 1/1, 4/4, 2/2: 1 genus in the United States.

Procyon *Storr.* Body stout; head rather short; snout pointed; tail bushy and ringed with black and white; fur thick and heavy: 8 species, ranging from northern South America to Canada; 3 species in the United States.

P. lotor (L.).   Raccoon; coon.   Color gray, the hairs being yellowish-brown tipped with black; tail ringed with white and black; a black-patch on cheek; fur rather coarse; length 800 mm.; tail 250 mm.; hind foot 120 mm.; weight about 20 lbs.; maximum weight 49 lbs.: United States east of the Rockies.   Raccoons are nocturnal, forest animals, frequenting the vicinity of water-courses.   They are omnivorous in their feeding habits and make their nests mostly in hollow trees, in which they have from 4 to 6 young annually; in the north they hibernate, but not in the south.

Subspecies of P. lotor

P. l. lotor (L.).   United States north of Florida and Texas.

P. l. elucus Bangs.   Color distinctly yellow: Gulf coast.

P. l. fuscipes Mearns.   Size large; color pale; tail long; feet dark brown; length 900 mm.: southern Texas; southward into Mexico.

P. l. hernandezi Wagler.   Size very large; black tail-rings very narrow: western Mexico and into Arizona and southern California.

P. pallidus Merriam.   Color pale gray, with no yellowish; length 855 mm.; tail 295 mm.; hind foot 128 mm.: southern California; a desert form.

P. psora Gray.   Size large; length 900 mm.; tail 310 mm.; hind foot 115 mm.; color dark grizzled gray: Pacific slope.

Subspecies of P. psora

P. p. psora Gray.   California.

P. p. pacifica Merriam.   Color much darker; black rings on tail continuous below: coastal region and Cascade Mountains of northern California, Oregon and Washington.

Family 4. Bassariscidæ.—Cacomistles.   Similar to the Procyonidæ, but differing in dental characters; body slender; digits webbed, densely furred; dentition 3/3, 1/1, 4/4, 2/2: 1 genus.

Bassariscus Coues.   Body slender; head short; muzzle pointed; ears large; tail very long, bushy and ringed black and white: 4 species and subspecies in Mexico and the United States.

B. astutus (Lichtenstein).   Civet cat; ring-tailed cat.   Color uniform blackish gray, often tinged with fulvous on the sides; under parts yellowish gray; length 850 mm.; tail 425 mm.; hind foot 72 mm.: Mexico; Texas to California and northward into Oregon; nocturnal, omnivorous animals, living mostly among rocks; often common.

Subspecies of B. astutus

B. a. flavus Rhoads. Size smaller; color blackish on the back, tawny on the sides: central and southern Texas to California; southern Colorado; southern Utah.

B. a. oregonus Rhoads. Dorsal region intensely black; color beneath brownish yellow; western Oregon and northern California.

Family 5. Mustelidæ.—Weasels, otters, skunks, etc. Body usually elongate; legs short; feet plantigrade or digitigrade; toes 5-5; claws never fully retractile; tail usually long; tongue with rasping papillæ; anal glands usually present which secrete a fetid liquid; color usually uniformly dark brown or black and white: numerous species; savage, carnivorous or omnivorous animals found in all the geographical regions except the Australian, and most numerous in the Temperate and Boreal zones, many being valuable fur-bearing animals; about 11 genera and 65 species in North America, about 45 species occurring in the United States, grouped in 6 subfamilies.

Key to the Subfamilies of Mustelidæ

a_1 Claws partly retractile.
  b_1 Feet digitigrade; body slender............................1. *Mustelinæ.*
  b_2 Feet plantigrade; body stout.............................2. *Guloninæ.*
a_2 Claws not retractile.
  b_1 Toes not fully webbed.
    c_1 Last upper molar very large and quadrangular; skunks....3. *Mephitinæ.*
    c_2 Last upper molar triangular; badgers....................4. *Taxidiinæ.*
  b_2 Toes fully webbed.
    c_1 Incisor teeth 3-3; otters...............................5. *Lutrinæ.*
    c_2 Incisor teeth 3-2; sea otters...........................6. *Enhydrinæ.*

Subfamily 1. Mustelinæ.—Weasels, martens and minks. Body slender; toes short and partly retractile: 3 genera.

Key to the Genera of Mustelinæ

a_1 Teeth 38; feet digitigrade..1. *Martes.*
a_2 Teeth 34; body slender and small; weasels (Fig. 158)..............2. *Mustela.*

1. Martes Pinel (*Mustela* L.). Martens. Body elongate and slender; tail long and bushy; ears short; dentition 3/3, 1/1, 4/4, 1/2 (Fig. 156); toes partly webbed; claws small, sharp and partly retractile: 8 species in North America, about 3 in the United States.

Key to the United States Species of Martes

a_1 Body slender.
  b_1 Light-colored cheek patches present.......................*M. americana.*
  b_2 No light-colored cheek patches present....................*M. caurina.*
a_2 Body stout...*M. pennanti.*

M. americana (Turton). Pine marten; American sable (Fig. 156). Color rich brown, darker middorsally; legs black; tail blackish and bushy; length 610 mm.; tail 205 mm.; hind foot 90 mm.; ears pointed: forests of northern North America from the Atlantic to the Rockies; from Hudson Bay and Labrador southward into Pennsylvania; Hudsonian, Canadian and Upper Transition zones; nest in hollow trees or

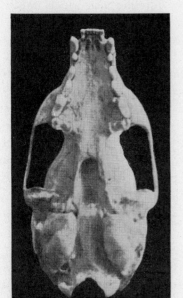

holes in the ground, and up to 8 young annually raised; 6 subspecies in British America.

M. caurina (Merriam). Pacific marten. Color rich dark brown; throat orange-buff; length 625 mm.; tail 220

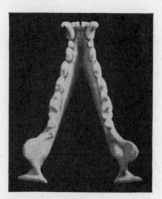

FIG. 156.—Skull of *Martes americana* (*from Elliot*).

mm.; hind foot 90 mm.: Pacific coast region from northern California to Alaska; central and southern Rockies.

Subspecies of M. caurina

M. c. caurina (Merr.). Pacific coast region.

M. c. origenes (Rhoads). Colors pale: central and southern Rockies.

M. c. sierræ Grinnell and Storer. Colors pale; breast with a large area of ochraceous orange; size small: Boreal zone of the Sierra Nevadas.

M. pennanti (Erxleben). Fisher; pekan. Body relatively stout; color dark brown or blackish, being lighter anteriorly; legs and tip of tail black; length 890 mm.; tail 375 mm.; hind foot 100 mm.: North America from the Atlantic to the Pacific; southward into Maine, New York and the Pennsylvania mountains; usually rare; Hudsonian, Canadian and Transition zones; 1 litter of 1 to 5 young raised.

Subspecies of M. pennanti

M. p. pennanti (Erx.).　Forests of northern America.

M. p. pacifica (Rhoads).　Size large; length 1,090 mm.: Pacific slope from California to Alaska.

2. Mustela L. (*Putorius* Cuvier).　Weasels and minks.　Body elongate and very slender, the two sexes differing very much in size; feet digitigrade; pads of feet separate; dentition 3/3, 1/1, 3/3, 1/2 (Fig. 158); color in summer sharply bicolor (except the mink, which is unicolor), brown above and white beneath, becoming, in many species, pure white in the winter: cosmopolitan; 22 species in North America, 15 in the United States.　Weasels are forest animals which feed on all kinds of small mammals and birds, and are noted for their ferocity and blood-thirstiness, which often leads them to kill much more than they can eat.　They are essentially terrestrial animals, but can run about in trees with the agility of squirrels.　Their dens are in hollow logs or in burrows in sheltered places, and they bear usually about 6 young a year, although sometimes as many as 12.

Key to the United States Species of Mustela

a_1 Length under 500 mm.; toes without webs; weasels.
 b_1 In the eastern States.
  c_1 From New England to North Carolina...............*M. noveboracensis.*
  c_2 New England, New York and northwards...........*M. cicognanii.*
  c_3 In Maine..*M. occisor.*
  c_4 In Florida.......................................*M. peninsulæ.*
  c_5 In western Pennsylvania.........................*M. allegheniensis.*
 b_2 In the central plains and the mountains.
  c_1 From Minnesota northwards......................*M. rixosa.*
  c_2 From Kansas northwards.........................*M. longicauda.*
  c_3 In the Sierras and Rockies......................*M. arizonensis.*
  c_4 In the Black Hills...............................*M. alleni.*
 b_3 On the Pacific slope.
  c_1 In California and Oregon.........................*M. xanthogenys.*
  c_2 In Oregon and Washington.......................*M. saturata.*
  c_3 In Washington..................................*M. washingtoni.*
  c_4 In the Puget Sound region.......................*M. streatori.*
a_2 Length greater than 500 mm.
 b_1 Color brown; minks................................*M. vison.*
 b_2 Color yellowish; ferrets...........................*M. nigripes.*

M. noveboracensis (Emmons).　Long-tailed weasel; common weasel (Fig. 157).　Color in summer brown above and white or yellowish beneath; posterior third or half of tail black; color in winter white towards the north and drab towards the south, except the end of the tail, which is always black; length 405 mm. (male); tail slender and 140 mm.; hind foot 47 mm.; female about a fifth smaller: eastern and central States; southward into North Carolina; westward to Illinois; Canadian, Transition and Upper Austral zones.

Subspecies of M. noveboracensis

M. n. noveboracensis (Em.). Eastern States from southern Maine throughout the Transition zone; westward to Illinois.

M. n. notia (Bangs). Belly yellow; winter coat drab: Austral zones of the eastern States.

M. cicognanii Bonaparte. Short-tailed weasel (Fig. 157). Color in summer brown above and white beneath, except the terminal third

FIG. 157.—Tail of *Mustela noveboracensis* (lower figure) and of *M. cicognanii* (upper figure) (*from Rhoads*).

of the tail which is black; color in winter white, except the terminal third of the tail which remains black; length 285 mm. (male); tail 77 mm.; hind foot 37 mm.; female about a fifth smaller: Boreal forests of North America from New England, New York and Minnesota northward; westward to Alaska and British Columbia; southward in the Rockies to Colorado.

M. occisor (Bangs). Similar to *M. noveboracensis;* tail very slender, the black tip very short, confined to the terminal tuft of hair; length (male) 460 mm.; tail 170 mm.; hind foot 50 mm.: southern Maine and northward; rare.

M. peninsulæ (Rhoads). Color chocolate brown above, yellow beneath; length (female) 375 mm.; tail 127 mm.; hind foot 44 mm.: Florida and Alabama.

M. allegheniensis (Rhoads). Color in summer brown above and white beneath and all white in winter; tail without a black tip, or with a few scattered blackish hairs; length 199 mm.; tail 19 mm.; hind foot 20 mm.: western Pennsylvania; rare.

M. rixosa (Bangs). Least weasel. Similar to *M. allegheniensis;* length 150 mm; tail 31 mm.; hind foot 22 mm.: Boreal America from

Hudson Bay to the Alaska coast; southward into Minnesota and Montana; the smallest carnivorous mammal.

M. longicauda Bonap.   Long-tailed weasel.   Color yellowish brown above and yellowish white beneath; extreme tip of tail black; length (male) 450 mm.; tail 165 mm.; hind foot 51 mm.: central plains from Kansas northwards.

Subspecies of M. longicauda

M. l. longicauda Bonap.   Great Plains from Kansas northwards.

M. l. spadix (Bangs).   Color dark: Minnesota at lower boundary of the Boreal zone.

M. arizonensis (Mearns).   Similar to *M. longicauda* but much smaller: Rocky Mountains south of British Columbia; Sierra Nevadas; in the high mountains.

M. alleni (Merriam).   Simiar to *M. arizonensis;* upper parts golden brown: Black Hills, South Dakota.

M. xanthogenys Gray.   Color umber brown, yellowish beneath; length (male) 402 mm.; tail 156 mm.; hind foot 40 mm.: Pacific slope.

Subspecies of M. xanthogenys

M. x. xanthogenys Gray.   Southern California.

M. x. munda (Bangs).   Smaller; colors darker: coast region of northern California.

M. x. oregonensis (Merr).   Size large: eastern Oregon.

M. saturata (Merr).   Similar to *M. longicauda,* but larger and darker: Oregon and Washington; a mountain form.

M. washingtoni (Merr).   Similar to *M. noveboracensis,* but with a longer tail and a shorter black tip: Mount Adams region, Washington.

M. streatori (Merr).   Similar to *M. cicognanii,* but smaller and darker, the white on the belly being reduced to a narrow, irregular strip: coast region of Washington and Oregon and the high Rockies.

Subspecies of M. streatori

M. s. streatori (Merr).   Costal region of Washington and Oregon.

M. s. lepta (Merr).   Size still smaller; black tip of tail very much smaller: Colorado, in the high mountains.

M. vison Scherber, Mink (Fig. 158).   Color uniformly dark brown; tail darker and bushy; breast and chin usually spotted white; length 610 mm.; tail 178 mm.; hind foot 63 mm.: North America from the Gulf of Mexico and the Mexican boundary to the Arctic Circle; westward to the Rockies and into California, British Columbia and

Alaska; along watercourses, where they feed on fish and all kinds of small animals. The nest is in a hollow log or a hole in the ground, and as many as 12 young may form the litter.

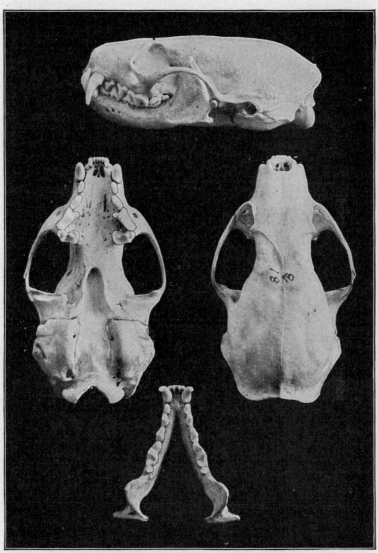

FIG. 158.—Skull of *Mustela vison* (*from Elliot*).

Subspecies of M. vison

M. v. vison Scherber. Boreal forests of northern North America; southward to Pennsylvania; Lower Arctic, Hudsonian and Canadian zones.

M. v. mink (Peale and Beauvois). Common mink. Larger and darker; length 640 mm.; tail 212 mm.; hind foot 73 mm.: eastern United States from the New England coast to North Carolina and central Georgia and Alabama; westwards to Missouri and northeastern Texas.

M. v. lutensis (Bangs). Colors pale; tail short; size small: coastal region from South Carolina to Florida.

M. v. letifera Hollister. Color light brown, with white spots on the throat and breast; size rather large: northern Illinois and southern Kansas.

M. v. lacustris (Preble). Color dark brown; white on the breast and belly; size rather large: northern Canada to southern North Dakota.

M. v. vulgivaga (Bangs). Size small; color light brown: Gulf coast from Texas to Florida.

M. v. energumenos (Bangs). Size small; color dark: New Mexico and Colorado, westward and northwestward to the Pacific coast.

M. nigripes (Audubon and Bachman). Black-footed ferret. Color pale yellowish or buff above and beneath, dark middorsally; feet, tip of tail and face black; length (male) 570 mm.; tail 133 mm.; hind foot 60 mm.: Great Plains from western Dakota and Montana to Texas; westward to the base of the Rockies; prairie dogs constitute its principal food.

Subfamily 2. Guloninæ.—Wolverines. Size large; body robust; ears very short: 1 genus.

Gulo Storr. Body stout; tail rather short and bushy; feet partly plantigrade; claws compressed: 3 species, 2 in the United States.

G. luscus (L.). Wolverine; glutton. Color dark brown or blackish, with a pale band on the sides; face brown; feet large; legs short; fur shaggy; length 1,025 mm.; tail 215 mm.; hind foot 200 mm.: Boreal forests of North America from Michigan, the Pennsylvania mountains and Colorado to the Arctic, and from the Atlantic to the Pacific; rare or extinct in the eastern States.

G. luteus Elliot. Color paler; length 950 mm.; tail 200 mm.; hind foot 170 mm.: Sierra Nevadas from Tulare County, California, northwards.

Subfamily 3. Mephitinæ.—Skunks. Body stocky, heavy behind; nose slender; ears small; legs short; claws long and non-retractile; tail usually long and bushy; fur mostly long, loose and silky; color black and white: 3 genera and 30 species, all North American; 20 species in the United States. Skunks are nocturnal animals which live on small mammals, birds eggs, insects, etc., and are found both in forests and open country.   Their anal glands secrete a malodorous pungent fluid which is discharged from the rectum and can sometimes be thrown 10 or 15 feet.   The northerly species hibernate in the winter.   The nest is a hole in the ground, a hollow log or a crevice in the rocks, and as many as 10 young are born in a litter.

Key to the Genera of Mephitinæ

a₁ Snout not proboscis-like.
  b₁ Skull with a convex upper outline; large skunks (Fig. 159)....1. *Mephitis.*
  b₂ Skull depressed, the upper outline being nearly straight; small
     skunks..2. *Spilogale.*
a₂ Snout proboscis-like; on the Mexican border..................3. *Conepatus.*

1. **Mephitis** Geoffroy and Cuvier.   Body stout; claws large and curved; a part of the sole applied to the ground in walking; skull convex; dentition 3/3, 1/1, 3/3, 1/2: about 9 species, all in the United States and Canada, being northerly in distribution.

Key to the Species of Mephitis

a₁ In the eastern and central States.
  b₁ From New England to Virginia and Indiana..........*M. nigra.*
  b₂ In Canada...*M. mephitis.*
  b₃ West Virginia to the Gulf..........................*M. elongata.*
a₂ In the States west of the Mississippi.
  b₁ On the Great Plains from Nebraska northwards.......*M. hudsonica.*
  b₂ From Louisiana and Texas northwards...............*M. mesomelas.*
  b₃ In New Mexico and Arizona........................*M. estor.*
                                            M. macroura milleri.
  b₄ On the Pacific slope...............................*M. occidentails.*

M. nigra (Peale and Beauvois).   Common skunk (Fig. 159).   Color black, with a white stripe on the nose and forehead and a white patch on the back of the neck, from which a broad white stripe extends backward a varying distance on each side of the body, often to the tail; tip of tail white; length 600 mm.; tail 229 mm.; hind foot 60 mm.: northeastern States; southward to Virginia; westward to Indiana.

M. mephitis (Schreber).   Color arrangement like *M. nigra*, but the white stripes are narrow and extend down the sides of the tail, which is mixed black and white; length 613 mm.; tail 188 mm.; hind foot 78 mm.: Nova Scotia and northern Ontario to Lake Winnipeg.

M. hudsonica (Richardson).   Color similar to *M. mephitis*, but the tip of the tail is black; length 726 mm.; tail 260 mm.; hind foot 82 mm.:

Manitoba to eastern British Columbia; southward into Colorado, Nebraska and Minnesota.

M. elongata (Bangs). Color similar to *M. nigra*, but the white stripes are very broad, sometimes entirely covering the back and tail;

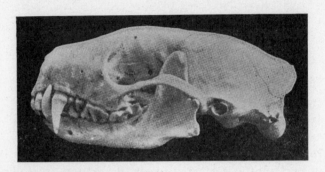

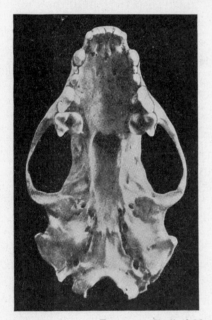

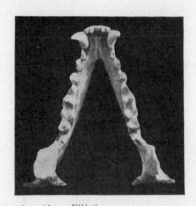

FIG. 159.—Skull of *Mephitis nigra (from Elliot)*.

length 703 mm.; tail 317 mm.; hind foot 74 mm.: West Virginia and North Carolina to the Gulf; westward along the Gulf coast to the Mississippi.

M. mesomelas Lichtenstein.   Dorsal white stripes narrow and short, usually extending to the middle of the back, but sometimes to the tail which usually lacks the white tip; length 576 mm.; tail 223 mm.; hind foot 63 mm.: Mississippi Valley from western Indiana into Iowa; southwestward of the river to the Gulf coast of Louisiana and Texas.

Subspecies of M. mesomelas

M. m. mesomelas Lich. From southern Louisiana to Missouri; westward to Matagorda Island, Texas; up the Red River Valley to Wichita Falls.

M. m. varians (Gray). Long-tailed skunk. Length 758 mm.; tail 393 mm.; hind foot 71 mm.: southwestern Texas and eastern New Mexico to Nebraska and Colorado.

M. m. avia (Bangs). Tail very short; length 625 mm.; tail 200 mm.; hind foot 65 mm.: prairies from Indiana to Iowa.

M. estor Merriam. Dorsal stripes very broad, occasionally entirely covering the back and tail; length 639 mm.; tail 285 mm.; foot 69 mm.: Arizona and western New Mexico.

M. occidentalis Baird. White stripes varying much in extent, frequently extending on to the tail; length 800 mm.; tail 310 mm.; hind foot 78 mm.: Pacific slope from Monterey Bay northwards to the Willamette Valley; westwards to the Sierras and Cascades.

Subspecies of M. occidentalis

M. o. occidentalis Baird. Central California to the Willamette Valley, Oregon.

M. o. spissigrada (Bangs). White stripes very broad, extending on to the sides of the tail; length 650 mm.: region of Puget Sound.

M. o. notata (Howell). White stripes very narrow, often ending in the middle of the back: northern Oregon and southern Washington, east of the Cascades.

M. o. major (Howell). Size large; stripes broad; length 705 mm.: eastern Oregon, and California to Utah.

M. o. holzneri Mearns. Size small: southern California.

M. macroura milleri (Mearns). Back of body and tail nearly all white, although in a considerable proportion of individuals the back is nearly all black; two color phases present; tail very long; length 675 mm.; tail 350 mm.; hind foot 65 mm.: southern Arizona into Mexico.

2. Spilogale Gray. Spotted skunks. Body small and slender; skull flattened and with a straight dorsal outline; color pattern in stripes and spots; dentition 3/3, 1/1, 3/3, 1/2: about 13 species, generally southerly in range; 10 species in the United States.

Key to the United States Species of Spilogale

a₁ In the States east of the Mississippi.
    b₁ In the Atlantic and Gulf States, except Florida..............*S. putorius.*
    b₂ In Florida...*S. ambarvalis.*
a₂ In the States west of the Mississippi.
    b₁ In the central States.
        c₁ From Nebraska and Minnesota southwards...............*S. interrupta.*
        c₂ In the coast region of Louisiana and Texas...............*S. indianola.*
        c₃ On the eastern slopes of the Rockies.....................*S. tenuis.*
    b₂ In the southwestern States.
        c₁ From western Texas to central Arizona..................*S. leucoparia.*
        c₂ In the Great Basin from northern Arizona to Idaho.......*S. gracilis.*
                                     S. arizonæ.
    b₃ On the Pacific slope.....................................*S. phenax.*

S. putorius (L.).   Color black, with 4 white narrow longitudinal stripes on the forward half of the body and 2 transverse stripes on the hinder half on each side; end of tail white; length 516 mm.; tail 206 mm.; hind foot 48 mm.: south Atlantic and Gulf States from western Virginia to western Georgia, and westward into Mississippi.

S. ambarvalis Bangs.   Size small; tail short; color like *S. putorius;* length 386 mm.; tail 120 mm.; hind foot 40 mm.: eastern Florida.

S. interrupta (Rafinesque).   White stripes much reduced, sometimes represented by a few spots; tail wholly black: southern Minnesota and eastern Nebraska to central Texas.

S. indianola Merriam.   Color similar to *S. interrupta*, but the tail has a white tip; length 472 mm.; tail 183 mm.; hind foot 48 mm.: Gulf coast of Louisiana and Texas.

S. tenuis Howell.   White markings very broad; length 450 mm.; tail 165 mm.; hind foot 51 mm.: eastern slopes of the Rockies in New Mexico and Colorado.

S. leucoparia Merr.   White markings very broad; no white of legs: central Texas to New Mexico.

S. gracilis Merr.   Like *S. leucoparia;* length 381 mm.; tail 143 mm.; hind foot 44 mm.: Great Basin from Arizona and California into Oregon and Idaho.

S. arizonæ Mearns.   Like *S. gracilis*, but larger: central New Mexico and Arizona, southward.

S. phenax Merr.   Dorsal pair of white stripes narrow, lateral pair much broader; length 470 mm.; tail 154 mm.; hind foot 52 mm.: Pacific slope.

Subspecies of S. phenax

S. p. phenax Merr.   California, except the southeastern desert and the extreme northern portions.

S. p. latifrons Merr.   White stripes less prominent: Oregon coast region.

S. p. olympica Merr.   Tail shorter: Olympic peninsula.

3. Conepatus Gray.   Snout long and proboscis-like, with a large bare pad on the upper side for rooting; color black, with a white tail and a wide middorsal white band; dentition 3/3, 1/1, 2/3, 1/2: 7 species in Mexico and Central and South America.

C. mesoleucus telmalestes Bailey.   Hog-nose skunk.   Length 670 mm.; tail 290 mm.; hind foot 75 mm.: central and southern Texas to Arizona.

Subfamily 4.   Taxidiinæ.—Badgers.   Body stocky; legs short; toes not retractile, with long claws; tail short: 1 genus.

Taxidea Storr.   Dentition 3/3, 1/1, 3/3, 1/2; skull attenuate in front: 1 species.

T. taxus (Schreber).   American Badger.   Color gray, mottled with black dorsally and with a white stripe running from the top of the nose to the shoulder; belly whitish; length 700 mm.; tail 135 mm.; weight about 15 lbs.: western North America from western Texas and Mexico to Hudson Bay and Lake Athabaska; eastward into Wisconsin, Michigan and Kansas; westward to the Pacific coast.   The badger lives in deep burrows in the ground and feeds on small animals of all kinds, especially rodents.   Towards the north they hibernate in the winter; a single litter of from 2 to 5 young is raised annually.

Subspecies of T. taxus

T. t. phippsi Figgins.   Larger and darker: southern Colorado.

T. t. taxus (Schreber).   Western America.

T. t. berlandieri (Baird).   A white middorsal stripe from nose to tail: western Texas and westward into California.

T. t. neglecta (Mearns).   Size smaller and with less black: California Oregon and Washington.

Subfamily 5.   Lutrinæ.—Otters.   Body elongate; legs short; head broad behind, with a sharp snout; ears small and round; toes webbed; tail long, broad and flattened; fur short and dense: 1 genus.

Lutra Brisson.   With the characters of the subfamily; toes 5-5; dentition 3/3, 1/1, 4/3, 1/2: many species, cosmopolitan; 1 species in the United States.

L. canadensis (Schreber). American otter. Color seal brown, grayish beneath; under surface of webs of toes densely hairy; length 1,100 mm.; tail 420 mm.; hind foot 120 mm.: North America from the Atlantic to the Pacific; northward to the tree line; aquatic animals, living along streams and lakes and eating fish. The animal's den is in the side of the bank with its opening often below the water; the number of young annually raised is from 1 to 5.

Subspecies of *L. canadensis*

L. c. canadensis (Schreber). Eastern North America north of South Carolina.

L. c. lataxina (F. Cuvier). Upper surface yellowish brown: south-eastern and Gulf States from North Carolina to Mississippi.

L. c. vaga (Bangs). Darker and redder: Florida and eastern Georgia.

L. c. pacifica (Rhoads). Size large; color lighter: Pacific slope from California to Alaska.

L. c. sonora (Rhoads). Size very large; length 1,300 mm.: Arizona and southern California.

L. degener Bangs. Color blackish; length 995 mm.: Newfoundland.

Subfamily 6. Enhydrinæ.—Sea otters. Body long and robust; toes webbed: 1 genus.

Enhydra Flemming. Body elongate but stout; tail rather short; hind feet short and very large; dentition 3/2, 1/1, 3/3, 1/2: 1 species almost extinct.

E. lutris (L.). Sea-otter. Color deep glossy brownish black; length 1,200 mm.; tail 300; muzzle beset with bristles: shores of the Pacific from Lower California to Alaska; almost extinct; the most valuable American fur animal. The sea otter feeds principally on shell-fish and sea-urchins; but one young is born.

Family 6. Felidæ.—Cats. Body more or less elongate, compact and lithe; feet digitigrade; toes 5-4; claws compressed, sharp and retractile; head short and round; tongue with rasping papillæ; pupil elliptical: cosmopolitan (except in Australia); many species, which are most numerous in the tropics and subtropics; about 29 species in North America and 16 in the United States and Canada, grouped in 2 genera.

Key to the United States Genera of Felidæ

a_1 Tail long...1. *Felis*.
a_2 Tail short...2. *Lynx*.

1. Felis L. Cats. Body slender; fur soft and compact; dentition 3/3, 1/1, 3/2, 1/1: about 50 species; 9 species and subspecies in the

United States. Of these species about 6 are different geographical races of pumas, which are the only native cats ranging over the whole country, while the other 3 species are Central American cats which occur along the Mexican border. The pumas are characterized among cats by the following features; large size, slender build, a small head, a long tail and absence of color markings. They are confined to America, ranging from southern Patagonia to southern British America. The domestic cat, *F. domestica*, is a descendant of the Egyptian wild cat, *F. maniculata*, but with a considerable admixture of the European wild cat, *F. catus*. The yellow tabby cat is probably the result of such a cross. The domestic cat usually bears from 3 to 6 at a birth. The puma bears from 2 to 5 young, which are often spotted and have ringed tails.

Key to the United States Species of Felis

a_1 Color uniform, without spots or stripes.
  b_1 Size large; legs long; pumas.
    c_1 In the northeastern States.........................*F. concolor*
    c_2 In Florida...*F. coryi.*
    c_3 In Louisiana......................................*F. arundivaga.*
    c_4 In the Far-west...................................*F. oregonensis.*
  b_2 Size smaller; legs short................................*F. cacomitli.*
a_2 Color not uniform; body spotted or striped.
  b_1 Size large; body spotted and without stripes; jaguar.....*F. hernandesii.*
  b_2 Size smaller; body with both spots and stripes.........*F. pardalis.*

F. concolor L. Puma; cougar; mountain lion; panther; painter; catamount. Color uniform yellowish brown or fulvous, darker mid-dorsally; under parts reddish or whitish; tail tipped with black or brown; length 2,400 mm.; tail 750 mm'.; hind foot 250 mm.; weight about 150 lbs.: eastern and central America; northward into southern Canada; extinct in all well settled regions, but may still exist in the Adirondacks and the higher Alleghanies of Pennsylvania and West Virginia.

F. coryi Bangs. Florida cougar. Size large; head large and massive; feet small; color of back very dark: central Florida.

F. arundivaga Hollister. Size large; color grayish fawn above; tail darker, with a dark brown median line; throat and breast white; face blackish, with a white streak over each eye: cane-brakes of Louisiana.

F. oregonensis Rafinesque. Western puma; mountain lion. Size large; color dull fulvous; head large and massive: Rocky Mountain and Pacific coast regions.

Subspecies of F. oregonensis

F. o. oregonensis Raf. Color very dark; belly whitish: coastal region from California to British Columbia.

F. o. hippolestes (Merriam). Largest of the pumas; length 2,550 mm.; tail 900 mm.; weight 220 lbs.; color dull yellowish brown; head with a high median crest: Rocky Mountains and Great Basin.

F. o. azteca (Merr). Size moderate; color dull fulvous; tail much darker and with a longer black tip; no white underneath; ears black: western Texas and Mexico.

F. o. californica (May). Color pale; length 1,950 mm.; tail 750 mm.: throughout California.

F. cacomitli Berlandier. Jaguarundi cat; eyra. Color (in red color phase) uniformly either gray or rusty rufous, there being 2 distinct color phases; length 1,060 mm.; tail 480 mm.; hind foot 140 mm.: South and Central America; southern Texas.

F. pardalis L. Ocelot; tiger cat. Color tawny or brown, with large blackish spots and stripes, each one enclosing a lighter one; length 1,200 mm.; tail 375 mm.: southern Texas to Patagonia.

F. hernandesii (Gray). Jaguar. Color tawny yellow, spotted with black rings; length 2,100 mm.; tail 600 mm.: southern United States to Patagonia; formerly numerous, still found from central Texas to northern Arizona; number of young at a birth 2.

2. Lynx. Kerr. Body short and thick; tail short; legs long; dentition 3/3, 1/1, 2/2, 1/1; ears with a tuft of long hairs at the tip: many species, all in the northern hemisphere, about 6 in North America; woodland animals, preying largely on rodents; number of young, 2 to 5.

Key to the United State Species of Lynx

a_1 Feet moderate in size; tail moderately short; skull narrow; fur
      short and dense.
   b_1 In the eastern States.
      c_1 Color dull, with little black on upper parts...............*L. ruffus.*
      c_2 Color rich, with much black on upper parts; size large; in
            Nova Scotia..*L. gigas.*
   b_2 In the Rocky Mountain States.........................*L. uinta.*
                                  L. baileyi.
   b_3 On the Pacific slope..*L. fasciatus.*
a_2 Feet very large; tail very short; fur long and loose; skull broad.
   b_1 Color gray..*L. canadensis.*
   b_2 Color very dark; in Newfoundland.......................*L. subsolanus.*

L. ruffus (Schreber). Wildcat; bobcat. Color reddish brown in winter and ash brown in summer, spotted and streaked with black;

tail ringed with black; length 900 mm.; tail 170 mm.; hind foot 180 mm.; weight up to 20 lbs.: Nova Scotia to the Gulf of Mexico and into Mexico, and from the Atlantic to the Pacific; in wooded regions.

Subspecies of L. ruffus

L. r. ruffus (Schr.). Eastern States; southward into Georgia.

L. r. floridanus (Rafinesque). Color darker: Florida and Georgia west to Louisiana.

L. r. texensis (Allen). Belly and inner surface of legs white, with brown spots: southern Texas.

L. r. californicus Mearns. Size large; color dark: coast region of southern California.

L. r. eremicus Mearns. Color pale: deserts of the Mexican border; southern California.

L. uinta Merriam. Mountain wildcat. Color buff, grizzled with gray and black, with black spots; white beneath; tail with 2 or 3 black bands: Wyoming; Colorado; Utah; New Mexico.

L. gigas Bangs. Color cinnamon rufus above, much spotted and streaked with black; length 1,000 mm.; tail 180 mm.; hind foot 200 mm.: Nova Scotia.

L. fasciatus Raf. Pacific wildcat. Color chestnut brown above, pale on the sides and white, spotted with black beneath; terminal third of tail black; length 890 mm.; tail 170 mm.: coastal California to British Columbia.

Subspecies of L. fasciatus

L. f. fasciatus Raf. Washington and Oregon.

L. f. pallescens Merr. Color hoary gray: northern California and northward; eastwards to Wyoming and Colorado.

L. f. oculeus Bangs. Back darker, without stripes or spots; sides gray; tip of tail white; length 770 mm.; tail 139 mm.; hind foot 158 mm.: coast region of California north of San Francisco.

L. baileyi Merr. Plateau wildcat. Similar to *L. ruffus*, but paler and with a shorter tail: Arizona to Texas; southern Colorado.

L. canadensis Kerr. Canada lynx. Color gray, mottled with brown; tail-tip black; length 1,000 mm.; tail 100 mm.; hind foot 225 mm.; weight up to 30 lbs.; legs thick; feet very large: northern America, in forested regions from Pennsylvania and northern Michigan to Hudson Bay and Alaska; southward in the Rockies as far as Colorado, and in the Sierras as far as Mount Whitney; extinct in the eastern States.

L. subsolanus Bangs.   Color black and hazel, much darker than *L. canadensis;* length 920 mm.; tail 110 mm; hind foot 220 mm.: Newfoundland.

Order 7.   Pinnipedia.—Seals. Aquatic mammals of large size and carnivorous habits, and closely related to the Order *Carnivora;* feet transformed to flippers; toes 5-5, joined by a thick membrane; hinder limbs directed backwards and used for swimming; usually no external ears present: about 50 species, in temperate and Arctic seas; in Lake Baikal (fresh water); about 11 species on the coasts of the United States and Canada, grouped in 2 families.

Key to the Families of Pinnipedia

a_1 External ears present...1. *Otariidæ.*
a_2 External ears absent..2. *Phocidæ.*

Family 1.   Otariidæ.—Hind limbs capable of being turned forward and used for walking; ears present; forelegs long; claws small and rudimentary, except those on digit 3 of the foot: 3 genera and species on the Pacific coast.

1. Zalophus Gill.   Ears short; dentition 3/2, 1/1, 4/4, 1/1; head rounded; nose narrow, pointed: 1 species.

Z. californianus (Lesson).   Sea-lion.   Color reddish brown in summer, lighter in winter; length 2,542 mm.; tail 110 mm.; hind foot 380 mm.; weight 500 lbs.; body slender; snout long: southern Mexico to northern California.

2. Eumetopias Gill.   Ears rather long; dentition 3/2, 1/1, 4/4, 1/1; upper molar separated by a wide space from the premolars: 1 species.

E. jubata (Schreber).   Steller's sea-lion.   Color reddish brown; length 3,000 mm.; weight 1,500 lb.: Bering Strait to Farollon Islands, California.

3. Callorhinus Gray.   Dentition 3/2, 1/1, 4/4, 2/1; facial portion of skull short: 1 species.

C. alascanus Jordan and Clark.   Fur seal.   Color chestnut brown; length 1,887 mm.; tail 51 mm.; hind foot 548 mm.: Bering Strait to California.   The animals breed on the Pribilof Islands in June, spending the summer and fall there; in the winter and spring they migrate southward, ranging as far south as southern California.

Family 2.   Phocidæ.—Hind limbs directed permanently backwards, and of no use in walking; ears absent; fore legs short; claws well developed: about 5 species on the American coasts.

Key to the American Genera of Phocidæ

a_1 Teeth 34.

 b_1 Molars with 2 to 4 cusps each.............................1. *Phoca.*

 b_2 Molars with 1 cusp each.................................2. *Halichœrus.*

a_2 Teeth 30; snout proboscis-like..............................3. *Cystophora.*

1. **Phoca** L.   Snout narrow and pointed; dentition 3/2, 1/1, 4/4, 1/1; forehead convex; incisors conical: cosmopolitan.

P. vitulina L.   Harbor seal.   Color yellowish gray, spotted with black; length 1,500 mm.: circumpolar; southward to Lower California and the Carolinas; common on the New England coast; ascending 'rivers; occasionally in Lake Champlain and Lake Ontario.

P. hispida Schreber.   Ringed seal.   Color blackish above, with large whitish spots; length 1,500 mm.; body slender; limbs long: circumpolar; southward to Newfoundland.

P. grœnlandica Erxleben.   Harp seal.   Color gray, with a black face and a black band across the shoulder and extending along the sides; length 1,500 mm.; body slender; weight 600 to 800 lbs.; circumpolar; southward to Newfoundland and the Magdalen Islands; the basis of the sealing industry in Newfoundland.

2. **Halichœrus** Nilsson.   Snout broad and short; teeth 34; molars conical, with a single cusp; incisors conical; claws well developed: 1 species.

H. grypus (Fabricius).   Gray seal.   Color gray, with irregular dark spots; length 2,500 mm.; weight up to 3,600 lbs.; flippers hairy only along the toes: North Atlantic; southward to Nova Scotia.

3. **Cystophora** Nilsson.   Snout elongated, forming a short proboscis and capable of inflation in the male; dentition 2/1, 1/1, 4/4, 1/1; incisors conical; molars and premolars small and separated from one another: 1 species.

C. cristata (Erxleben).   Hooded seal.   Color bluish black, with whitish spots; length 2,400 mm.: North Atlantic; southward occasionally to Long Island.

Order 8.   Rodentia.—Rodents.   Small or medium-sized mammals with long chisel-like incisor teeth, no canines, and grinders (premolars and molars) which are separated from the incisors by a wide space, the incisors having persistent papillæ and growing continuously (Fig. 168); feet mostly pentadactylous and plantigrade; placenta discoidal: about 1,400 species grouped in about 21 families, constituting a third of all species of mammals and occurring on all the continents; about 400 species in the United States.

Key to the United States Families of Rodentia

a₁ Tail present.
  b₁ Two upper incisors present.
    c₁ Tail cylindrical or compressed laterally (except flying-squirrels).
      d₁ No quills in the fur.
        e₁ Body stout; fore feet with digging claws; pocket
          gophers.................................... 2. *Geomyidæ.*
        e₂ Fore feet not with digging claws.
          f₁ Not more than 3 well-developed grinders in
            each jaw.
            g₁ No cheek-pouches present.
              h₁ Hind legs not greatly elongated; rats and
                mice............................. 1. *Muridæ.*
              h₂ Hind legs greatly elongated; jumping
                mice............................. 4. *Zapodidæ.*
            g₂ Large cheek-pouches present; pocket mice.   3. *Heteromyidæ.*
          f₂ At least 4 well developed grinders in each jaw.
            g₁ Tail very short; mountain beavers........ 6. *Apoldontiidæ.*
            g₂ Tail long or moderate; squirrels; marmots.. 7. *Sciuridæ.*
      d₂ Long quills present in the fur; porcupines.......... 5. *Erethizontidæ.*
    c₂ Tail large and flattened; beavers.................... 8. *Castoridæ.*
  b₂ Four upper incisors present; rabbits and hares.......... 9. *Leporidæ.*
a₂ External tail wanting; pikas............................10. *Ochotonidæ.*

Family 1.   Muridæ.

—Rats and mice.   Small, slender rodents with a long tail, with feet not specially modified and with naked soles; snout elongated; nostrils separated by a furrow; eyes and ears large; upper lip usually divided; dentition 1/1, 0/0, 0/0, 3/3: over 700 species and 100 genera, comprising half of all rodents and being the largest family of mammals; distribution cosmopolitan; 150 species in the United States, grouped in 4 subfamilies.

Key to the Subfamilies of Muridæ

a₁ Molars of upper jaw with a more or less tuberculate biting surface
  (Fig. 160).
  b₁ Tubercles arranged in 3 longitudinal rows.................1. *Murinæ.*
  b₂ Tubercles either arranged in 2 rows (Fig. 160) or flattened....2. *Cricetinæ.*
a₂ Molars with a flattened surface and not tuberculate (Fig. 167).
  b₁ Tail long; body slender....................................3. *Neotominæ.*
  b₂ Tail short; body stout.....................................4. *Microtinæ.*

Subfamily 1.   Murinæ.

—Old world rats and mice.   Form slender; molars of upper jaw with 3 longitudinal rows of tubercles on their crowns; tail long and scaly or scantily haired; thumb rudimentary: 130 species, in all parts of the old world except Madagascar; a few species have followed man to the new world.

1. **Mus** L.   With the characters of the subfamily; tail scantily haired; size small: 4 semidomesticated species in the United States.

✳*M. musculus* L.   House-mouse.   Body brownish gray in color; under parts ashen; length 170 mm.; tail 85 mm.; hind foot 17 mm.: everywhere in houses; often in fields and woods; about 5 litters annually of 4 to 9 each.

2. **Rattus** Fischer (*Mus* L.).   With the characters of the subfamily; tail scaly; size large: 3 American species.

R. norvegicus (Erxleben).   (*M. decumanus* Pallas.)   Common rat; brown rat.   Body brown above and gray beneath; length 400 mm.; tail 200 mm.; hind foot 43 mm.: very common.   This rat made its appearance in Europe in eastern Russia in 1727, and rapidly spread westward, driving out and replacing the black rat, which up to that time had been the common house-rat.   It appeared in America about the time of the Revolutionary War.

R. rattus (L.).   Black rat.   Body slenderer, black in color; length 400 mm.; tail 215 mm.; hind foot 37 mm.: during colonial times the common house-rat in America, but now almost exterminated by the larger, fiercer brown rat.

R. alexandrinus (Geoffroy).   Roof-rat.   Body brown above, white beneath; length 425 mm.; tail 237 mm.; hind foot 40 mm.: southern United States; common in some places.

Subfamily 2. Cricetinæ.—American rats and mice.   Body slender; ears and eyes large; legs and tail long; tail well haired; upper molars usually with tubercles arranged in 2 longitudinal rows (Fig. 160): about 50 species in the United States; and very many subspecies.

Key to the Genera of Cricetinæ

a_1 Tubercles on surface of upper molars in 2 distinct longi-
    tudinal rows (Fig. 160).
　　b_1 Upper incisors longitudinally grooved (Fig. 161)........2. *Reithrodontomys.*
　　b_2 Upper incisors not thus grooved.
　　　　c_1 Soles of feet with 4 plantar tubercles..............1. *Onychomys.*
　　　　c_2 Soles of feet with 5 or 6 plantar tubercles (Fig. 163).
　　　　　　d_1 Belly pure white; fur fine......................3. *Peromyscus.*
　　　　　　d_2 Belly not pure white; fur coarse................4. *Oryzomys.*
a_2 Tubercles of molars form flattened S-shaped loops.........5. *Sigmodon.*

1. **Onychomys** Baird.   Grasshopper mice; scorpion mice.   Body stout; fur dense and velvety; tail short; fore feet strong; ears hairy: 2 species, in western America; nocturnal burrowing animals which feed largely on insects, scorpions and other small animals; several litters of from 2 to 6 young each raised each year; the animals do not hibernate.

Key to the Species of Onychomys

a_1 Tail usually less than half the length of the head and trunk.....*O. leucogaster*.
a_2 Tail usually more than half the length of the head and trunk....*O. torridus*.

O. leucogaster (Weid) (Fig. 160). Body light mouse-brown above, being darker middorsally, and snow-white beneath; a melanistic color phase also occurs; length 150 mm.; tail 40 mm.; hind foot 20 mm.: western America, from eastern Dakota and Kansas to eastern California; Mexico; 11 subspecies.

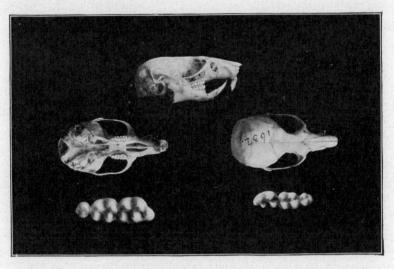

FIG. 160.—Skull and tuberculate molars of *Onychomys leucogaster* (*from Elliot*).

Subspecies of O. leucogaster

O. l. leucogaster (Wied). Size large; length 164 mm.; color dark: eastern and central North Dakota into Manitoba.

O. l. missouriensis (Audubon and Bachman). Size smaller; color pale: western North Dakota and Montana and northwards.

O. l. articeps (Rhoads). Like *O. l. missouriensis*, but still paler, buff in color: Wyoming and South Dakota; southward to southwestern Texas.

O. l. brevicaudus Merriam. Size small; length 141 mm.; color darker than *O. l. articeps:* southern Idaho, northern Utah and Nevada.

O. l. fuscogriseus Anthony. Color darker; size small: eastern and central Washington, Oregon and northern California.

O. l. melanophrys Merr. Color dark, being pinkish-cinnamon: southern Utah and Colorado and northern New Mexico and Arizona.

O. l. ruidosæ (Stone and Rehn). Color dark: southern New Mexico and southeastern Arizona.

O. l. longipes (Merr.). Size large; length 190 mm.; tail 48 mm.; hind foot 25 mm.; color dull: central and southern Texas.

O. l. breviauritus Hollister. Like *O. l. longipes*, but darker and with a shorter tail, are and hind foot: eastern Nebraska and central Kansas and Oklhaoma.

O. torridus (Coues). Body fulvous brown above and white beneath; length 150 mm.; tail 50 mm.; hind foot 20 mm.: southwestern United States; Mexico.

Subspecies of O. torridus

O. t. torridus (Coues). Southwestern Texas, southern New Mexico, southeastern Arizona and northern Mexico.

O. t. perpallidus Mearns. Size larger: western Arizona.

O. t. pulcher (Elliot). Size small; length 136 mm.; color very pale: deserts of southern California.

O. t. longicaudus (Merriam). Size large; color pale: southwestern Utah; northwestern Arizona, Nevada and Inyo and Mono counties, California.

O. t. tularensis Merr. Color grayish drab above: upper San Joaquin Valley, California.

O. t. ramona (Rhoads). Color very dark: southwestern California.

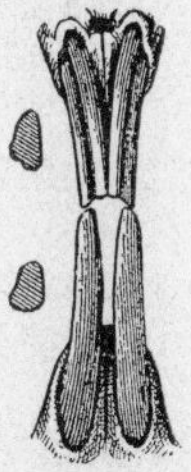

FIG. 161. Incisor teeth of *Reithrodontomys megalotis* (from Mearns).

2. **Reithrodontomys** Giglioli. American harvest mice. Body small and slender; tail long, being a third or a half the body length; ears prominent; anterior face of upper incisor with a deep longitudinal groove (Fig. 161); sole of hind foot with 6 plantar tubercles: 50 species, in tropical and sub-tropical America; 6 species and 17 subspecies in the United States; mainly nocturnal animals which live in open, grassy places, often near water, and feed upon grains, fruits and vegetables. Most species build a globular nest of grass often elevated above the ground in weeds or bushes and raise from 3 to 7 young in a litter and several litters a year. They resemble the house-mouse in appearance, but may be distinguished by the browner colors, more hairy tail and grooved upper incisors.

R. humulis (Audubon and Bachman) (Fig. 162). Eastern harvest mouse. Color dark brown above mixed with pinkish cinnamon, darker on the head and middorsally; whitish beneath; length 120 mm.; tail 57 mm.; hind foot 16 mm.: southern States.

R. h. humulis (Aud. and Bach.).   Ear 9 to 10 mm. long: coastal plain from Virginia to central Florida.

R. h. impiger (Bangs).   Ears smaller: mountains of northern Virginia and West Virginia.

R. h. merriami (Allen).   Ears smaller; under parts darker: central Kentucky to central Alabama and westward to the east Texas coast.

R. albescens Cary.   Color very pale; length 125 mm.: South Dakota to central Texas.

R. megalotis (Baird) (Fig. 161).   Western harvest mouse.   Color brownish buff on the back and buff on the sides; white beneath and on the feet; length 140 mm.; tail 65 mm.; hind foot 17 mm.; ear 12 mm.: western States to the Pacific; southward into Mexico.

Subspecies of R. megalotis

R. m. megalotis (Baird).   Southern Idaho southward to eastern California and the Mexican border; then eastward to southwestern Texas.

R. m. aztecus (Allen).   Ears and skull larger: northern New Mexico, northeastern Arizona, southeastern Utah and western Colorado.

R. m. dychei (Allen).   More black on the upper parts; tail shorter: eastern Iowa and Missouri to central Colorado and Wyoming; northward to North Dakota and Montana.

R. m. nigrescens Howell.   More blackish: eastern Washington, Oregon and northern California and western Idaho.

R. m. longicaudus (Baird).   Colors darker; length 145 mm.; tail 75 mm.; hind foot 17 mm.: western California, west of the Sierras.

R. catalinæ Elliot.   Similar to *R. m. longicaudus*, but larger; length 169 mm.; tail 94 mm.: Santa Catalina Island.

R. raviventris Dixon.   Upper parts very dark; under parts pinkish; length 130 mm.; tail 64 mm.; hind foot 16 mm.: salt marches of San Francisco Bay.

FIG. 162.—
Reithrodontomys humulis
(after Stone & Cram).

Subspecies of R. raviventris

R. r. raviventris Dix.   Southern part of San Francisco Bay.

R. r. halicœtes Dix.   Size larger; length 156 mm.; under parts white: salt marshes of San Pablo, Suisun Bay and the lower San Joaquin and Sacramento Rivers.

R. fulvescens (Allen).   Color buff above, white beneath; length 183 mm.; tail 102 mm.; hind foot 19 mm.: Mexico and southern States.

Subspecies of R. fulvescens

R. f. intermedius (Allen).   Color pale: southern Texas.

R. f. aurantius (Allen).   Color darker: eastern Texas and Oklahoma, southern Arkansas and Louisiana west of the Mississippi.

3. Peromyscus Gloger.   Wood mice; deer mice; vesper mice; white-footed mice.   Body small and slender; tail long, being a third or a half the total length; eyes and ears large; internal cheek pouches present; hind feet and legs long, the former (except in *P. floridanus*) with 6 plantar tubercles (Fig. 163): about 100 species, all North American; about 15 species in the United States, with many subspecies; nocturnal animals which live on the ground in a great variety of situations, feeding principally on grains and seeds.   They do not form permanent runways, although they may use those of other animals.   They breed throughout the year, raising from 4 to 6 in a litter, and do not hibernate, and may exceed in numbers all the other mammals in a region.   They frequently enter and live in dwellings, and may be distinguished from the house-mouse by their snow-white feet and under parts.

FIG. 163.—Hind foot of *Peromyscus leucopus*, showing the plantar tubercles *(from Howell).*

P. maniculatus (Wagner).   Color brown or brownish gray above, the middorsal region being darker; under parts and feet white; length 160 to 200 mm.; tail 70 to 120 mm.; hind foot 19 to 21 mm.; mammæ 6; tail and body sharply bicolor: North America from Hudson Bay and Alaska to southern Mexico, which is the widest range of perhaps any North American mammal; mostly in woodlands; 27 subspecies.

Subspecies of P. maniculatus

P. m. maniculatus (Wag.).   Tail short, averaging less than 90 mm. in length: Hudsonian zone of northeastern Canada.

P. m. gracilis (LeConte).   Tail very long; length 200 mm.; tail 112 mm.: northern and central New York, northern Vermont, Michigan, Wisconsin and Minnesota into Canada; Canadian zone.

P. m. abietorum (Bangs).   Similar to *P. m. gracilis* but paler and grayer: central Maine to Nova Scotia.

P. m. nubiterræ Rhoads.   Like *P. m. gracilis*, but smaller: Alleghenies from western Pennsylvania to Georgia, Canadian zone.

P. m. oreas (Bangs). Size large; color very dark; length 215 mm.; tail 120 mm.; hind foot 23 mm.: western Washington from the Columbia River into British Columbia.

P. m. artemisia (Rhoads). Color brownish fawn: northwestern Wyoming to western Washington and British Columbia.

P. m. austerus (Baird). Color very dark: coast region of Puget Sound.

P. m. rubidus Osgood. Like *P. m. oreas*, but paler and tail and hind foot shorter: coast region from San Francisco Bay to the Columbia.

P. m. gambeli (Baird). Like *P. m. rubidus*, but smaller and paler: central Washington to Lower California; coast region south of San Francisco Bay.

P. m. sonoriensis (LeC.). Size small; color ochraceous buff: Great Basin region.

P. m. rufinus (Merriam). Like *P. m. sonoriensis*, but darker: southern Rocky Mountain region.

P. m. nebrascensis (Coues). Like *P. m. sonoriensis:* eastern base of the Rockies from Canada through western Nebraska to western Texas.

P. m. bairdi (Hoy and Kennicott). Color very dark; back black: prairie region of the upper Mississippi Valley; south to Oklahoma; east to eastern Ohio; north to Manitoba.

P. m. pallescens (Allen). Like *P. m. bairdi*, but smaller (length 126 mm.) and somewhat paler: central Texas.

P. polionotus (Wagner). Size very small; length 130 mm.; tail 47 mm.; hind foot 16 mm.; color uniformly brownish fawn; under parts creamy white; feet and forelegs white; tail mostly bicolor; mammæ 6: southeastern States.

Subspecies of *P. polionotus*

P. p. polionotus (Wag.). Open fields of northern Florida and southern *Georgia*.

P. p. niveiventris (Chapman).. Size larger and color paler: sandy beach region of eastern Florida.

P. p. rhoadsi (Bangs). Length 124 mm.; color darker than *P. niveiventris:* west-central Florida.

P. p. albifrons Osg. Like *P. p. rhoadsi:* coast of western Florida and Alabama.

P. leucopus (Rafinesque). Common white-footed or deer mouse (Fig. 164). Color brownish gray above; under parts and feet pure white; length 166 mm.; tail 77 mm.; hind foot 20 mm.; mammæ 6: eastern and central States; very common.

Subspecies of P. leucopus

P. l. leucopus (Raf.). Western Kentucky southward to southern Louisiana; westward to Oklahoma; eastward through Mississippi and Alabama to eastern Virginia.

P. l. noveboracensis (Fischer). Larger and paler: north-central and eastern States; westward to Kansas and South Dakota; southward to southern Missouri and North Carolina; northward to central Minnesota, Ontario and Maine.

P. l. fusus Bangs. Size larger; length 194 mm.: Martha's Vineyard.

P. l. aridulus Osg. Like *P. l. noveboracensis*, but paler and larger; length 184 mm.: South Dakota and Montana to Oklahoma.

P. l. texanus (Woodhouse). Color darker; molar teeth small: southern Texas and eastern Mexico.

P. l. tornillo (Mearns). Like *P. l. texanus*, but larger and paler: western Texas and eastern New Mexico to Colorado.

P. l. arizonæ (Allen). Like *P. l. tornillo*, but darker: southeastern Arizona and southwestern New Mexico.

P. l. ochraceus Osg. Color ochraceous buff: eastern and central Arizona.

P. gossypinus (LeC.). Cotton mouse. Color rufescent cinnamon above; under parts tinged with cream; tail not distinctly bicolor; feet white; length 181 mm.; tail 81 mm.; hind foot 23 mm.; mammæ 6: southeastern and south-central States.

Subspecies of P. gossypinus

P. g. gossypinus (LeC.). Coast region and peneplain of southern States from Virginia to central Louisiana, except peninsular Florida.

P. g. megacephalus (Rhoads). Larger and paler: northern Alabama and western Tennessee to eastern Oklahoma and Texas and western Louisiana.

P. g. palmarius Bangs. Small and paler: peninsular Florida.

P. g. anastasæ (Bangs). Color pale ochraceous buff; size small: Anastasia Island, Florida and Cumberland Island, Georgia.

FIG. 164.—*Peromyscus leucopus (Rhoads).*

P. boylii (Baird).   Color light brown above; feet white; tail long, equal to or longer than the head and body; length 197 mm.; tail 103 mm.; hind foot 22 mm.; mammæ 6: southwestern States and Mexico.

Subspecies of P. boylii

P. b. boylii (Baird).   West slopes of the Sierras from Yosemite to Mount Shasta, thence along the east slope of the Coast Range southward to San Francisco Bay.

P. b. rowleyi (Allen).   Like *P. b. boylii*, but paler: mountains of southern California to western Texas; southern Nevada, Utah and Colorado.

P. b. attwateri Allen.   Like *P. b. boylii;* hind foot larger: central Texas to Arkansas and Kansas.

P. pectoralis laceianus Bailey.   Color pinkish buff above mixed with dusky; under parts pure white; length 187 mm.; tail 96 mm.; hind foot 23 mm.: west-central Texas into Mexico.

P. truei (Shufeldt).   Rock mouse.   Color ochraceous buff above, mixed with fine dusky lines; under parts creamy white; feet white; tail slightly bicolor; length 186 mm.; tail 92 mm.; hind foot 23 mm.; ears very large, equal in length to hind foot; mammæ 6: Pacific and southwestern States and Mexico.

Subspecies of P. truei

P. t. truei (Schuf.).   Eastern California to eastern New Mexico and southeastern Colorado.

P. t. gilberti (Allen).   Size larger and color darker: mountains of interior California and the coast south of San Francisco Bay; northward to central Oregon.

P. t. martirensis (Allen).   Size large; tail long: mountains of southwestern California.

P. nasutus (Allen).   Not quite as large as *P. truei;* tail finely annulated; color grayish brown; mammæ 6: mountains of Colorado, eastern Arizona and western Texas.

P. nuttalli (Harlan).   Golden mouse.   Color ochraceous above, creamy white suffused with ochraceous below; ears ochraceous; length 181 mm.; tail 85 mm.; hind foot 20 mm.; mammæ 6: southeastern Virginia and northern North Carolina; westwards to central Kentucky.

Subspecies of P. nuttalli

P. n. nuttalli (Harl.). Distribution as given above.

P. n. aureolus (Audubon and Bachman). Size smaller: southeastern States, from North Carolina, east of the mountains, to northern Florida; Gulf slope to eastern Texas and north into Missouri.

P. floridanus (Chap.). Size large; color pale ochraceous buff; under parts white; length 200 mm.; tail 86 mm.; hind foot 26 mm.; mammæ 6; plantar tubercles 5: central Florida, from coast to coast.

P. crinitus (Merr.). Color buff above, white beneath; mammæ 4; length 190 mm., tail 95 mm.; hind foot 21 mm.: Great Basin, from eastern Oregon and southern Idaho to Lower California.

P. californicus (Gambel). Size very large, being the largest in the country; length 243 mm.; tail 133 mm.; hind foot 27 mm.; color russet above, mixed with black; under parts creamy white; ears very large; mammæ 4: coast region of California from San Francisco into Lower California.

P. eremicus (Baird). Color ochraceous buff above; white beneath; tail long; length 183 mm.; tail 101 mm.; hind foot 20 mm.; mammæ 4: deserts of southern California to western Texas.

P. taylori (Thomas). Size very small, being the smallest of the genus, and one of the smallest of rodents; length 97 mm.; tail 38 mm.; hind foot 14 mm.; color pale drab; under parts smoky gray: coastal region of Texas.

4. Oryzomys Baird. Body rat-like, long and slender; tail long; belly not pure white; fur coarse: 50 species, mostly in Mexico and Central America; 1 species in the United States; the litter numbers 3 to 7.

O. palustris (Harlan). Rice or marsh rat (Fig. 165). Body dark brown above, paler beneath; length 240 mm.; tail 115 mm.; hind foot 30 mm.: southeastern States; in coastal marches and wet lands.

Subspecies of O. palustris

O. p. palustris (Har.). Southern New Jersey to the Gulf States and northwards to southern Illinois.

O. p. natator Chapman. Color tawny; body larger: South Carolina to Florida and southern Texas.

O. p. coloratus Bangs. Color rich reddish brown; size large; length 301 mm.: central Florida.

O. p. texensis Allen. Color paler, grayish: coast of Mississippi, Louisiana and Texas; Mississippi Valley into Missouri.

5. Sigmodon Say and Ord.   Body large and rat-like; ears large; tail long; molars with crowns flattened and showing S-shaped loops: 11 species, mostly in Mexico; 1 species in the United States.

S. hispidus S. and O.   Cotton rat (Fig. 166).   Color yellowish brown above sprinkled with black, whitish beneath; fur long and coarse;

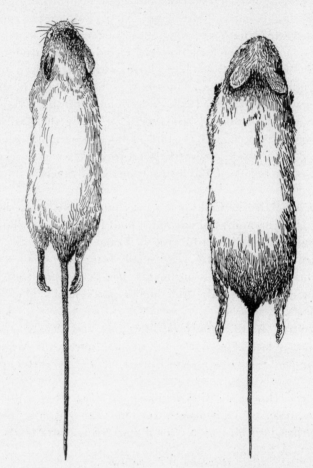

FIG. 165.—*Oryzomys palustris (after Stone & Cram).*   FIG. 166.—*Sigmodon hispidus (after Stone & Cram).*

length 252 mm.; tail 102 mm.; hind foot 32 mm.: south Atlantic and Gulf States; westward to Kansas, Texas and into Mexico; 11 subspecies.

Subspecies of *S. hispidus*

S. h. hispidus S. and O.   North Carolina to Florida and Louisiana.
S. h. littoralis Chapman.   Color darker: southeastern Florida.

S. h. spadicipygus Bangs. Size smaller; rump rufous: extreme southern Florida.

S. h. texianus (Audubon and Bachman). Size smaller; rump reddish: Texas, Oklahoma and Kansas.

S. h. berlandieri (Baird). Color pale: western Texas and eastern New Mexico.

S. h. eremicus Mearns. Color yellowish; size larger: along the lower Colorado.

S. h. arizonæ Mearns. Size large; length 320 mm.; colors pale: Arizona.

S. minimus Mearns. Size small; fur not hispid; color grizzled gray; length 185 mm.; tail 95 mm.; hind foot 31 mm.: southern New Mexico and Arizona.

Subfamily 3. Neotominæ.—W o o d r a t s; mountain rats. Body large, but slender; eyes and ears large; tail long; crowns of molar teeth flattened (Fig. 167): 5 genera, all in North America, 1 in the United States; mostly in the west.

Neotoma Say and Ord. With the characters of the subfamily: 28 species, about 10 in the United

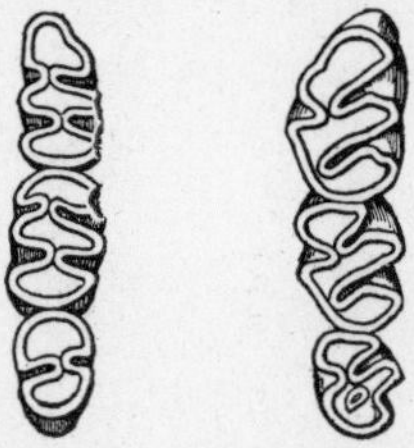

FIG. 167.—Non-tuberculate teeth of *Neotoma*.

States, mostly in the western States; most species live in rocky or mountainous regions, building large conical nests of sticks, often in trees above the ground, to which well-defined runways lead. Their food consists of grass, bark, seeds, fruit, etc. Wood rats have several litters a year of from 2 to 5 young each. They sometimes enter houses and resemble the common rat, but may be distinguished by usually greater size, larger ears and eyes, a shorter and fully furred, bicolor tail and white feet and under parts.

Key to the United States Species of Neotoma

a_1 Tail cylindrical and not bushy.
  b_1 Size large; length more than 320 mm.
    c_1 In the eastern and central States.
      d_1 From Pennsylvania to Alabama....................*N. pennsylvanica.*
      d_2 In the Gulf States; Texas to South Dakota.........*N. floridana.*
    c_2 In the far-western States.
      d_1 Hind feet white.
        e_1 Not on the Pacific coast; in the States on the Mexican border.
          f_1 Throat and breast pure white...............*N. micropus.*
                              N. albigula.
          f_2 Throat and breast plumbeous...............*N. mexicana.*

e$_2$ In the Pacific coast region....................*N. intermedia.*
d$_2$ Hind feet dusky..............................*N. fuscipes.*
b$_2$ Size small; length under 320 mm.
 c$_1$ From California to Utah...........................*N. desertorum.*
 c$_2$ In Arizona and New Mexico.......................*N. lepida.*
a$_2$ Tail flattened and bushy...............................*N. cinerea.*

N. pennsylvanica Stone. Wood or cave rat. Color grayish buff above and white beneath, darkest middorsally; feet white; length 430 mm.; tail 198 mm.; hind foot 43 mm.: Appalachian Mountain region from the Hudson River in southern New York to Alabama; Transition zone; nocturnal animals nesting in caves and rocky crevices, where they heap together a great mass of sticks and leaves, in which is the nest; probably omnivorous.

N. floridana (Ord.). Color pale cinnamon above; underneath parts and feet white; length 409 mm.; tail 189 mm.; hind foot 38 mm.; tail slightly bicolor and scantily haired: southern and central States.

Subspecies of N. floridana

N. f. floridana (Ord.). Atlantic coast region from South Carolina to Sebastian, Florida.

N. f. rubida. Bangs. Color redder: lower Mississippi Valey, northward to Arkansas, and the Gulf coast from Alabama to Texas.

N. f. illinoensis Howell. Color grayer; tail bicolor: southern Illinois to northern Arkansas.

N. f. attwateri (Mearns). Color darker and teeth smaller; tail white beneath, sharply bicolor: central Texas to Missouri.

M. f. baileyi (Merriam). Color grayer; fur longer; tail shorter, bicolor: South Dakota to Oklahoma.

N. micropus Baird. Color pale drab; under parts white; tail blackish above, grayish beneath; length 351 mm.; tail 163 mm.; hind foot 41 mm.: central and western Texas and New Mexico into Mexico; northward into Kansas and Colorado.

N. albigula Hartley. Color pinkish buff above; under parts and feet white; tail sharply bicolor; length 328 mm.; tail 152 mm.; hind foot 33 mm.: southwestern States.

Subspecies of N. albigula

N. a. albigula Hart. Southwestern Texas to western Arizona and into Mexico.

N. a. venusta (True). Size larger: western Arizona and south-eastern California.

N. a. warreni Merr. Color decidedly grayer: northeastern New Mexico and southeastern Colorado.

N. mexicana Baird. Color grayish buff; under parts dull white; feet white; tail brownish above, white below; length 327 mm.; tail 149 mm.; hind foot 34 mm.; fur on throat and breast plumbeous: deserts of the southwest.

Subspecies of *N. mexicana*

N. m. mexicana Baird. Western Texas, southern New Mexico and Arizona.

N. m. fallax (Merr.). Size larger; color grayer: mountains of Colorado and New Mexico.

N. m. pinetorum (Merr.). Size larger; color less gray: central and eastern Arizona.

N. desertorum Merr. Size small; ears large; fur long; color pinkish buff; belly and feet white; tail bicolor; length 293 mm.; tail 131 mm.; hind foot 30 mm.: deserts of Nevada, Utah and southern California.

N. lepida Thomas. Color yellowish buff above; under parts creamy or pinkish white; feet white; length 286 mm.; tail 136 mm.; hind foot 29 mm.: New Mexico and Arizona.

Subspecies of *N. lepida*

N. l. lepida Thom. Northern New Mexico and Arizona.

N. l. stephensi (Goldman). Size larger; color darker and grayish instead of yellowish: central Arizona and western New Mexico.

N. fuscipes Baird. Size large; length 438 mm.; tail 209 mm.; hind foot 42 mm.; color ochraceous buff, very dark middorsally; throat and chest pure white; belly creamy or pinkish buff; forefeet and toes of hind feet white; hind feet dusky: Pacific slope.

Subspecies of *N. fuscipes*

N. f. mohavensis Elliot. Color grayer: Mohave Desert, California.

N. f. fuscipes Baird. Pacific coast region from San Francisco Bay to Salem, Oregon.

N. f. streatori Merr. Smaller; color paler; tail sharply bicolor: west slopes of the Sierra Nevadas.

N. f. annectens Elliott. Like *N. f. fuscipes*, but with distinctive cranial characters: from San Francisco Bay to Monterey Bay, and inland southward.

N. f. macrotis (Thomas). Size small; color grayish brown; tail bicolor: coastal region south of Monterey Bay.

N. cinerea (Ord). Color grayish buff above, white beneath; length 390 mm.; tail 160 mm.; hind foot 43 mm.; tail flattened and bushy: hind foot densely furred on sole: northwestern States and British Columbia; 9 subspecies.

Subspecies of N. cinerea

N. c. cinerea (Ord). Rocky Mountains from northern Montana and the Dakotas to Arizona; central Nevada and western California.

N. c. occidentalis (Baird). Color darker: British Columbia to northern California; eastward into Idaho and northern Nevada.

N. c. fusca (True). Color very dark: coastal region west of the Cascades in Oregon.

N. c. arizonæ (Merr.). Size very small: northern Arizona and New Mexico and southern Utah and Colorado.

N. c. orolestes (Merr.). Color ochraceous: Rocky Mountain region from New Mexico to Montana.

N. c. rupicola (Allen). Color paler; size smaller: southwestern South Dakota; western Nebraska; eastern Colorado.

N. intermedia Rhoads. Color grayish brown; under parts white; feet white; tail black above, dull white below; length 325 mm.; tail 160 mm.; hind foot 31 mm.: coastal region of California from Monterey Bay southward to Cape San Lucas.

Subfamily 4. Microtinæ.—Meadow or field mice; voles; lemmings. Body stout, with a thick head and short ears and a short tail; crowns of molars flattened and showing triangular loops of enamel: distribution circumpolar; over 70 species in the United States; very common animals, living in a great variety of locations, but most abundant in well-watered grass lands, all remarkable for their great fecundity, breeding usually throughout the year; their food consists mainly of green vegetation, roots and bark and they are often a plague to the agriculturist. This subfamily includes the Scandinavian lemmings, which at irregular intervals migrate across the country in great armies, eventually reaching the sea and all drowning, and also the Alpine marmot, which lives in the high mountains and hibernates 8 or 10 months of the year.

Key to the United States Genera of Microtinæ

a_1 Tail round.

  b_1 Molars without roots (prongs) (Fig. 168).

    c_1 Lower incisors long; their roots extending under the posterior molars.

      d_1 Plantar tubercles mostly 6.

        e_1 Mammæ mostly 8...............:..................1. *Microtus.*

        e_2 Mammæ 4.......................................3. *Pitymys.*

      d_2 Plantar tubercles 5.

        e_1 Mammæ 8...2. *Lagurus.*

        e_2 Mammæ 6.......................................4. *Neofiber.*

    c_2 Lower incisors short, their roots ending on the inner side of the molars.......................................5. *Synaptomys.*

  b_2 Molars with roots (prongs) (Fig. 169).

    c_1 Back not red or chestnut in color; molars large..........6. *Phenacomys.*

    c_2 Back red in color; molars small and weak..............7. *Evotomys.*

a_2 Tail flattened laterally; size large; muskrats..................8. *Ondatra.*

1. Microtus Schrank. Meadow or field mice; voles. Cranium slender; lower incisors very long, with roots ending on the outer side

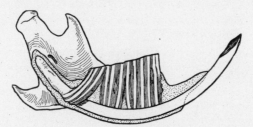

FIG. 168.—Lower jaw of *Microtus pennsylvanicus*, showing the molars without roots but open below so that they grow continuously (*from Miller*).

of the molars, which are rootless (Fig. 168); tail very short but longer than the hind foot; plantar tubercles 5 or 6; thumb with nail: over

FIG. 169.—Lower jaw of *Phenacomys orophilus*, showing the molars possessing roots (*from Miller*).

150 species, ranging northward to Arctic regions and southward to the tropics; 30 species and very many subspecies in the United States,

mostly northerly in range; both diurnal and nocturnal animals which build nests under bush heaps or stones, to which runways, often more or less subterraneous, lead; they feed on grasses, roots and bark, and also at times on grain, and they do not hibernate. Field mice at times become excessively numerous in a district, when they may destroy forage crops, and also fruit trees and shrubbery by gnawing off the bark at the base of the trunk. Several litters, numbering from 4 to 11 each, are born annually.

Key to the United States Species of Microtus

a_1 Plantar tubercles 6.
  b_1 Mammæ 8.
    c_1 In the eastern and central States.
      d_1 In the States east of the Mississippi.
        e_1 Nose not yellow.
          f_1 Present from the Atlantic to the Rockies....*M. pennsylvanicus.*
          f_2 On Muskeget Island Massachusetts........*M. breweri.*
        e_2 Nose conspicuously yellow...................*M. chrotorrhinus.*
      d_2 In the States between the Mississippi and the Rockies.
        e_1 Present from the Atlantic to the Rockies.......*M. pennsylvanicus.*
        e_2 In the Black Hills, South Dakota............*M. longicaudus.*
        e_3 In the Rocky Mountains....................*M. mordax.*
    c_2 In the Pacific States.
      d_1 Throughout California........................*M. californicus.*
      d_2 In the southern Sierras......................*M. dutcheri.*
      d_3 In Idaho and Nevada........................*M. nanus.*
      d_4 In Oregon and Washington.
        e_1 From Puget Sound to Yaquina Bay...........*M. townsendii.*
        e_2 In the Willamette Valley....................*M. canicaudus.*
        e_3 In northern California and southern Oregon....*M. angusticeps.*
        e_4 In eastern Oregon in Utah...................*M. montanus.*
  b_2 Mammæ 4; in Arizona...............................*M. mogollonensis.*
a_2 Plantar tubercles 5.
  b_1 Mammæ 8.
    c_1 In the Boreal zone of the Rockies and Cascades......*M. richardsoni.*
    c_2 In the Puget Sound region.........................*M. oregoni.*
                                                      M. serpens.
  b_2 Mammæ 6.
    c_1 In the central Mississippi Valley....................*M. ochrogaster.*
    c_2 From South Dakota and Kansas to the Rockies......*M. haydeni.*
    c_3 In Louisiana.......................................*M. ludovicianus.*
    c_4 In Minnesota and South Dakota....................*M. minor.*

M. pennsylvanicus (Ord). Common field or meadow mouse (Fig. 170). Color chestnut brown above, darker middorsally, grayish beneath; feet brownish; length 180 mm.; tail 50 mm.; hind foot 21 mm.; nammæ 8: eastern and central States; southward to North Carolina; westward to the Rockies; northward to Hudson Bay; common in meadows.

Subspecies of M. pennsylvanicus

M. p. pennsylvanicus (Ord). Transition zone from the Atlantic coast to the Great Plains.

M. p. nigrans Rhoads. Larger, with notably larger hind feet and darker coloration: coast region of northern North Carolina and southern Virginia.

M. p. fontigenus (Bangs). Size smaller: eastern Canada, Hudsonian zone.

M. p. acadicus Bangs. Smaller and paler: Nova Scotia and Prince Edwards Island.

M. p. modestus (Baird). Color paler, more yellowish: Rocky Mountains and western plains from New Mexico to British Columbia; Transition zone.

M. breweri (Baird). Color pale grayish; fur long and coarse; length 182 mm.; tail 54 mm.; hind foot 22 mm.: Muskeget Island, Massachusetts.

M. ochrogaster (Wagner). Prairie meadow mouse. Color grizzly gray; belly fulvous; fur coarse; length 150 mm.; tail 32 mm.; hind foot 20 mm.; mammæ 6: southern Wisconsin to Oklahoma and eastern Kansas and Nebraska; eastward to Indiana; common in dry prairie land.

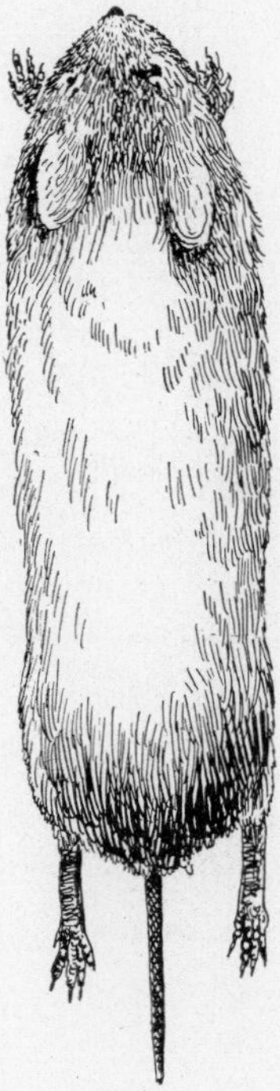

M. chrotorrhinus (Miller). Color glossy brown; nose, ears and rump conspicuously yellowish; length 165 mm.; tail 45 mm.; hind foot 19 mm.: Mount Washington, the Catskills and into Canada; Hudsonian zone.

FIG. 170.—*Microtus pennsylvanicus (after Stone & Cram).*

M. haydeni (Baird). Color light gray; belly silvery white; length 180 mm.; tail 47 mm.; hind foot 22 mm.: western South Dakota to Kansas; westward into southern Montana, Wyoming and eastern Colorado; in dry prairies.

M. longicaudus (Merriam). Color dark brown above, whitish below; length 180 mm.; tail 65 mm.; hind foot 21 mm.: Boreal cap of Black Hills.

M. ludovicianus Bailey. Color dark gray above, dark buff below: length 164 mm.; tail 33 mm.; hind foot 19 mm.: coast prairies of Louisiana.

M. minor (Merr.). Size very small; length 120 mm.; tail 30 mm.; hind foot 16 mm.; color peppery gray above, buff below: northern border of the Great Plains from Minneapolis to eastern North Dakota and Alberta.

M. californicus (Peale). Color dull buff or brownish; belly whitish; tail bicolor, dark brown and gray; length 171 mm.; tail 49 mm.; hind foot 21 mm.; mammæ 8; fur coarse: Pacific slope; in dry meadows.

Subspecies of M. californicus

M. c. californicus (Peale). Coastal region of central California.

M. c. constrictus Bailey. Smaller and grayer: northwest coast of California, near Cape Mendocino.

M. c. eximius Kellogg. Tail black: coastal region of northern California and southern Oregon.

M. c. æstuarinus Kellogg. Size large; color dark: San Joaquin and Sacramento valleys.

M. c. vallicola Bailey. Larger and darker: Owens Valley region, California.

M. c. sanctidiegi Kellogg. Color brown or buff; size large: San Diego region; north to the San Bernardino Mountains.

M. c. kernensis Kellogg. Color lighter; size large: Kern River basin; west to Bakersfield, California.

M. townsendii (Bachman). Color dark brown; belly grayish; tail black; length 226 mm.; tail 66 mm.; hind foot 26 mm.; ears conspicuous: region west of the Cascades from British Columbia to Yaquina Bay, Oregon; Transition zone.

M. mordax (Merr.). Color dark gray; belly whitish; tail long; feet small; length 185 mm.; tail 70 mm.; hind foot 22 mm.: Rocky Mountains from latitude 60 to New Mexico and the eastern slopes of the Cascades and Sierras; common on the banks of mountain streams; Hudsonian and Canadian zones.

Subspecies of M. mordax

M. m. mordax (Merr.). Eastern Oregon and northern and central Nevada.

M. m. sierræ Kellogg. Color darker: northern and eastern California and Oregon.

M. m. bernardinus Merr. San Bernardino Mountains.

M. m. abditus Howell. Size very large; color darker: coastal region of Oregon.

M. m. macrurus (Merr.). Larger and darker: coastal region of Washington, and northwards to Alaska.

M. angusticeps Bailey. Color dark brownish gray, darkest on the face; tail distinctly bicolor; length 170 mm.; tail 56 mm.; hind foot 22; skull very narrow: coastal region of northwestern California and southern Oregon.

M. montanus (Peale). Color dark gray; belly whitish; length 175 mm.; tail 52 mm.; hind foot 21 mm.: eastern Oregon; northern California to Nevada.

Subspecies of M. montanus

M. m. arizonensis Bailey. Color more ferrugineous: eastern Arizona; Transition zone.

M. m. rivularis (Bailey). Larger and lighter colored: Washington County, Utah; Lower Sonoran zone.

M. nanus (Merr.). Color grizzled gray; length 151 mm.; tail 41 mm.; hind foot 18 mm.: Rocky Mountains from central Idaho to central Nevada and southern Colorado; Canadian zone.

M. n. canescens Bailey. Color lighter and clearer: northern Washington and British Columbia, east of the Cascades.

M. canicaudus Miller. Color bright yellowish brown; belly whitish gray; tail uniform grayish; length 135 mm.; tail 33 mm.; hind foot 20 mm.: Wiliamette Valley and southern Washington; Transition zone.

M. dutcheri Bailey. Color dark brown; belly buffy brown; tail bicolor; length 167 mm.; tail 35 mm.; hind foot 20 mm.: Hudsonian zone of the southern Sierras; in wet alpine meadows.

M. richardsoni (DeKay). Color grayish sepia; belly whitish; tail long; feet large; fur long and heavy; length 234 mm.; tail 81 mm.; hind foot 29 mm.: Boreal zones of the Rockies and the Cascades.

Subspecies of M. richardsoni

M. r. macropus (Merr.). Color dark sepia; size smaller: Rockies from the Wasatch into Canada.

M. r. arvicoloides (Rhoads). Color dark sepia: Boreal zone of the Cascades.

M. mogollonensis (Mearns). Color dull rusty brown; belly cinnamon or gray; mammæ 4; length 131 mm.; tail 28 mm.; hind foot 18 mm.: plateau country of central Arizona.

M. oregoni (Bachman). Color dark brown and grizzled; belly dusky; length 140 mm.; tail 42 mm.; hind foot 17 mm.: Pacific coast region from northern California to Puget Sound; in dry open forests.

M. serpens Merr.   Color sooty gray; belly dusky; length 130 mm.; tail 31 mm.; hind foot 18 mm.: northern Washington and southern British Columbia between the Cascades and Puget Sound.

2. Lagurus Gloger.   Similar to *Microtus;* cranium low and wide; plantar tubercles 5; mammæ 8; colors pale; fur lax; tail very short; size small: 4 species.

L. curtatus (Cope).   Color buffy gray; whitish beneath; length 141 mm.; tail 27 mm.; hind foot 17 mm.: eastern California and western Nevada; Transition zone.

L. pallidus (Merriman).   Color very pale buffy gray; length 121 mm.; tail 25 mm.; hind foot 18 mm.: western Dakota and Montana, in high prairies.

L. pauperrimus (Cooper).   Color buffy gray; length 115 mm.; tail 20 mm.; hind foot 16 mm.: eastern Washington and Oregon; Transition zone.

3. Pitymys McMurtrie.   Like *Microtus;* cranium flat and wide; plantar tubercles 5; mammæ 4; fur short and dense; ears very small; tail very short: 3 species, 1 in Mexico.

P. pinetorum (LeConte).   Pine mouse.   Color bright russet brown; belly dusky; ears concealed in the fur; length 113 mm.; tail 18 mm.; hind foot 15 mm.: Georgia and Mississippi to Indiana and New York; common in fields and open woods.   The pine mouse has an underground nest and raises several litters of from 1 to 4 young a year; the runways are also underground, and often resemble mole's tunnels; the food consists of grasses, roots and bark, and great damage is often done to orchards and gardens.

FIG. 171.—Lower jaw of *Synaptomys cooperi (from Miller).*

Subspecies of P. pinetorum

P. p. pinetorum (LeConte).   Georgia and the Carolinas.

P. p. scalopsoides (Audubon and Bachman).   Size larger; color darker: North Carolina to New York; westward to Illinois.

P. p. auricularis (Bailey).   Colors dark and rich, ears large: Mississippi to Indiana, between the Alleghany Mountains and the Mississippi River.

P. nemoralis (Bailey).   Color full chestnut; belly washed with bright cinnamon; length 130 mm.; tail 24 mm.; hind foot 18 mm.: westward of the Mississippi River from Arkansas to Iowa.

4. Neofiber True. Size very large; tail long; plantar tubercles 5; mammæ 6; skull massive: 1 species.

N. alleni True. Color dark brown; belly pale buff; length 320 mm.; tail 121 mm.; hind foot 40 mm.: Florida; in marshes and bogs.

5. Synaptomys Baird. Lemmings. Each upper incisor with a longitudinal groove in its outer surface; lower incisors extend back along the inner side of the molars (Fig. 171), which are without roots; tail very short, covered with short hairs: about 4 species in the United States.

S. cooperi Baird (Fig. 172). Body small and mouse-like, but with a very much shorter tail than the house-mouse, grizzled gray in color; length 120 mm.; tail 18 mm.; hind foot 18 mm.; plantar tubercles 6; head very large: northern and central States and Canada; in woody marshes and swamps; Boreal and Transition zones.

Subspecies of S. cooperi

S. c. cooperi Baird. Minnesota to the Atlantic; south through New York and Michigan.

S. c. helaletes Merriam. With larger head and feet, and longer tail: length 130 mm.; tail 21 mm.; hind foot 20 mm.: Dismal Swamp in Virginia and North Carolina.

S. c. stonei Rhoads. Like the above, but smaller: central Wisconsin and Illinois to the Atlantic; Massachusetts to North Carolina.

S. c. gossii (Coues). Like *S. c. helaletes*, but redder: northeastern Arkansas and southern Illinois into Iowa and Dakota.

S. sphagnicola Preble. Color sepia brown mixed with black; under parts grayish white; length 132 mm.; tail 17 mm.; hind foot 17 mm.: Mount Washington, New Hampshire.

FIG. 172.—*Sy-naptomys cooperi (after Stone & Cram).*

6. Phenacomys Merriam. Similar to *Microtus;* molars with 2 roots (Fig. 169) and large and strong; front teeth without grooves; body short and thick; tail short; ears just appearing above the fur: 14 species and subspecies, in Canada and the western mountains of the United States.

P. intermedius Merriam. Color yellowish brown, whitish below; length 142 mm.; tail 30 mm.; hind foot 17 mm.: western States and Canada, in the mountains.

Subspecies of P. intermedius

P. i. intermedius Merr.   British Columbia to northern California and Utah; central Montana to New Mexico.

P. i. levis Howells.   Similar to the above; color brownish drab; feet white: central Alberta into Montana.

P. i. olympicus (Elliot).   Color dark drab; length 155 mm.; tail 42 mm.: Olympic and Cascade Mountains.

P. i. celsus Howells.   Color light brown: Sierra Nevadas.

P. albipes Merr.   Color grizzled brown; grayish beneath; feet white; length 168 mm.; tail 62 mm.; hind foot 19 mm.: coastal region from Humboldt County, California, north to the Columbia River.

P. longicaudus True.   Color bright rusty brown; feet brown, length 148 mm.: coniferous forests in the coastal region of western Oregon and northwestern California.   The mouse is arboreal in habits, building a large nest of twigs from 30 to 100 feet from the ground in which it raises several litters of young a year, numbering from 1 to 4 each.

7. Evotomys Coues.   Red-back mice.   Body small and reddish in color, with a short tail; molars rooted, and small and weak, the lower incisors extending along the outer side of them; incisors without grooves: circumpolar; about 24 species and subspecies in the United States and Canada, which nest in underground burrows in which they raise several broods a year, each numbering from 3 to 8 young; they feed on seeds, roots, etc., and lay up stores for winter use.

FIG. 173.—*Evotomys gapperi (after Stone & Cram)*.

† *E. gapperi* (Vigors) (Fig. 173).   Color bright chestnut above; sides buff, sharply defined from the color of the back; length 140 mm.; tail 40 mm.; hind foot 18 mm.: Canada and northern United States; southward into the Pennsylvania mountains; westward to eastern Oregon; in cool forests and swamps.

Subspecies of E. gapperi

E. g. gapperi (Vigors).   Pennsylvania to Canada; westward to the Rockies.

E. g. ochraceus Miller.   Color pale rusty rufous: Upper Boreal zone of White Mountains, New Hampshire and eastward.

E. g. rhoadsi Stone.   Ears large, projecting conspicuously above the fur; color dark chestnut; skull and teeth heavy: southern New Jersey to New York.

E. g. loringi Bailey.   Size very small; colors bright: Minnesota and eastern Dakotas, along the edge of timbered valleys.

E. g. galei (Merriam).   Size larger; colors lighter: Boreal zone of Colorado to northern Montana.

E. g. saturatus Rhoads.   Size larger; colors lighter: Blue Mountains, Oregon; northern Idaho.

E. carolinensis Merr.   Color dark chestnut, fading into lighter; length 150 mm.; tail 45 mm.; hind foot 21 mm.: mountain forests of the southern Alleghenies.

E. brevicaudus (Merr.).   Color pale reddish, mixed with black; belly cream; length 125 mm.; tail 31 mm.; hind foot 19 mm.: Black Hills; Boreal zone.

E. idahoensis Merr.   Color pale hazel, lined with black; length 153 mm.; tail 48 mm.; hind foot 20 mm.: mountains of south-central Idaho.

E. mazama Merr.   Color cinnamon rufous; length 157 mm.; tail 52 mm.; hind foot 18 mm.: crest of the Cascades in Oregon.

E. obscurus Merr.   Color olive gray above; length 155 mm.; tail 47 mm.; hind foot 17 mm.: eastern Oregon and northeastern California.

E. californicus Merr.   Color sepia above, dark chestnut on the back; length 161 mm.; tail 50 mm.; hind foot 21 mm.: coast of Oregon and northern California.

E. occidentalis Merr.   Color dark chestnut above; sides gray; under parts salmon buff; length 145 mm.; tail 45 mm.; hind foot 18 mm.: Puget Sound and coast region of Washington.

E. nivarius Bailey.   Color light chestnut above; sides gray; length 150 mm.; tail 50 mm.; hind foot 18 mm.: high peaks of the Olympic Mountains, Washington.

8. Ondatra Link (*Fiber* Cuvier).   Muskrats.   Body large and stout; legs short; feet large, the feet and toes being fringed with short, stiff hairs; hind toes partly webbed; tail flattened laterally, with few hairs; fur thick, with longer hairs projecting from it; anal musk glands present: 3 species, with many subspecies, all in North America; the most important fur-bearing animals in the country.

O. zibethica (L.).   Common muskrat.   Color brown, variable, darker dorsally, whitish beneath; length 560 mm.; tail 250 mm.; hind foot 81 mm.: North America, from the Arctic barrens and Hudson Bay to the Mexican boundary; very common.   The animals live in swamps and ponds and streams, in the banks of which they may burrow to form the nest where the young are born. They also form large dome-shaped houses two or three feet high and five or six feet in diameter by heaping up sticks and reeds, the upper portion of which contains a chamber above the level of the water where they spend much of the winter. Their food consists of roots and water-plants, and also shell-fish and other small animals; they raise several litters annually of from 3 to 13 each, and do not hibernate, 14 subspecies.

Subspecies of O. zibethicus

O. z. zibethica (L.). Northeastern and central States; westward to Minnesota and the Great Plains; southward to Georgia and Arkansas, except along the Atlantic seaboard south of Delaware Bay.

Fig. 174.—Incisors of (1) *Geomys bursarius* and (2) *Thomomys talpoides* (from Merriam).

O. z. macrodon Merriam. Colors rich and bright; black phase often common; in size the largest of the genus; length 620 mm.; tail 274 mm.; hind foot 88: Atlantic coast region from Delaware Bay to Pamlico Sound.

O. z. osoyoosensis Lord. Color glossy brown to black: Puget Sound region and Rocky Mountains.

O. z. occipitalis Elliot. Paler and more reddish than *F. z. osoyoosensis:* northern Willamette Valley and coast of Oregon.

O. z. mergens Hollister. Color pale; size large: northern part of Great Basin.

O. z. pallida Mearns. Color uniform rusty red; size small: Colorado River Valley; eastward to Rio Grande.

O. z. ripensis Bailey. Color light brown; size small: Pecos Valley, Texas.

O. z. cinnamomina Holl. Color pale, with much red: Great Plains from Manitoba to northern Texas; east to central Iowa.

O. rivalicia Bangs. Color dark brownish black; length 547 mm.; tail 233 mm.; hind foot 78 mm.: coast region of Louisiana; moults twice annually.

Family 2. Geomyidæ.—Pocket gophers. Thick-bodied rodents with short legs, fore feet fitted for digging, small ears and eyes, and a pair of large fur-lined cheek-pouches which are not connected with the mouth but open on the cheeks at the sides of the mouth; dentition 1/1, 0/0, 1/1, 3/3: 9 genera and about 100 species, all American, half of which occur in the southern United States, the rest in Mexico and Central America. The animals live in burrows in the ground, in which they dig with great facility, using both the strong, clawed fore feet and the incisors. Their food consists chiefly of roots, tubers and grasses, and they frequently do great damage to potato and vegetable fields. The cheek-pouches are useful in carrying food to their winter store houses, substances being put into them with their fore feet. They are mostly nocturnal and live in communities and do not hibernate; the young number from 1 to 7 in a litter.

Key to the Genera of Geomyidæ of the United States

a₁ Outer surface of the upper incisors grooved (Fig. 174).
  b₁ Upper incisors with 2 grooves each......................1. *Geomys.*
  b₂ Upper incisor with a single deep groove..................2. *Cratogeomys.*
a₂ Outer surface of the upper incisors not grooved or with a single
  fine groove...3. *Thomomys.*

1. Geomys Rafinesque. Upper incisors with a large groove near the middle and one near the median margin; ears rudimentary; fore claws very large: 16 species and subspecies, all in the United States.

FIG. 175.—*Geomys tuza (from Merriam).*

G. tuza (Barton) (Fig. 175). Color brown above, yellowish beneath; tail almost naked; length 270 mm.; tail 89 mm.; hind foot 33 mm.: Georga, Florida and Alabama; common.

G. t. tuza (Bart.). Pine barrens of Georgia; Austroriparian zone.

.G. t. mobilensis Merriam. Color very dark: Alabama and Florida.

G. t. floridanus (Audubon and Bachman). Size larger; color darker: peninsular Florida.

G. bursarius (Shaw) (Fig. 174). Color dark reddish brown; feet white; length 270 mm.; tail 80 mm.; hind foot 35 mm.; upper incisors with 2 grooves; very common; 1 litter annually of 1 to 7 young: upper Mississippi Valley; southward to eastern Kansas and southeastern Missouri; westward into the Dakotas; eastward to Lake Michigan.

G. breviceps Baird. Color dark russet brown; length 230 mm.; tail 70 mm.; hind foot 28 mm.; size small: lower Mississippi Valley and Gulf coast of Louisiana and Texas; northward into Kansas.

Subspecies of G. breviceps

G. b. sagittalis Merr. Size smaller: Gulf coast about Galveston Bay.

G. b. attwateri Merr. Size larger: coastal plain and islands from Nueces Bay to Matagorda Bay.

G. texensis Merr. Color dark brown mixed with black; feet and under parts white; length 203 mm.; tail 60 mm.; hind foot 28 mm.: central and southern Texas.

G. arenarius Merr. Colors pale; length 258 mm.; tail 88 mm.; hind foot 33 mm.: valley of the upper Rio Grande.

G. lutescens (Merr.). Colors pale drab or fulvous; beneath whitish; length 270 mm.; tail 85 mm.; hind foot 32 mm.: Great Plains from South Dakota to Texas; eastern Wyoming and Colorado; Upper Sonoran zone.

2. Cratogeomys Merriam. Upper incisors with a single groove: 1 species in the United States.

C. castanops Baird. Color yellowish brown; buff beneath; length 262 mm.; tail 65 mm.; hind foot 37 mm.: Great Plains from the Arkansas River into Mexico.

3. Thomomys Wied. Outer surface of upper incisors not grooved or with one faint groove near the median margin (Fig. 174); ears distinct but very small; claws moderate: many species, all in the Rocky Mountain or Pacific States or along the Mexican border.

T. bottæ (Eydoux and Gervais). Color yellowish brown, darker towards the head; lips and lining of the pockets white; length 260 mm; tail 89 mm.; hind foot 33 mm.; mammæ 4 pairs: California; 13 subspecies.

Subspecies of T. bottæ

T. b. bottæ (E. and G.). Coast region from Freestone to San Diego.

T. b. laticeps (Baird). Color warmer and brighter: coast region north of Eel River, northern California.

T. b. minor Bailey. Size smaller; color darker: coast region from Cape Mendocino to Cazadero.

T. b. leucodon (Merriam). Smaller, lighter: from Fairfield and Placerville to Grants Pass, Oregon.

T. b. navus (Merr.). Much smaller; color lighter: Sacramento Valley.

T. b. mewa Merr. Size smaller; color darker: east side of San Joaquin Valley.

T. b. angularis (Merr.). Size large; color light: west side of San Joaquin Valley; also Santa Clara and San Juan Valleys.

T. bulbivorus (Richardson). Color dark brown, above and below; length 300 mm.; tail 90 mm.; hind foot 42 mm.; mammæ 4 pairs: Willamette Valley.

T. townsendii (Bachman). Color dark gray above, buff below; length 305 mm.; tail 100 mm.; hind foot 38 mm.; mammæ 4 pairs; in dark color phase black all over: southern Idaho and Oregon and northern Nevada.

T. alpinus Merr. Color yellowish brown, being darker along the back and lighter on the belly; mammæ 4 pairs; length 222 mm.; tail 61 mm.; hind foot 30 mm.: upper levels of the southern Sierras.

T. perpallidus (Merr.). Color buff or cream above, whitish beneath; length 241 mm.; tail 84 mm.; hind foot 31 mm.; mammæ 4 pairs: deserts of southern California to New Mexico and Colorado: 14 subspecies.

Subspecies of T. perpallidus

T. p. perpallidus (Merr.). Colorado desert, southern California.

T. p. perpes (Merr.). Size small; color gray: eastern California from Owens Valley to Hesperia.

T. p. canus (Bailey). Color grayish buff; size rather large: western and central Nevada.

T. p. aureus (Allen). Color golden buff; size rather large: southern Nevada and Utah, western Colorado, New Mexico and Arizona.

T. fulvus (Woodhouse). Color dark tawny or light chestnut; length 219 mm.; tail 70 mm.; hind foot 30 mm.; mammæ 4 pairs: Arizona to Texas; 8 subspecies.

Subspecies of T. fulvus

T. f. fulvus (Woodh.). Central Arizona and western and central New Mexico.

T. f. toltecus (Allen). Color paler and grayer: southeastern Arizona and southwestern New Mexico.

T. talpoides (Richardson) (Fig. 174).   Color dark gray or grayish brown; under parts whitish or pure white; tail white tipped or all white; length 214 mm.; tail 60 mm.; hind foot 28 mm.; mammæ 6 pairs: South Dakota, Colorado and Wyoming northward into Canada; 8 subspecies.

Subspecies of T. talpoides

T. t. talpoides (Rich.).   Western Montana into Canada.

T. t. rufescens (Wied).   Size large; length 240 mm.; color dark gray: North and South Dakota and Manitoba.

T. t. clusius (Coues).   Size small; color hazel gray: eastern Colorado and Wyoming.

T. t. bullatus Bailey.   Color pale and bright: eastern Montana and Wyoming and western South Dakota.

T. ocius (Merr.).   Color very pale buffy gray, whitish underneath; length 204 mm.; tail 60 mm.; hind foot 26 mm.; mammæ 7 pairs: Green River basin in Wyoming, Colorado and Utah.

T. pygmæus Merr.   Color hazel-brown; length 177 mm.; tail 46 mm.; hind foot 22 mm.; the smallest species; mammæ 6 pairs: southwestern Wyoming and southeastern Idaho; Transition zone.

T. fossor Allen.   Color dark brown; length 221 mm.; tail 63 mm.; hind foot 29 mm.; mammæ 5 pairs: mountains of Colorado and Utah; Boreal zone.

T. quadratus Merr.   Color light russet; length 210 mm.; tail 64 mm.; hind foot 27 mm.; mammæ 5 pairs: northern California, eastern Oregon and Nevada.

Subspecies of T. quadratus

T. q. quadratus Merr.   Eastern Oregon and northern California.

T. q. fisheri Merr.   Color paler; size smaller: northern Nevada.

T. douglasii (Richardson).   Color uniform dull hazel; length 215 mm.; tail 64 mm.; hind foot 30 mm.; mammæ 4 pairs: western Washington; 7 subspecies.

T. monticola Allen.   Color dull hazel above, buff beneath; length 212 mm.; tail 70 mm.; hind foot 27 mm.; mammæ 4 pairs: California and Oregon; 5 subspecies.

Subspecies of T. monticola

T. m. monticola Allen.   Sierra Nevada of California and Nevada; southward to Mammouth Pass.

T. m. mazama (Merr.).   Color darker and richer: Cascade and Sis-kiyou Mountains; southward to the Trinity Mountains; northward to the Columbia.

T. m. pinetorum Merr.   Nose and cheeks conspicuously gray: mountains on the west side of Sacramento Valley.

T. fuscus (Merr.).   Color light brown; length 203 mm.; tail 70 mm.; hind foot 27 mm.; mammæ 4 pairs: Wyoming to Washington and northward into Canada; 5 subspecies.

Subspecies of T. fuscus

T. f. fuscus (Merr.).   Western Montana and Wyoming, northern and central Idaho, eastern Oregon and Washington, British Columbia.

T. f. saturatus Bailey.   Size larger; color darker: higher parts of the Cœur d'Alene Mountains.

T. hesperus Merr.   Color dark rich auburn; length 210 mm.; tail 60 mm.; hind foot 24 mm.: coast region of northwestern Oregon.

Family 3. Heteromyidæ.—Small, slender rodents with a long tail and with a pair of cheek-pouches, which are lined with fur on the inside and open at the side of the mouth on each cheek; eyes and ears usually large; fur harsh in many species, with numerous bristles or spines: 6 genera and about 100 species, all in America, mostly in more or less arid regions of the western States and Mexico.

Key to the United States Genera of Heteromyidæ

a_1 Progression by walking...................................1. *Perognathus.*
a_2 Progression by leaping.
   b_1 Tail with a terminal pencil............................2. *Dipodomys.*
   b_2 Tail without terminal pencil...........................3. *Microdipodops.*

1. Perognathus Wied.   Pocket mice (Fig. 176).   Body slender and murine; tail at least as long or nearly as long as the rest of the body; ears small; legs and feet long; dentition 1/1, 0/0, 1/1, 3/3; molars rooted and tuberculate; upper incisors strongly sulcate; hair harsh in some species and soft in others: many species, all in North America; about 25 species and very many subspecies in the United States, all west of the Mississippi; nocturnal, burrowing animals, dwelling on plains and deserts and feeding on seeds; several litters of young raised annually, numbering from 2 to 8 each.

P. fasciatus Wied.   Color olivaceous; pure white below; fur soft; soles of feet hairy; length 134 mm.; tail 64 mm.; hind foot 17 mm.: eastern Montana and Wyoming and western Dakota; Upper Sonoran and Transition zones.

P. flavescens (Merriam). Color buff; white below; feet and legs white; length 129 mm.; tail 61 mm.; hind foot 17 mm.: South Dakota to northern Texas; westward to the Rockies.

P. merriami Allen. Color ochraceous buff; belly, feet and fore legs white; length 116 mm.; tail 57 mm.; hind foot 16 mm.: central and southern Texas to southeastern New Mexico.

P. flavus Baird. Color pinkish buff; pure white below; fur very soft; length 112 mm.; tail 50 mm.; hind foot 15 mm.: eastern Utah and Wyoming and western South Dakota; south to Mexico.

P. apache Merr. Color rich buff; length 139 mm.; tail 67 mm.; hind foot 18 mm.: eastern Arizona, western New Mexico and southern Utah and Colorado.

P. panamintinus Merr. Color grayish buff; underparts white; fur long and silky; length 143 mm.; tail 78 mm.; hind foot 20 mm.: southern California and Nevada.

P. longimembris (Coues). Color uniform, being buff above and white below; length 145 mm.; tail 74 mm.; hind foot 18 mm.: southern California; Sonoran zone.

P. parvus (Peale). Color gray or buff, having two color phases; length 171 mm.; tail 91 mm.; hind foot 22 mm.: central and eastern California, Oregon, Washington, and the Great Basin; Upper Sonoran zone.

Subspecies of P. parvus

FIG. 176.
Perognathus penicillatus (after Stone & Cram).

P. p. parvus (Peale). Yakima River, Washington to southeastern Oregon.

P. p. mollipilosus (Coues). Size smaller, color darker: northeastern California to Klamath Basin.

P. p. olivaceus (Merr). Color lighter: Great Basin from southern Idaho and Oregon to Owens Valley, California.

P. p. magruderensis Osgood. Size larger; length 198 mm.: southeastern California and Nevada.

P. lordi (Gray). Color pale buff; length 183 mm.; tail 97 mm.; hind foot 23 mm.: plains of the Columbia; Upper Sonoran and Transition zones.

P. formosus Merr. Color grizzled sepia; white below; length 189 mm.; tail 106 mm.; hind foot 24 mm.; tail very long, heavily crested: southern Nevada, Utah and California; Lower Sonoran zone.

P. hispidus Baird. Color ochraceous; under parts white; fur harsh but without bristles; soles of hind feet naked; length 222 mm.; tail

108 mm.; hind foot 26 mm.: Great Plains from the Dakotas to Mexico; westward to the base of the Rockies.

P. penicillatus Woodhouse (Fig. 176). Color buff; length 205 mm.; tail 110 mm.; hind foot 25 mm.; tail long and crested: southern California, Arizona and Nevada.

P. intermedius Merr. Color drab; fur harsh, with spines on the rump; length 179 mm.; tail 102 mm.; hind foot 22 mm.: southern Arizona and New Mexico.

P. fallax Merr. Color dark drab; length 192 mm.; tail 104 mm.; hind foot 23 mm.: southern California.

P. femoralis Allen. Size very large; tail and ears very long; color dark drab; under parts dirty white; length 223 mm.; tail 126 mm.; hind foot 27. mm.: extreme southern California.

P. californicus Merr. Color dark drab; under parts yellowish white; rump and flanks supplied with bristles; length 192 mm.; tail 103 mm.; hind foot 24 mm.: central and southern California.

Subspecies of *P. californicus*

P. c. californicus Merr. Vicinity of San Francisco Bay.

P. c. dispar Osgood. Size larger; color paler: coast valleys of California; southward to San Bernardino.

P. c. ochrus Osgood. Color paler; length 200 mm.: Kern County, California.

2. Dipodomys Gray. Kangaroo rats (Fig. 177). Body slender; hind legs and tail very long, the tail black dorsally and ventrally and white on the sides and ending with a penicillate tuft; hind foot with either 4 or 5 toes; fur soft; soles of feet hairy; fore legs very short; dentition 1/1, 0/0, 1/1, 3/3; color brownish or yellowish, with a conspicuous white stripe across the thigh; eyes large: about 50 species and subspecies, mostly in western America; burrow-

FIG. 177.—*Dipodomys agilis (after Stone & Cram).*

ing, nocturnal animals with remarkable jumping powers, making jumps 4 to 6 feet long. They inhabit deserts and dry plains, feeding on seeds and leaves, and raise from 2 to 6 young in a litter.

D. agilis Gambel (Fig. 177).   Color yellowish brown, mixed with dusky; hind foot with 5 toes; length 300 mm.; tail 180 mm.; hind foot 42 mm.: southern and western California; Transition and Sonoran zones.

Subspecies of D. agilis

D. a. agilis Gamb.   Southwestern California; north to Santa Barbara.

D. a. simulans (Merriam).   Color darker; length 285 mm.; tail 172 mm.: San Diego County.

D. a. cabezonæ (Merr.).   Color buffy ochraceous; length 282 mm.; tail 171 mm.: southern California deserts.

D. a. perplexus (Merr.).   Color yellowish brown; length 320 mm.; tail 195 mm.: southern Sierras and Tejon Mountains.

D. a. venustus (Merr.).   Color cinnamon brown; length 316 mm.; tail 191 mm.: Santa Lucia Mountains.

D. microps (Merr.).   Color pale buff; length 270 mm.; tail 150 mm.; hind foot 40 mm.: Mohave Desert, California.

D. deserti Stephens.   Color pale yellowish brown; hind foot with 4 toes; length 342 mm.; tail 200 mm.; hind foot 52 mm.: Colorado and Mohave Deserts, California.

D. heermanni LeConte.   Color cinnamon buff; length 293 mm.; tail 180 mm.; hind foot 45 mm.: northern California.

Subspecies of D. heermanni

D. h. heermanni LeConte.   Hind foot with 5 toes: west base of the central Sierra Nevadas; Upper Sonoran zone.

D. h. californicus (Merr.).   Hind foot with 4 toes; length 312 mm.; tail 195 mm.: central California coastal region north of San Francisco.

D. h. dixoni (Grinnell).   Hind foot with 5 toes; length 282 mm.; tail 170 mm.: northern portion of the San Joaquin Valley.

D. h. goldmani (Merr.).   Color drab brown; length 312 mm.; tail 185 mm.: Salinas River Valley.

D. morroensis (Merr.).   Color dark buff; length 292 mm.; tail 177 mm.: San Luis Obispo County, California.

D. panamintinus (Merr.).   Color buffy clay; length 301 mm.; tail 180 mm.: Panamint Mountains, California.

D. stephensi (Merr.).   Hind foot with 5 toes; dark clay in color; length 295 mm.; tail 180 mm.; hind foot 43 mm.: San Jacinto Valley, California.

D. ingens (Merr.). Hind foot with 5 toes; size very large; color ochraceous buff; length 330 mm.; tail 185 mm.: Fresno, San Luis Obispo and Santa Barbara Counties, California.

D. spectabilis Merr. Color ochraceous buff; length 350 mm.; tail 211 mm.; hind foot with 4 toes: western Texas, to Arizona.

D. elator Merr. Hind foot with 4 toes; color clay; length 290 mm.; tail 170 mm.: northern Texas and southern Oklahoma.

D. merriami Mearns. Hind foot with 4 toes; color clay; length 240 mm.; tail 143 mm.: California to Texas.

Subspecies of D. merriami

D. m. merriami Mearns: Mohave Desert, southeastern Nevada and southwestern Arizona.

D. m. exilis Merr. Color darker: San Joaquin Valley, California.

D. m. parvus Rhoads. Color buffy gray; length 248 mm.; tail 154 mm.: southern California.

D. m. nitratoides Merr. Color darker; dusky crescent over nose; size smaller: Tulare County, California.

Subspecies of D. ordii

D. ordii Woodhouse. Hind foot with 5 toes; color clay; length 244 mm.; tail 140 mm.; hind foot 39 mm.: western States.

D. o. ordii Wood. Southern Texas to Arizona.

D. o. columbianus (Merr.). Color darker; length 232 mm.; tail 130 mm.: northern portion of the Great Basin.

D. o. utahensis (Merr.). Color clay; length 260 mm.; tail 147 mm.; hind foot 40 mm.: northern Utah.

D. o. richardsoni (Allen). Color paler; length 267 mm.; tail 144 mm.; hind foot 40 mm.: western Texas, north into Utah and Wyoming.

D. o. montanus (Baird). Color yellowish brown; length 245 mm.; tail 137 mm.: Castilla County, Colorado.

D. o. longipes (Merr.). Color bright ocracheous buff; length 275 mm.; tail 165 mm.; hind foot 42 mm.: Painted Desert, Arizona.

3. Microdipodops Merriam. Kangaroo mice. Size very small; penicillate, four-striped tail lacking; mastoid region very much inflated; dentition 1/1, 0/0, 1/1, 3/3; hind foot with 5 toes: 4 species.

M. californicus Merr. Color olivaceous; under parts snow white; length 160 mm.; tail 92 mm., terminal third blackish; hind foot 25 mm.: southern California.

M. pallidus Merr. Color pale buff; tail without a dark tip; length 171 mm.; tail 102 mm.; hind foot 25 mm.: Churchill County, Nevada.

M. megacephalus Merr.   Color yellowish brown; under parts white; tail bicolor, terminal third blackish; length 150 mm.; tail 80 mm.; hind foot 24 mm.: northern California and Nevada and southeastern Oregon.

Family 4.   Zapodidæ.—Jumping mice.   Small mouse-like rodents with very long hind legs and tail and short fore legs, which progress by leaping; ears and eyes large; upper incisors much curved, compressed and deeply sulcate: 2 genera and about 15 species, in the northern United States and Canada; 1 species in China.

Key to the Genera of Zapodidæ

a₁ One very small premolar present............................1. *Zapus.*
a₂ No premolars present......................................2. *Napæozapæ.*

1. Zapus Coues.   Tail longer than the rest of the body; hind foot nearly half as long as the head and body; dentition 1/1, 0/0, 1/0, 3/3; premolars very small: about 10 species, which live in meadows and make nests in burrows in the ground or in tufts of grass or hollow logs; progress is made by leaps, which may be 10 feet in length; they hibernate in the winter; 1 or 2 litters annually of 5 or 6 young each.

Z. hudsonius (Zimmermann).   Meadow jumping-mouse.   Body about the size of a house-mouse; color yellowish brown above, with a broad dark dorsal band; white beneath; tail tipped with brown and bicolor; feet white; length 217 mm.; tail 132 mm.; hind foot 30 mm.: eastern and central States; westward to the Rockies and Alaska.

Subspecies of Z. hudsonius

Z. h. hudsonius (Zimm.).   Hudson Bay to New Jersey, and in the mountains to North Carolina; west to Iowa and Missouri and Alaska.

Z. h. americanus (Barton).   Size small; length 191 mm.: from Raleigh, N. C. along the coastal plain to Connecticut.

Z. h. campestris Preble.   Size large; length 222 mm.: Great Plains from Manitoba to Nebraska; westward to Colorado and Wyoming.

Z. princeps Allen.   Color yellowish brown, with a broad dark dorsal band; length 245 mm.; tail 147 mm.; hind foot 32 mm.: Rocky Mountain region from New Mexico to Alberta.

Subspecies of Z. princeps

Z. p. oregonus Preble.   Color lighter; length 250 mm.: Blue Mountains, Oregon.

Z. trinotatus Rhoads. Color dark ochraceous buff on the sides; dorsal band very distinct; length 248 mm.; tail 153 mm.; hind foot 33 mm.: coastal region, British Columbia to Humboldt Bay.

Subspecies of Z. trinotatus

Z. t. alleni (Elliot). Tip of tail often white: Sierras from Mount Shasta to Kern River.

Z. luteus Miller. Color brighter; length 225 mm.; tail 136 mm.; hind foot 32 mm.: northern New Mexico.

Z. montanus Merriam. Color dark ochraceous buff; dorsal area sharply defined; tail sharply bicolor; length 228 mm.; tail 135 mm.; hind foot 31 mm.: Cascade Range in Oregon.

Z. orarius Preble. Color dark ochraceous, dorsal area and lower parts strongly suffused with the color of the sides; length 220 mm.; tail 127 mm.; hind foot 30 mm.: coast from San Francisco to Humboldt Bay California.

Z. pacificus Merr. Color similar to *Z. orarius;* length 225 mm.; tail 141 mm.: hind foot 31 mm.: south-western Oregon and northern California.

2. Napæozapus Preble. Similar to *Zapus*, but without premolars: 1 species and several subspecies.

N. insignis (Miller) (Fig. 178). Color of sides yellowish buff; back dark; belly white; tip of tail white; length 238 mm.; tail 146 mm.; hind foot 31 mm.: Nova Scotia to Maryland; westward to Lake Superior; in meadows and forests, near streams.

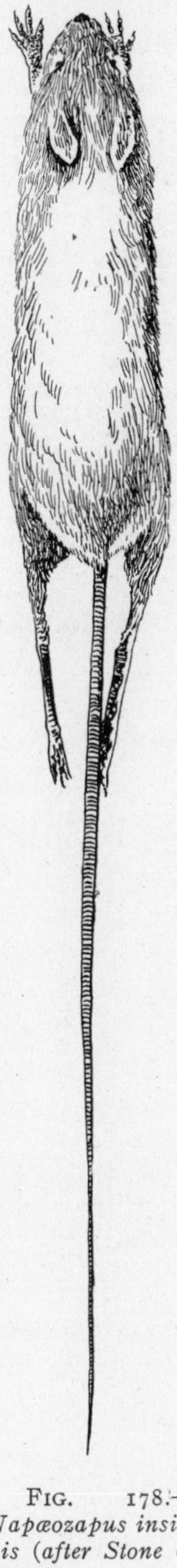

Family 5. Erethizontidæ.—Porcupines. Large, short-legged rodents with long, stiff spines or quills mingling with the coarse hair; feet plantigrade; dentition 1/1, 0/0, 1/1, 3/3; molars with long roots: 3 genera, of which 2 are tropical; habits arboreal and nocturnal.

Erethizon F. Cuvier. Tail short and thick and not prehensile; toes 4 in front, 5 behind: 2 species.

E. dorsatum (L.). Common porcupine; hedgehog. Color uniform blackish; quills tipped with black; length 900 mm.; tail 150 mm.; hind foot 90 mm.; quills 50 to 100 mm. long and mostly concealed by the fur; average weight 18 lbs.; maximum weight 40 lbs.: northern America; Lower Hudsonian, Canadian

Fig. 178.—*Napæozapus insignis* (after Stone & Cram).

and Upper Transition zones; westward to the Great Plains. Porcupines climb trees for bark and twigs, which they feed on, but they are clumsy climbers and live largely on the ground, nesting in holes among the rocks; from 1 to 4 young raised annually; they do not hibernate.

E. epixanthum Brandt. Western porcupine. Similar to *E. dorsatum;* tips of long hairs greenish yellow; midventral line brownish; length 825 mm.; tail 165 mm.: from the upper Missouri into New Mexico; westward to the Pacific; northward from California to Alaska.

Subspecies of E. epixanthum

E. e. couesi Mearns. Smaller and paler: Arizona.

Family 6. Aplodontiidæ.—Mountain beavers; boomers. Form stout, heavy; limbs short; head broad, flat, triangular; tail very short; eyes very small; feet plantigrade, 5-toed; dentition 1/1, 0/0, 2/1, 3/3: 1 genus.

Aplodontia Richardson. With the characters of the family: about 1 species; burrowing, mainly nocturnal, animals which live in colonies in dense wet forests, in which they construct numerous runways and tunnels, and feed on bark, leaves and twigs, laying up large stores for winter use; they raise 2 or 3 young annually and do not hibernate.

A. rufa (Rafinseque). Color umber; belly gray; whiskers white; length 350 mm.; hind foot 53 mm.: Pacific Coast States.

Subspecies of A. rufa

A. r. rufa (Raf.). Western slope of the Cascade Mountains from British Columbia into northern California.

A. r. olympica Merriam. Color darker: Olympic Mountains.

A. r. ranieri (Merr.). Color grayer; length 373 mm.; hind foot 63 mm.: on Mount Ranier.

A. r. pacifica Merr. Color fulvous brown; belly plumbeous; length 325 mm.; hind foot 52 mm.: Pacific coast of Oregon.

A. r. humboldtiana (Taylor). Color ochraceous to pinkish buff; length 345 mm.; hind foot 54 mm.: coastal region of northwestern California.

A. r. californica (Peters). Color grayer: the Sierra Nevada, California.

Family 7. Sciuridæ.—Squirrels, marmots, etc. Arboreal or terrestrial rodents, with mostly long, bushy tails; skull with postorbital processes; molars rooted and with tubercular biting surfaces: 15 or 20 genera and about 250 species, grouped in 2 subfamilies; cosmopolitan, except in the Australian region; about 9 genera and 90 species in the United States and Canada.

Key to These Subfamilies

a₁ No flying membrane present.................................1. *Sciurinæ.*
a₂ Flying membrane present; flying squirrels....................2. *Pteromyinæ.*

Subfamily 1. Sciurinæ.—Squirrels; chipmunks; ground squirrels; prairie dogs; woodchucks: 9 genera.

Key to These Genera

a₁ Tail long; body slender.
  b₁ Cheek-pouches absent; tail very long...............1. *Sciurus.*
  b₂ Cheek-pouches present; tail moderate.
    c₁ Thumb with well developed nail; chipmunks.
      d₁ Premolars 1/1; eastern chipmunks...........2. *Tamias.*
      d₂ Premolars 2/1; western chipmunks (Fig. 181)..3. *Eutamias.*
    c₂ Thumb with rudimentary nail (Fig. 182); ground
      squirrels.
      d₁ Back and sides broadly striped.
        e₁ Tail not curved over the back............4. *Callospermophilus.*
        e₂ Tail curved over the back................5. *Ammospermophilus.*
      d₂ Back and sides not broadly striped, either finely
        striped or spotted or uniform in color.
        e₁ Size large; length over 500 mm...........6. *Otospermophilus.*
        e₂ Size small; length under 300 mm..........7. *Citellus.*
a₂ Tail short; body stout and heavy.
  b₁ Length 400 mm. or less; prairie dogs..............8. *Cynomys.*
  b₂ Length over 600 mm.; woodchucks.................9. *Marmota.*

1. Sciurus L. Squirrels. Body slender; tail long and bushy, the hairs being longest on the sides; ears and eyes large; thumb rudimentary; dentition 1/1, 0/0, 2/1, 3/3: over 100 species; cosmopolitan, excepting the Australian region; 10 species and numerous subspecies in the United States; about 30 species in Mexico and Central America; arboreal and mostly diurnal rodents which feed on seeds, nuts and buds, and often on young birds, bird-eggs and insects, and which build their nests in trees; they probably do not usually hibernate, and usually lay up stores of food.

Key to the Species of Sciurus in the United States

a₁ Upper premolars 2 in number, making 5 grinders on each side in
  upper jaw (Fig. 179).
  b₁ Size small; color red.
    c₁ In the eastern, central and Rocky Mountain States.
      d₁ In the northeastern, north-central and Rocky Moun-
      tain States; common red squirrel.................*S. hudsonicus.*

      d_2 In the central Rockies and southwestern States.......*S. fremonti.*
      c_2 On the Pacific slope.................................*S. douglasii.*
   b_2 Size large; color gray, sometimes black.
      c_1 Ears not tufted.
         d_1 In the eastern and central States; common gray squirrel.*S. carolinensis.*
         d_2 On the Pacific slope.................................*S. griseus.*
      c_2 Ears tufted with long black hairs.
         d_1 Belly white; ears black...........................*S. aberti.*
         d_2 Belly dark; ears reddish.........................*S. kaibabensis.*
a_2 Upper premolar 1 in number, making 4 grinders on each side in
   upper jaw (Fig. 180).
   b_1 In the eastern and central States; common fox squirrel......*S. niger.*
   b_2 In Arizona..*S. apache.*
                                                       S. arizonensis.

S. hudsonicus (Erxleben). Red squirrel. Color reddish brown above and whitish beneath; tail relatively narrow and short; ears tufted in winter; length 315 mm.; tail 115 mm.; hind foot 47 mm.; several litters of young raised a year, from 4 to 6 each: northern America from Labrador to Alaska and British Columbia; southward to Virginia and Tennessee; westward to Utah, eastern Oregon and Washington.

Subspecies of S. hudsonicus

S. h. hudsonicus (Erx.). Colors pale; fringe of tail yellowish: eastward of Rocky Mountains in Canadian and Hudsonian zones.

S. h. gymnicus Bangs. Size small; length 290 mm.; outer fringe of tail red; colors deep; belly gray in winter: northeastern States, Canadian zone; southward into New York State, Michigan and Minnesota.

S. h. loquax Bangs. Outer fringe of tail yellowish; colors pale; belly pure white at all seasons: eastern States, Transition and Upper Austral zones.

S. h. minnesota Allen. Size large; colors pale; under side of tail gray; length 345 mm.: Minnesota to Iowa, eastward to Indiana.

S. h. dakotensis Allen. Size large; colors very pale; center of tail yellowish red: Black Hills and Wyoming.

S. h. baileyi Allen. Fringe of tail black; dorsal band pale; size large: central Wyoming and eastern Montana.

S. h. ventorum Allen. End of tail black; size large: Yellowstone Park region into the Wasatch Mountains.

S. h. richardsoni Bachman. Upper surface of tail mostly black; size large: western Montana into eastern Washington and Oregon.

S. h. streatori Allen. Terminal third of tail black: Columbia River, northward into British Columbia.

S. fremonti Audubon and Bachman. Similar to *S. hudsonicus,* but large; dorsal band pale yellowish rufous; length 335 mm.; tail 140 mm.; hind foot 55 mm.: Colorado, Utah, New Mexico and Arizona; Canadian zone.

Subspecies of *S. fremonti*

S. f. fremonti Aud. and Bach. Color grayish; white beneath: mountains of Colorado and northeastern Utah.

S. f. lychnuchus Stone and Rehn. Color dull ferruginous; fringe of tail black: White Mountains, New Mexico.

S. f. neomexicanus Allen. Size smaller: Taos Range, New Mexico.

S. f. mogollenensis (Mearns). Dorsal band brighter: higher mountains of central Arizona; Canadian and Boreal zones.

S. f. grahamensis (Allen). Like *S. f. mogollonesis,* but paler: fir zone, Graham Mountains, Arizona.

S. douglasii Bachman. Pine squirrel; redwood squirrel. Similar to the red squirrel; color brown or brownish gray above and buff or gray beneath; fur soft and dense; tail short, fringed with hellow; length 315 mm.; tail 125 mm.; hind foot 50 mm.: Pacific slope from British Columbia to Lower California; in coniferous forests.

Subspecies of *S. douglasii*

S. d. douglasii Bach. Washington and Oregon, along the coast.

S. d. mollipilosus (Audubon and Bachman). Color dark brown; belly gray; white tail fringe: coast region of northern California and southern Oregon.

S. d. cascadensis Allen. Size large; tail fringe white: Cascade Mountains.

S. d. albolimbatus Allen. Tail fringe white; belly buff; size large: Sierras of northern California; southeastern Oregon.

S. carolinensis Gmelin. Gray squirrel (Fig. 179). Color gray above with a rusty middorsal region and white beneath; two color phases may occur, the black color phase not uncommon in many localities; tail very long and bushy, edged with white; length 500 mm.; tail 220 mm.; hind foot 70 mm.: eastern and central States; westward into Oklahoma and Nebraska; 2 litters of from 4 to 6 young each are raised.

Subspecies of *S. carolinensis*

S. c. carolinensis Gmelin. Size smaller; length 455 mm.: Austral zone; southward to northern Florida; westward into Oklahoma and Nebraska.

S. c. leucotis (Gapper). Larger and grayer; the black color phase often common: Transition and lower edge of Canadian zones; southward into the Pennsylvanian mountains; westward to Minnesota.

S. c. hypophæus Merriam. Size large; color dark; only a small white streak on the belly: Minnesota forest belt.

S. c. extimus Bangs. Size small; length 438 mm.; color light: southern Florida.

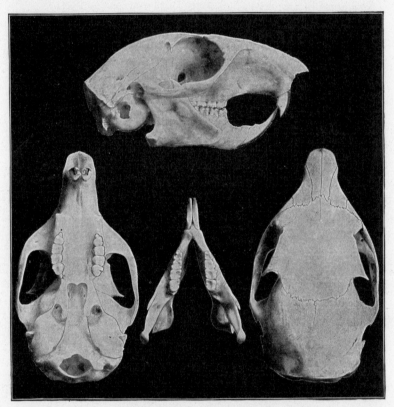

Fig. 179.—Skull of *Sciurus carolinensis* (*from Elliot*).

S. c. fuliginosus (Bachman). Color blackish, grizzled with brown; brown beneath: the bayou region of Louisiana.

S. griseus Ord. Western gray squirrel. Size large; color gray above white beneath; length 550 mm.; tail 250 mm.; hind foot 80 mm.: Pacific slope.

Subspecies of S. griseus

S. g. griseus Ord. Southwestern Washington to Lower California; Transition zone and upper border of Austral, except the coast belt south of San Francisco.

S. g. anthonyi (Mearns). Color gray, suffused with yellowish-brown: Laguna Mountains, southern California.

S. g. nigripes (Bryant). Color much darker; upper surface of feet blackish: coast region south of San Francisco.

S. aberti Woodhouse. Tufted ear squirrel. Color gray with a broad reddish dorsal band; white beneath, with a black or reddish line separating the gray from the white; ear long and pointed, terminating with a long black tuft; length 525 mm.; tail 220 mm.; hind foot 73 mm.: northern Arizona and New Mexico and Colorado; in coniferous forests; Transition zone.

Subspecies of *S. aberti*

S. a. aberti Wood. Mountains of northeastern Arizona and western New Mexico.

S. a. ferreus True. Size smaller; no reddish dorsal band: northern Colorado.

S. a. mimus Merr. Reddish dorsal band absent; size smaller: southwestern Colorado; northern New Mexico.

S. kaibabensis Merr. Similar to *S. aberti;* belly black; 2 annual litters of 3 or 4 each: north of the Grand Canyon, Arizona.

S. niger L. Fox squirrel (Fig. 180). Color reddish brown above and rusty or rusty white beneath; rarely (in the south) black; tail long and bushy; length 675 mm.; tail 300 mm.; hind foot 87 mm.; weight 2 or 3 lbs.; usually 1 litter a year of 2 to 4 young: eastern and central States; westward to the eastern border of the Great Plains.

Subspecies of *S. niger*

S. n. niger L. Color more grayish varying to black; nose and ears white: southeastern States, east of the Alleghenies; north to Virginia.

S. n. neglectus (Gray). Color more reddish: southern New York and New England to central Virginia.

S. n. rufiventer (Geoffrey). Size smaller; length 540 mm.; color deeper ferruginous: Mississippi Valley from the Alleghanies to the Great Plains; southward to northern Louisiana.

S. n. texianus (Bachman). Length 625 mm.; colors pale: coast region of Mississippi and Louisiana.

S. apache Allen. Color of the fox squirrel; upper surface with a broad dorsal band, which may be obscured in the summer; length 554 mm.; tail 279 mm.; hind foot 77 mm.: southern Arizona and Mexico; Transition zone.

S. arizonensis Coues.   Color grizzled gray; belly white; tail black above, edged with white, brown beneath; length 540 mm.; tail 300 mm.; hind foot 71 mm.: Arizona and New Mexico.

   2. **Tamias** Illiger.   Chipmunks.   Body small; tail short and not bushy; large internal cheek pouches present; dentition 1/1, o/o, 1/1,

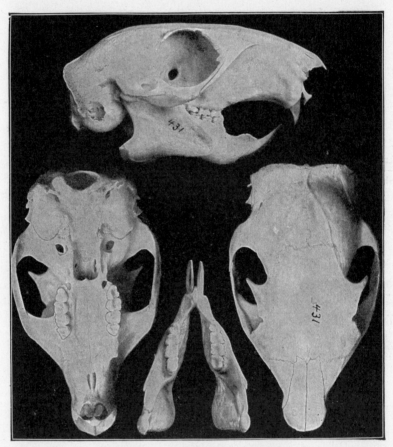

FIG. 180.—Skull of *Sciurus niger* (*from Elliot*).

3/3: 1 species; terrestrial squirrels which make their nests in deep burrows in the ground, in which they hibernate a longer or shorter time in winter; stores of food layed up.

   T. striatus (L.).   Common chipmunk.   Color reddish brown, with a middorsal black stripe and with a lateral whitish, longitudinal stripe bordered above and below on each side by a black stripe; end of tail blackish; rump ferruginous; length 250 mm.; tail 90 mm.; hind foot 33 mm.: eastern and central States; Upper Austral and Transition zones; westward into Nebraska and Oklahoma; several litters of young a year, of 4 to 6 each; the food consists mainly of seeds and fruits, but also of insects, snails, young birds and birds eggs, and other small animals.

Subspecies of T. striatus

T. s. striatus (L.).   Southeastern States.

T. s. griseus Mearns.   Size larger; color less reddish: upper Mississippi Valley, westward of the Great Lakes; southward to eastern Kansas and Missouri.

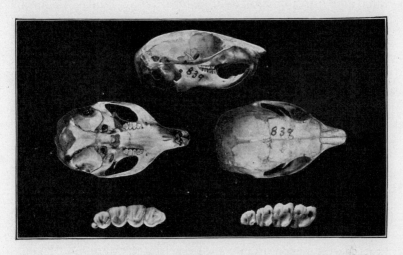

FIG. 181.—Skull of *Eutamias dorsalis* (premolars and molars below, those of the upper jaw being at the left) (*from Elliot*).

T. s. lysteri (Richardson).   Color pale and dull; rump yellowish brown: New England to Lake Huron; Upper Transition and Lower Canadian zones.

T. s. venustus Bangs.   Upper surface dark gray; size large: Oklahoma.

T. s. fisheri Howell.   Colors pale and gray: middle Atlantic States to southern Virginia; westward to Ohio.

3. Eutamias Trouessart.   Western chipmunks.   Similar to *Tamias* in coloration; dentition 1/1, 0/0, 2/1, 3/3; nail of thumb well developed: about 57 species and subspecies; in western America.

E. dorsalis (Baird) (Fig. 181).   Color rusty gray with a dark brown dorsal stripe; other stripes faint; under parts grayish white; length 237 mm.; tail 105 mm.; hind foot 35 mm.: Utah to the Sierras; southward into New Mexico and Arizona.

E. townsendii (Bachman).   Color dark yellowish brown with 5 black dorsal stripes; light stripes almost obsolete; tail black, fringed with white; belly white; length 257 mm.; tail 107 mm.; hind foot 35 mm.; 1 annual litter, possibly more, of 2 to 6 each: British Columbia to central California.

Subspecies of E. townsendii

E. t. townsendii (Bach.).   British Columbia to the Columbia River; coastal region.

E. t. senex (Allen).   Color uniform gray: Boreal zone of the Sierra Nevada and Cascade Ranges from Mariposa County, California to Cook County, Oregon.

E. t. cooperi (Baird).   Color grizzled gray; 3 dorsal stripes distinct, the others not: Cascade Mountains near Mount Ranier; Boreal zone.

E. t. ochrogenys Merr.   Colors dull; stripes inconspicuous: humid coastal region of northwestern California and southern Oregon.

E. merriami (Allen).   Color pale yellowish gray; ears high, pointed; length 250 mm.; tail 117 mm.; hind foot 34 mm.: mountains of southern California.

Subspecies of E. merriami

E. m. merriami (Allen).   Mountains of San Diego County and northwards to San Luis Obispo.

E. m. pricei (Allen).   Color grayish brown; with 5 black dorsal stripes: coastal region from San Francisco to Monterey, California.

E. quadrimaculatus (Gray).   Color of head and rump gray, rest of back ferruginous; ears very large; black markings on the side of the face conspicuous; length 262 mm.; tail 120 mm.; hind foot 35 mm.: central California from Yosemite Park to Quincy.

E. speciosus (Allen).   Color with much white and gray; tip of tail black; length 234 mm.; tail 120 mm.; hind foot 32 mm.: San Bernardino and San Jacinto Mountains to central California, Boreal zone.

Subspecies of E. speciosus

E. s. speciosus (Allen).   San Bernardino and San Jacinto Counties, California.

E. s. frater (Allen).   Dark colors more distinct; size smaller: western Nevada to central California; Lake Tahoe.

E. s. callipeplus (Merr.).   Shoulders ochraceous; flanks fulvous; size small: Yosemite Valley to Mount Pinos.

E. panamintinus (Merr.). Color pale gray; facial stripes indistinct; length 208 mm.; tail 96 mm.; hind foot 31 mm.: west side of Great Basin in California and Nevada.

E. amœnus (Allen). Color gray; stripes conspicuous; flanks ochraceous brown; belly white; length 207 mm.; tail 70 mm.; hind foot 30 mm.: central California into Canada; eastwards into Montana; Transition and Boreal zones.

Subspecies of *E. amœnus*

E. a. amœnus (Allen). Northwestern California, central and eastern Oregon and Washington.

E. a. monœsis Grinnell and Storer. Colors paler: eastern portion of central Sierra Nevadas; Canadian zone.

E. a. luteiventris (Allen). Wyoming and Montana, northwards into Alberta.

E. a. caurinus (Merr.). Olympic Mountains, Washington.

E. cinereicollis (Allen). Color gray; flanks yellowish brown; length 247 mm.; tail 102 mm.; hind foot 35 mm.: San Francisco and Mogollon Mountains, Arizona.

E. umbrinus (Allen). Color yellowish brown; outer dark stripes obsolete; length 249 mm.; tail 100 mm.; hind foot 32 mm.: Wasatch and Uinta Ranges, Utah.

E. quadrivittatus (Say). Color gray, yellowish on the sides; stripes conspicuous: length 237 mm.; tail 100 mm.; hind foot 31 mm.: Colorado and northern New Mexico and Arizona.

E. minimus (Bachman). Size small; color pale, being gray, rusty yellow on the flank; tail black above, yellowish below; length 200 mm.; tail 85 mm.; hind foot 29 mm.: eastern Washington to the Dakotas; south into Arizona and New Mexico.

Subspecies of *E. minimus*

E. m. minimus Bachman. Wyoming, northeastern Utah and western Colorado.

E. m. borealis (Allen). Size small; colors darker: North Dakota to Idaho; north to Alaska; in forests.

E. m. caryi Merr. Color paler and grayer: San Luis Valley, Colorado,

E. m. consobrinus (Allen). Size larger; colors darker: eastern border of the Great Basin in Utah, Colorado and New Mexico.

E. m. pictus (Allen). Colors pallid: Great Basin from western Utah westward; northward to eastern Washington.

E. m. pallidus (Allen).   Color ochraceous buff; length 220 mm.; tail 120 mm.; hind foot 35 mm.: South Dakota, Montana, Wyoming and western Nebraska, in the Great Plains.

E. alpinus (Merr.).   Like *E. m. pictus*, but paler; tip of tail black; length 189 mm.: high Sierras, California.

4. Callospermophilus Merriam.   Golden chipmunks; rock squirrels. Body heavy, with 1 white and 2 black stripes on each side; head, fore limbs and neck uniform reddish or yellowish brown; dentition 1/1, 0/0, 2/1, 3/3: about 12 species and subspecies, in mountain States of the far-west, in forests of pine and fir; in feeding habits similar to chipmunks; they hibernate often from 5 to 7 months; a single litter of 4 to 7 young raised.

C. lateralis (Say).   Color of back reddish brown; lateral stripe broad and bordered above and below by a black stripe; under parts pale brownish gray; length 275 mm.; tail 100 mm.; hind foot 43 mm.: California, Arizona and New Mexico north into Canada; Transition and Lower Boreal zones.

Subspecies of C. lateralis

C. l. saturatus (Rhoads).   Size larger; length 317 mm.; colors darker: central Washington, Cascade Mountains.

C. l. castanurus (Merr.).   Head and shoulders chestnut; length 284 mm.; tail 92 mm.; hind foot 43 mm.: Wasatch Mountains, Utah.

C. l. cinerascens (Merr.).   Head and shoulders chestnut; color of back grizzled gray: from Yellowstone Park, north through Idaho, Montana and northwards.

C. l. wortmani (Allen).   Color yellowish gray, mixed with black; neck and shoulders deep ochraceous; length 280 mm.; tail 95 mm.; hind foot 42 mm.: Wyoming and northwestern Colorado.

C. chrysodeirus (Merr.).   Head, neck and shoulders ochraceous; black stripes more distinct: eastern Oregon and northern California.

C. bernardinus (Merr.).   Similar to the above; length 275 mm.; tail 90 mm.; hind foot 42 mm.: southern California.

5. Ammospermophilus Merriam.   Antelope chipmunks; ground squirrels.   Size small; one whitish lateral stripe; tail very short and carried curved over the back; skull very broad; dentition 1/1, 0/0, 2/1, 3/3: 7 species and subspecies, in arid plains; several litters of young raised a year, of from 4 to 12 each.

A. leucurus (Merr.).   Color grizzled yellowish brown above and yellowish white beneath; tail grizzled blackish above and white below;

length 209 mm.; tail 69 mm.; hind foot 38 mm.: Oregon to Mexico;
Sonoran zone; in deserts.

Subspecies of A. leucurus

A. l. cinnamomeus (Merr.). Upper parts uniform pale cinnamon,
lined with black: northern Arizona, southern California, Utah and
Colorado.

A. l. interpres (Merr.). Similar to *A. leucurus*, but darker; tail
bushy, with 2 free black bands; length 226 mm.; tail 80 mm.; hind foot
37 mm.: western Texas and eastern New Mexico.

A. harrisii (Audubon and Bachman). Similar to *A. l. leucurus;* tail
iron gray above and below; length 230 mm.; tail 80 mm.; hind foot 40
mm.: southern Utah and Nevada into Arizona and northwestern New
Mexico.

A. nelsoni (Merr.). Color yellowish brown; under parts white;
length 228 mm.; tail 68 mm.; hind foot 40 mm.: San Joaquin Valley,
California, south to Bakersfield.

6. Otospermophilus Brandt. Rock squirrels. Size large; colors
grayish or brownish, without stripes, mottled or faintly spotted; ears
small; tail long, flat and moderately bushy; dentition 1/1, 0/0, 2/1, 3/3:
1 species and several subspecies; terrestrial squirrels inhabiting the
western States from the Columbia River and Colorado south into
Mexico.

O. grammurus (Say). Color mottled gray; length 500 mm.; tail
200 mm.; hind foot 60 mm.: central and southern Rockies and Great
Basin.

Subspecies of O. grammurus

O. g. grammurus (Say). Eastern Colorado and south into Arizona,
southeastern California, New Mexico and western Texas.

O. g. utah (Merriam). Size small; back reddish: Wasatch Mountains, Utah and western Colorado.

O. g. buckleyi (Slack). Back and shoulders with much more black;
flanks grayish; size large: southern and western Texas.

O. g. beecheyi (Richardsoni). Color mottled gray and brown,
indistinctly spotted; size smaller: western central California in Sacramento and San Joaquin Valleys.

O. g. douglasii (Rich.). Like *O. g. beecheyi*, but with darker shoulders;
length 375 mm.: Columbia River south to San Francisco.

O. g. nesioticus (Elliot). Like *O. g. beecheyi*, but darker: Santa
Catalina and Santa Barbara Islands, California.

O. g. juglans (Bailey).   Color brownish gray; length 500 mm.; tail 225 mm.: Mogollon Mountains, New Mexico.

7. Citellus Oken. (*Spermophilus* Cuvier).   Ground squirrels; gophers.   Small body and slender; cheek-pouches large; thumb rudimentary (Fig. 182); dentition 1/1, 0/0, 2/1, 3/3: about 80 species, mostly in the more or less arid regions of northern and western America, northern Asia and Europe: over 50 species and subspecies in the United States and Canada.   Ground squirrels feed on grains, seeds, fruits, plants, etc. and are very destructive to crops; they also often eat insects and other small animals.   They breed in deep burrows, in which they raise from 5 to 13 young in a litter, and usually one litter a year.   In the more northerly latitudes they hibernate in the winter, often 6 or more months, but in warmer regions may remain active throughout the year.

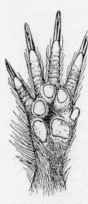

FIG. 182.—Fore foot of *Citellus spilosoma* (*from Mearns*).

C. tridecemlineatus (Mitchill).   Gopher.   Color yellowish-brown, with about 6 yellowish longitudinal stripes alternating with rows of yellow spots, making about 13 stripes in all; belly yellowish; ears small; length 275 mm.; tail 107 mm.; hind foot 32 mm.: central States, from eastern Michigan to the Rockies; southward to northern Missouri and central Texas; northward into Saskatchewan; a single litter of young raised a year.

Subspecies of C. tridecemlineatus

C. t. tridecemlineatus (Mitch.).   Southern Michigan to Dakota.

C. t. alleni (Merriam).   Size small; colors dark: Bighorn Mountains, Wyoming.

C. t. parvus (Allen).   Size small; length 204 mm.: southeastern Montana to western Colorado, Wyoming and Utah; Upper Sonoran zone.

C. t. pallidus (Allen).   Size small; colors pale: Great Plains from eastern Montana and western Dakota into northeastern Utah and northern Colorado.

C. t. olivaceus (Allen).   Color dusky brown above: Black Hills.

C. t. badius (Bangs).   Size large; length 276 mm.; colors dark: Missouri and Oklahoma.

C. t. texensis (Merr.).   Size large; color deep ferruginous: eastern Texas and Oklahoma.

C. franklini (Sabine).   Body yellowish brown, speckled with black but not striped; tail with 3 black lines; length 375 mm.; tail 137 mm.; hind foot 50 mm.: central prairie region from Saskatchewan into Oklahoma; eastward to Indiana; 1 litter annually of 4 to 8 each.

C. spilosoma (Bennett) (Fig. 182). Color reddish brown with ill-defined spots arranged in longitudinal series; under parts yellowish white; ears very short; length 255 mm.; tail 75 mm.; hind foot 32 mm.: southern California to Texas.

Subspecies of C. spilosoma

C. s. macrospilotus (Merr.). Color dark; spots large and far apart; also with a drab-gray color phase: southern Arizona and New Mexico.

C. s. major (Merr.). Dorsal spots indistinct: eastern New Mexico and western Texas to Colorado.

C. s. pratensis (Merr.). Size small; length 197 mm.; colors dark: northwestern Arizona.

C. s. arens (Bailey). In 2 color phases, a reddish and a gray; spots small: southwestern Texas.

C. s. annectans (Merr.). Color grayish brown; spots buff: southern coast region of Texas and New Mexico.

C. tereticaudus (Baird). Color grizzled grayish brown, without spots; tail very long; length 248 mm.; tail 112 mm.; hind foot 35 mm.: southern California to southern Arizona.

C. neglectus (Merr.). Like *C. tereticaudus* but with a much shorter tail; length 200 mm.; tail 74 mm.; hind foot 32 mm.: western Arizona.

C. cryptospilotus (Merr.). Color pale buff, without spots; length 190 mm.; tail 60 mm.; hind foot 32 mm.: Painted Desert, Arizona.

C. obsoletus (Kennicott). Color light gray, spotted indistinctly; length 212 mm.; tail 62 mm.: Black Hills and western Nebraska; westward to Utah.

C. elegans (Kenn.). Color uniform dusky yellowish brown, without spots; length 275 mm.; tail 67 mm.; hind foot 46 mm.: Wyoming, northern Utah and northwestern Colorado; Transition and Upper Sonoran zones.

C. armatus (Kenn.). Color uniform dark gray, without spots; length 275 mm.; tail 62 mm.: Utah, Wyoming, Idaho and Montana.

C. richardsonii (Sab.). Similar to *C. elegans*, but paler: North Dakota and Montana; Canada.

C. columbianus (Ord). Color yellowish brown, with many white blotches; length 370 mm.; tail 102 mm.; hind foot 55 mm.: western Montana to Washington.

C. mollis (Kenn.). Color dusky yellowish brown, without spots; ears rudimentary; length 208 mm.; tail 45 mm.: Utah and Nevada.

Subspecies of C. mollis

C. m. stephensi (Merr.).   Head and shoulders pinkish buff: Nevada.

C. m. canus (Merr.).   Color dusky grizzled gray: northern Oregon.

C. m. yakimensis (Merr.).   Color buffy gray: eastern Washington.

C. townsendi (Bachman).   Color dark reddish brown, speckled with white; ears very small; length 305 mm.; tail 90 mm.; hind foot 37 mm.: plains of the Columbia River to Montana.

C. beldingi (Merr.).   Sides and under parts yellowish gray; dorsal band bright rufous; length 260 mm.; tail 70 mm.; hind foot 40 mm.: central Sierras, California.

C. chlorus Elliot.   Color olive gray above and grayish white below; ears very small, blackish; length 255 mm.; tail 100 mm.; hind foot 37 mm.: southern California.

C. mohavensis (Merr.).   Color grizzled gray above, whitish beneath; length 250 mm.; tail 75 mm.; hind foot 38 mm.: Mojave Desert, California.

C. mexicanus parvidens (Mearns).   Color olivaceous gray with about 9 rows of white spots; belly white; length 325 mm.; tail 130 mm.; hind foot 44 mm.: valley of the lower Rio Grande and the Gulf coast northward to Corpus Christi.

8. Cynomys Rafinesque.   Prairie dogs.   Body stout; tail very short and flat; ears small; cheek-pouches shallow; skull strongly convex; dentition 1/1, 0/0, 2/1, 3/3; 5 toes on each foot, all with claws: about 5 species, inhabiting the more or less arid plains of the western States and Mexico.   They are burrowing animals which live in colonies and feed on grasses and other plants, including grains, often to the great detriment of crops.   They are not strictly hibernating animals, except during severe cold; a single litter of from 4 to 6 young is raised.   The rattlesnake and burrow-owl are often found in their burrows, and feed on their young.

C. ludovicianus (Ord).   Color dark pinkish cinnamon above and whitish beneath; tail tipped with black; length 388 mm.; tail 86 mm.; hind foot 62 mm.: Great Plains from central Texas to central North Dakota; westward to the eastern base of the Rockies.

Subspecies of C. ludovicianus

C. l. ludovicianus (Ord).   Eastward to about the 97th meridian; westward to central Montana, Wyoming and Colorado; introduced into Iowa, Louisiana, South Carolina and Nantucket Island; chiefly Upper Sonoran, but also Transition and Lower Sonoran zones.

C. l. arizonensis Mearns. Colors brighter: southwestern Texas to southeastern Arizona.

C. leucurus Merriam. Color yellowish buff or grayish; terminal two-thirds of tail white; length 358 mm.; tail 57 mm.; hind foot 62 mm.: Wyoming and into northern Colorado and northeastern Utah; Transition zone.

C. parvidens Allen. Like *C. leucurus*, but smaller and reddish in color and less grayish; length 338 mm.; tail 43 mm.; hind foot 59 mm.: central Utah.

C. gunnisoni (Baird). Color as in *C. leucurus;* terminal half of tail with a gray center, bordered and tipped with white; length 340 mm.; tail 53 mm.; hind foot 56 mm.: central Colorado and north-central New Mexico; Transition zone, also Upper Sonoran and Canadian zones.

Subspecies of C. gunnisoni

C. g. zuniensis Hollister. Color more cinnamon and less buff; size larger: western Colorado, northern New Mexico and Arizona.

9. Marmota Blumenbach (*Arctomys* Schreber). Woodchucks; ground-hogs. Body large and heavy; tail short; legs short and stout; cheek pouches small; dentition 1/1, 0/0, 2/1, 3/3; skull nearly flat on top: about 10 species in northern America, Europe and Asia; 4 species in the United States. A woodchuck digs a deep burrow, usually in a field, which may extend 25 feet or more into the ground, in which it has its nest and hibernates in the winter. Its food consists of grasses, clover, etc.; a single litter of from 3 to 9 young is raised.

Key to the American Species of Marmota

a_1 Upper parts grizzled brownish, yellowish, drab or buff.
    b_1 Sides of neck without conspicuous buffy patches............*M. monax.*
    b_2 Sides of neck with conspicuous buffy patches..............*M. flaviventris.*
a_2 Upper parts mainly black and white........................*M. caligata.*

M. monax (L.). Common woodchuck. Color grizzly gray, varied with chestnut, yellowish and black; under parts chestnut, length 675 mm.; tail 145 mm.; hind foot 83 mm.; weight about 9 lbs.: eastern and northern America from Hudson Bay to Georgia; westward in the United States to eastern Kansas and in Canada to Alaska.

Subspecies of M. monax

M. m. monax (L.). Middle eastern States from New Jersey to western Iowa and eastern Oklahoma; southward to western North Carolina and northern Georgia and Alabama.

M. m. preblorum Howell.   Colors paler; length 515 mm.: New England; northward to southern Maine and central Vermont.

M. m. rufescens How.   Colors redder; length 548 mm.: New York State westward through Michigan to eastern North Dakota; western Massachusetts.

M. m. canadensis (Erxleben).   Size small; colors strongly reddish; length 513 mm.: northern Michigan, Wisconsin, Minnesota and New England, and Canada; northwestward to Alaska.

M. m. petrensis How.   Like *M. m. canadensis*, but with a larger skull: northern Idaho and Montana; British Columbia.

M. flaviventris (Audubon and Bachman).   Yellow-bellied woodchuck.   Color yellowish brown above, yellowish beneath; sides of neck with large buffy patches; length 700 mm.; tail 170 mm.; hind foot 85 mm.: Rocky Mountain and Pacific States.

Subspecies of M. flaviventris

M. f. flaviventris (Aud. and Bach.).   The Cascade Range in Oregon and northern Sierras in California.

M. f. sierræ How.   Colors redder: higher Sierras from Kern River to Mono Lake.

M. f. avara (Bangs).   Colors paler; size smaller: eastern Oregon and Washington.

M. f. parvula How.   Size smaller; colors like *M. f. sierræ* but paler: central Nevada.

M. f. engelhardti (Allen).   Size smaller; under parts darker: Utah and southern Idaho.

M. f. nosophora How.   Colors more ochraceous above and redder below that *M. f. engelhardti:* mountain regions of Montana, Idaho and Wyoming.

M. f. dacota (Merriam).   Color like *M. f. nosophora,* buffy above; size large; length 643 mm: Black Hills to Bridger Pass, Wyoming.

M. f. luteola How.   Size large; under parts yellowish: mountains of northern Colorado and southern Wyoming.

M. f. warreni How.   Size large; colors deep red with buff: western Colorado.

M. f. obscura How.   Size large; color dark brown, mixed with white: northern New Mexico and southern Colorado.

M. caligata (Eschscholtz).   Whistler.   Color of fore part of back white, hinder and sides of body part cinnamon, mixed with black; under parts white; feet and top of head black; length 755 mm.; tail 250 mm.; hind foot 110 mm.: Alaska to Washington and Montana.

Subspecies of M. caligata

M. c. nivaria How.   High mountains of northwestern Montana and northern Idaho.

M. c. cascadensis How.   Head and feet browner and under parts darker: Cascade Range, Washington; southward to Mount Rainier.

M. c. olympus (Merr.).   Color brownish drab; feet brown: upper slopes of Olympic Mountains.

Subfamily 2.   Pteromyinæ.—Flying squirrels: 1 genus.

Glaucomys Rafinesque.   Flying squirrels.   Small rodents with a broad furry membrane stretching between the front and hind legs and extending out from the sides; tail flattened; ears large; dentition 1/1, 0/0, 2/1, 3/3: about 15 species; in the northern hemisphere; 2 species and many subspecies in the United States, nocturnal animals which make their nests in holes in trees; from 2 to 6 young form a litter, of which there probably are several a year.

Key to the Species of Glaucomys

a_1 Belly pure white..*G. volens.*
a_2 Belly dirty white...*G. sabrinus.*

G. volans (L.).   Color drab above ringed with reddish; beneath creamy white; underside of flying membrane pinkish; length 230 mm.; tail 100 mm.; hind foot 30 mm.; fur soft and dense: eastern and central States from southern Maine to Florida; westward to the plains.

Subspecies of G. volans

G. v. volens (L.).   Eastern and central States from Maine to North Carolina; west to Kansas and Nebraska.

G. v. saturatus Howell.   Darker in color: from North Carolina and Tennessee to the Gulf coast of Alabama to Lousiana.

G. v. texensis How.   Color yellowish: eastern Texas.

G. v. querceti Bangs.   Color more uniform russet: coastal region, Georgia and Florida.

G. sabrinus (Shaw).   Color drab above and dirty white beneath; length 312 mm.; tail 137 mm.; hind foot 42 mm.: northeastern and central States and Canada; southward into Massachusetts and northern New York; north to Alaska and Hudson Bay; Pacific Slope.

Subspecies of G. sabrinus

G. s. sabrinus (Shaw).   Extreme northwestern Wisconsin; Canada, north to Hudson Bay.

G. s. macrotis Mearns.   Color reddish: New England, New York, Michigan, Wisconsin.

G. s. bangsi (Rhoads).   Color grayer: Idaho, western Wyoming and Montana.

G. s. olympicus Elliot.   Color very dark; size large: coastal region of Washington and Oregon.

G. s. oregonensis (Bachman).   Color dark and reddish: coastal region of Oregon and Washington.

G. s. fuliginosus (Rhoads).   Color browner; length 317 mm.: Cascade Range from British Columbia into California.

G. s. klamathensis (Merriam).   Color brown, tinged with fulvous: region of the Klamath Lakes, Oregon.

G. s. californicus (Rhoads).   Colors pale; length 286 mm.: southern California.

G. s. lascivus (Bangs).   Color dark; size small: northern California; Sierra Nevada Range.

G. s. stephensi (Merr.).   Color redder: coastal region, northern California.

Family 8. Castoridæ.—Beavers. Large, stout rodents with a large flattened and scaly tail; all feet with 5 toes; hind feet webbed and with a double-clawed second toe; dentition 1/1, 0/0, 1/1, 3/3: 1 genus.

Castor L. With the characters of the family: 3 American species and 14 subspecies.

C. canadensis Kuhl. Body covered with a dense, soft fur and dark brown in color; length 1,100 mm.; tail 410 mm.; hind foot 175 mm.; average weight 35 lbs.: North America from Hudson Bay and Alaska into the southern Alleghanies in the east and into Mexico in the west; exterminated in well-settled regions. Beavers are aquatic and nocturnal, and feed on bark and twigs. The nest is usually in a conical lodge built of sticks and mud in a pond formed by throwing a dam of sticks and earth across a stream. Along streams with high banks the nest is often a chamber in the bank above the water level, and connected with the stream by a tunnel whose entrance is under the water. From 2 to 5 young are raised annually.

Subspecies of C. canadensis

C. c. canadensis Kuhl. Northeastern and central America; Hudsonian, Canadian and Transition zones.

C. c. carolinensis Rhoads. Size larger; color lighter; tail broader: North Carolina to Louisiana and Texas.

C. c. frondator Mearns. Color lighter; russet brown above: Montana to Mexico.

C. c. pacificus Rhoads. Size large; length 1143 mm.; color reddish chestnut: Pacific slope from California to Alaska.

C. c. michiganensis Bailey. Colors very dark; ears and feet black; length 1, 175 mm.; tail 475 mm.; hind foot 185 mm.; weight about 58 lbs: Upper Peninsula, Michigan.

C. c. missouriensis Bailey. Colors paler; size smaller: Missouri River drainage from Nebraska to Montana.

C. subauratus Taylor. Size very large; length 1171 mm.; color hazel and gray with a golden sheen: San Joaquin County, California.

Family 9. Leporidæ.—Rabbits and hares. Large rodents with 4 upper incisors (Fig. 183), a large pair in front and a small pair immediately behind them; upper lip divided; front legs short, with 5 toes; hind legs very long and with 4 toes; tail rudimentary; ears very long; dentition 2/1, 0/0, 3/2, 3/3: 5 genera and about 70 species, found throughout the world; 3 genera and 16 species and many subspecies in the United States. The American rabbits and hares (with the exception of *Brachylagus idahoensis*) do not

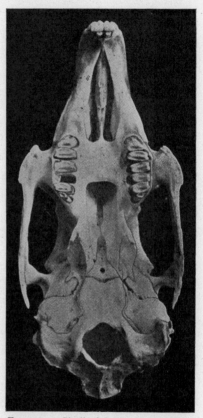

FIG. 183.—Skull of *Lepus* (*from Elliot*).

burrow as do their European relatives, but frequently make their nests in holes in the ground.

Key to the Genera of Leporidæ

a₁ Size large; hind foot over 125 mm. long.....................1. *Lepus.*
a₂ Size small; hind foot about 90 mm. long....................2. *Sylvilagus.*
a₃ Size very small; hind foot about 70 mm. long...............3. *Brachylagus.*

1. Lepus L. Size large; ears and hind legs very long; no interparietal bone in the adult; third to fifth ribs broad and flattened: circumpolar; 32 species and subspecies in America, and 20 in the

United States; the young, when born, are well furred and have their eyes open.

Key to the Species of Lepus

a_1 In the eastern and central States; varying hares..............*L. americanus.*
a_2 In the far-western States.
   b_1 Under 500 mm. in length.
      c_1 Color brown summer and winter.......... ....*L. washingtoni.*
      c_2 Color brown in summer and white in winter .... *L. bairdi.*
   b_2 Over 550 mm. in length; jack-rabbits.
      c_1 White-tailed jack-rabbits..............................*L. townsendii.*
      c_2 Black-tailed jack-rabbits.
         d_1 Color of flanks whitish and different from that of back.*L. alleni.*
         d_2 Color of flanks like that of back.....................*L. californicus.*

L. americanus Erxleben. White rabbit; varying hare; snowshoe rabbit. Color grayish or reddish brown in summer and white in winter; length 470 mm.; tail 43 mm.; hind foot 133 mm.: northern America from Bering Strait to the Atlantic; southward to British Columbia, central Minnesota and Michigan; throughout New England and New York and in the mountains into Virginia; mainly the Canadian zone, in swamps and wet thickets; from 2 to 7 young in a litter; 12 subspecies.

Subspecies of L. americanus

L. a. americanus Erx. Color in summer pale tawny brown; borders of ears conspicuously white: Hudson Bay to northern Quebec and Ontario, and in Michigan to Saganaw Bay; westward to the Canadian Rockies; in the Bighorn Mountains, Wyoming.

L. a. virginianus (Harlan). Color in summer bright rusty brown; borders of ears whitish; length 518 mm.: New England south of the Penobscot; New York and southward into Virginia and West Virginia.

L. a. struthopus Bangs. Color in summer dull tawny brown; length 474 mm.: Maine east of the Penobscot and eastward into Newfoundland; Canadian zone.

L. a. phæonotus Allen. Color in summer dull yellowish buff; length 464 mm.: northern Minnesota and Wisconsin and western half of the northern peninsula of Michigan; Canadian zone.

L. washingtoni Baird. Color in summer dull dark rusty brown; in winter similar, but slightly paler; length 450 mm.; tail 41 mm.; hind foot 125 mm.: Washington from the Cascades to the sea; Canadian and Transition zones.

L. w. klamathensis Merriam. Colors paler: Klamath Lake region to central eastern California; Canadian zone.

L. bairdi Hayden. Color in summer dusky grayish or rusty brown; in winter pure white; length 459 mm.; tail 39 mm.; hind foot 146 mm.: Rocky Mountains from Washington, Idaho and Montana to New Mexico; Canadian and Hudsonian zones.

L. alleni Mearns. Antelope jack rabbit. Size large; ears and legs very long; color of top of back yellowish brown; sides, rump and shoulders gray; under parts pure white; base of tail black; length 606 mm.; tail 63 mm.; hind foot 131: deserts of southern Arizona and Mexico.

L. townsendii Bachman. White-tailed jack rabbit. Color in summer pale yellowish gray; entire tail white; tip of ear black; in winter pure white in the northern portion of its range, in the south little changed; length 605 mm.; tail 92 mm.; hind foot 149 mm.: northern and western States west of the Mississippi River to eastern California. The jack rabbits weigh about 6 pounds and are remarkable for their speed, clearing 20 feet at a leap. They feed on bark, leaves and herbage and as they often do very great damage to crops are much hunted for purpose of extermination, and also for the fur and meat.

Subspecies of L. townsendii

L. t. townsendii Bach. Color uniform gray, without any yellowish: Great Basin; eastward to the summit of the Rockies.

L. t. sierræ (Merr.). Size large; color uniform gray; length 635 mm.: high Sierras from Mount Shasta to Mount Whitney.

L. t. campanius Hollister. Color buffy yellowish gray: Great Plains east of the Rockies in Canada and the United States.

L. californicus Gray. Black-tailed jack rabbit. Color dark ochraceous brown or dark buffy brown in winter and paler in summer; under parts dull dark buff; top of tail black; length 604 mm.; tail 95 mm.; hind foot 131 mm.: Nebraska and Texas to the Pacific; northward to Washington; southward into Mexico; 1 to 6 young in a litter.

Subspecies of L. californicus

L. c. californicus Gray. Coast region of California from Cape Mendocino to Gaviota Pass; eastward to the Sierras; northward to the Willamette.

L. c. deserticola (Mearns). Colors very pale, being ashy gray above; length 542 mm.: Great Basin from southeastern California and Nevada to central Arizona and Utah; northward into Idaho.

L. c. wallawalla (Merr.).   Like *L. c. deserticola* but darker, more pinkish: northeastern California and northwestern Nevada and northward to Washington.

L. c. richardsoni (Bach.).   Color light yellowish buff: San Joaquin Valley, California.

L. c. bennetti (Gray).   Color paler, more grayish; length 556 mm.: coast of California from Gaviota Pass into Lower California.

L. c. eremicus (Allen).   Color much paler, dull grayish: southern Arizona, east of Phœnix; Mexico.

L. c. texianus (Waterhouse).   Color pale gray: central and western Texas, New Mexico, northeastern Arizona and southwestern Colorado.

L. c. merriami (Mearns).   Color dark buffy brown: southern Texas from the Trinity River to the Rio Grande; Mexico.

L. c. melanotis (Mearns).   Color bright ochraceous buff: Great Plains from eastern South Dakota to Oklahoma and northern Texas and westward to the Rockies.

2. Sylvilagus Gray.   The cottontails.   Size moderate; interparietal bone district; anterior ribs narrow and rod-like; ears and legs relatively short: about 15 species, about 9 in the United States, the others in Mexico; the young, when born, are blind and naked.

Key to the United States Species of Sylvilagus

a_1 Tail comparatively large and loosely haired and cottony-white beneath; feet well haired.

  b_1 In States east of the Mississippi.

    c_1 Color gray...*S. floridanus.*

    c_2 Color pinkish buff; black patch between the ears........*S. transitionalis.*

  b_2 In States west of the Mississippi.

    c_1 Ear between 50 mm. and 60 mm. long.

      d_1 Color gray.......................................*S. floridanus.*

      d_2 Color buff, in the Rockies and Great Basin..........*S. nuttalli.*

    c_2 Ear more than 65 mm. long..........................*S. auduboni.*

a_2 Tail comparatively short, densely haired; white or gray beneath.

  b_1 In the coastal belt of the Pacific coast...................*S. bachmani.*

  b_2 In the coastal belt of the south Atlantic coast............*S. palustris.*

  b_3 In the south-central States............................*S. aquaticus.*

S. floridanus (Allen) (*Lepus sylvaticus* Bachman).   Common rabbit; gray rabbit; cottontail.   Color dark gray or rusty brown; tail white beneath; length 375 mm.; tail 45 mm.; hind foot 90 mm.: eastern and central States and southern Canada; several litters of from 2 to 6 each are raised annually.

Subspecies of S. floridanus

S. f. floridanus (Allen). Peninsular Florida.

S. f. mallurus (Thomas). Size larger; upper parts darker, more reddish: Atlantic States from Long Island and the lower Hudson Valley into Florida east of the Alleghanies.

S. f. mearnsi (Allen). Length 446 mm.; upper parts paler, more pinkish-buff; ears shorter: central States from the Alleghanies to eastern Nebraska; southward from Kentucky to eastern Kansas; northward from southern New York to southern Minnesota.

S. f. similis Nelson. Color pale buffy gray; length 408 mm.: eastern North and South Dakota, Nebraska, northern Kansas and Colorado.

S. f. alacer (Bangs). Color dark pinkish buff; length 418 mm.: southern and Gulf States from Georgia to Oklahoma; northward to central Missouri and Kansas; westward to central Texas.

S. f. chapmani (Allen). Color grayish brown without any rusty; length 403 mm.: middle and southern Texas; Mexico.

S. f. holzneri (Mearns). Color pale buffy gray: southern Arizona.

S. cognatus Nel. Size Large; length 458 mm.; color light buffy gray: high mountains of central New Mexico.

S. transitionalis (Bangs). Common rabbit. Color uniform rich pinkish buff or yellowish brown with a distinct black spot between the ears; length 388 mm.; tail 39 mm.; hind foot 95 mm.: New England States; northward to Rutland, Vermont, and southwestern Maine; eastern New York south of Lake George, and along the Alleghanies into Georgia; mainly Transition zone.

S. nuttalli (Bach.). Color dark buffy brown; length 352 mm.; tail 44 mm.; hind foot 89 mm.: Rocky Mountain and Great Basin region.

Subspecies of S. nuttalli

S. n. nuttalli (Bach.). Eastern Washington and Oregon and western Idaho, northeastern California and northwestern Nevada.

S. n. grangeri (Allen). Size larger; color buffy gray: Nevada and Utah, except the southern portions, southern Idaho and Wyoming and Montana.

S. n. pinetis (Allen). Darker than *S. c. grangeri;* length 386 mm.: pine forests from central Arizona through northern New Mexico and Colorado.

S. auduboni (Baird). Color dark buffy brown; white beneath; length 418 mm.; 72 mm;. hind foot 86 mm.: western, southwestern and Rocky Mountain States; 2 to 7 young in a litter; 10 subspecies.

Subspecies of S. auduboni

S. a. auduboni (Baird).   Interior of north-central California, including the region of San Francisco Bay.

S. a. vallicola Nel.   Color pale yellowish brown; length 402 mm.; tail 55 mm.; hind foot 91 mm.: central-interior California; Lower Sonoran zone.

S. a. sanctidiegi (Miller).   Size small; colors pale: coast region of southwestern California.

S. a. arizonæ (Allen).   Color very pale; ears very large: deserts of southern California and Nevada and southwestern Arizona.

S. a. minor (Mearns).   Size small; color pale grayish: southern New Mexico and western Texas.

S. a. cedrophilus Nel.   Color dark buff: central New Mexico and Arizona.

S. a. warreni Nel.   Color buffy brown: southwestern Colorado, northwestern New Mexico, northeastern Arizona and southeastern Utah.

S. a. baileyi (Merr.).   Color uniform pale creamy buff; length 411 mm.: plains of eastern Montana, Wyoming and Colorado and western North Dakota into western Kansas.

S. a. neomexicanus Nel.   Color dark buffy gray, slightly rusty: southern Kansas into central Texas and eastern New Mexico.

S. a. parvulus (Allen).   Color yellowish gray: southern Texas and Mexico.

S. bachmani (Waterhouse).   Brush rabbit.   Size small; ears, tail and legs short; color dark grayish brown with a tinge of reddish; length 328 mm.; tail 31 mm.; hind foot 74 mm.: a narrow belt along the coast or near it from the Columbia River to Cape St. Lucas; Transition and Upper and Lower Sonoran zones.

Subspecies of S. bachmani

S. b. bachmani (Water.).   Coastal region from Monterey to Santa Monica; also western foothills of the Sierras.

S. b. ubericolor (Miller).   Color darker and more reddish: coastal region from Monterey Bay to the Columbia River; also the head of the Sacramento Valley.

S. b. cinerascens (Allen).   Color lighter grayish brown: coastal region from Lower California to Santa Monica, also western side of the San Joaquin Valley.

S. palustris (Bach.). Marsh rabbit; pontoon. Body rather large and yellowish or reddish brown in color; beneath gray; legs short; length 436 mm.; tail 33 mm.; hind foot 91 mm.: under side of tail gray, sometimes brownish: coastal portions of the southern States from Dismal Swamp to Mobile Bay; in swampy woods; habits aquatic, the animals taking very readily to water and swimming well.

Subspecies of S. palustris

S. p. paludicola (Miller and Bangs). Color dark reddish brown: peninsular Florida.

S. aquaticus (Bach.). Swamp rabbit; cane-cutter. Color grayish brown; under side of tail pure white; length 550 mm.; tail 60 mm.; hind foot 106: river bottoms from western Georgia to central Texas and Oklahoma; northward to Tennessee and central Arkansas and in the Mississippi and Ohio River bottoms to Illinois.

Subspecies of S. aquaticus

S. a. littoralis Nel. Color much darker and reddish: narrow coast belt from Mississippi to Matagorda Bay, Texas.

3. Brachylagus Miller. Size small; ears short; tail very small and nearly unicolor: 1 species.

B. idahoensis (Merriam). Color drab or pinkish drab in winter and hair very long and soft; color in summer brownish gray; length 291 mm.; tail 18 mm.; hind foot 71 mm.: sagebrush plains of southern Idaho and Oregon and northern and central Nevada; makes its own burrows in the ground, being the only American rabbit or hare to do so.

Family 10. Ochotonidæ.—Pikas. Small compact rodents with short legs and without external tail; skull depressed; molars rootless; clavicles well developed: about 26 species, in Europe, Asia and America.

Ochotona Link. Dentition 2/1, 0/0, 2/2, 3/3: about 26 species and subspecies in the United States, which live in the high western mountains from Alaska to New Mexico, mainly above timber line, feeding upon herbage, of which they collect large winter stores; they do not hibernate; a single litter of from 2 to 4 young raised annually.

O. princeps Richardson. Body stout, with short fore and hind legs; toes 5-4; palms and soles densely haired; color gray or buff and variable; under parts whitish; length 190 mm.; hind foot 30 mm.: Rocky Mountains; Cascades; Sierra Nevadas; 16 subspecies.

Subspecies of O. princeps

O. p. princeps (Richardson). Western Montana and northern Idaho; north into Canada.

O. p. brunnescens (Howell). Color brownish: Cascade Range from British Columbia south to central Oregon.

O. p. saxatilis (Bangs). Size large; length 200 mm.; color pale yellowish brown: mountains of Colorado, north into Wyoming; west into Utah.

O. p. ventorum (Howell). Color lighter: northwestern Wyoming into Montana and Idaho.

O. p. figginsi (Allen). Color pale; size small: central Idaho.

O. schisticeps (Merriam). Color gray suffused with fulvous; top of head slate-gray; length 188 mm.; hind foot 29 mm.; tail vertebræ 9 mm.: Cascade and Sierra Nevada Mountains; 9 subspecies.

O. s. cinnamomea Allen. Color pale cinnamon rufous, darker in the middorsal region; top of head gray; similar to *O. schisticeps*, but smaller and lacking the slate-gray area on the head: Beaver Range, Utah, above 10,000 feet elevation.

Order 9. Ungulata.—Hoofed animals. Mammals of large size with 1 to 4 hoofs on each foot; molar teeth with broad crowns and adapted to the mastication of grasses and grains: about a dozen families, grouped in 2 suborders, and distributed throughout the world except in the Australian region, of which 4 occur in North America and 2 in the United States and Canada. The order contains the most important domestic animals.

Key to the Suborders of Ungulata

a_1 Number of hoofs on each foot either 2 or 4; even-toed ungulates.1. *Artiodactyla*.
a_2 Number of hoofs on each foot 1 or 3; odd-toed ungulates; no
    native species in the United States; horses; tapirs; rhinoc-
    eroses...2. *Perissodactyla*.

Suborder Artiodactyla.—Even-toed ungulates. Third and fourth digits prolonged beyond the others and support the animal's body; premolar and molar teeth usually not alike; stomach complex: about 300 species grouped in 2 divisions; about 40 species in the United States and Canada.

Key to the Divisions of Artiodactyla

a_1 Upper incisors and canines presents.........................1. *Suina*.
a_2 Upper incisors and canines absent...........................2. *Ruminantia*.

Division 1. Suina.—Pigs. Non-ruminant *Artiodactyla* with incisor, canine, premolar and molar teeth in both jaws; no horns present; metacarpals and metatarsals not fused; body large and robust; hairs bristle-like; skin very thick: 3 families, 1 of which only has native representatives in the United States, the other two families being the *Hippopotamidæ* and the *Suidæ*.

Family Tayassuidæ.—Peccaries. Small pigs with 3 toes on the hind feet and 4 toes on the fore feet; large musk gland in the middle of the rump; dentition 2/3, 1/1, 3/3, 3/3: 2 American genera.

Pecari Reichenbach. With the characters of the family: about 4 species, in Mexico, Central and South America.

P. angulatus (Cope). Collared peccary; muskhog. Color mixed black and white above, black predominating on the face and mane and back; white band over the shoulders to the middle of the back; under parts, nose and hoofs black; length 960 mm.; weight 50 lbs.: southwestern Texas and into New Mexico and Arizona; gregarious animals, omnivorous in feeding habits, which are found in dense forests and also among scattered thickets on sandy plains; number of young 2.

Division 2. Ruminantia.—Ruminant *Artiodactyla* with, in most species, no incisors or canines in the upper jaw; metacarpals and metatarsals, in most species (all American), fused to form the single "cannonbone"; horns present in very many species; stomach complex, being divided into 4 compartments, the ruminating habit of the animals consisting in the swallowing of the food first into the capacious first compartment or paunch; its return to the mouth for further mastication (the chewing of the cud), and the second swallowing of it into the other three compartments, where it is digested: 2 subdivisions and 3 families in this country.

Key to the Subdivisions of Ruminantia

a_1 Horns of solid bone which are shed periodically; deer..........1. *Cervina*.
a_2 Horns hollow and composed of horn and usually not shed; cattle;
    antelopes...2. *Cavicornia*.

Subdivision 1. Cervina. Deer. The males, and in the reindeers the females also, possess solid bone antlers which are shed every spring: 1 family.

Family Cervidæ.—With the characters of the subdivision: about 60 species, which are found in all the geographical regions except the Australian and African. The animals occur chiefly in forest regions and on grassy plains where they live on herbs, leaves, buds and young bark; about 25 species in the United States and Canada, grouped in 4 genera.

Key to the Genera of Cervidæ

a₁ Antlers cylindrical and not palmate.
    b₁ Antlers directed backwards, the prongs forwards.............1. *Cervus.*
    b₂ Antlers directed forwards, the prongs upwards..............2. *Odocoileus.*
a₂ Antlers more or less palmate.
    b₁ Males only with horns; lowest prongs not extending over the
       face...3. *Alces.*
    b₂ Both sexes with horns; lowest prongs extending over the face..4. *Rangifer.*

1. Cervus L. Antlers present only in the male, cylindrical, the first prong being just above the base and projecting over the brow; dentition 0/4, 1/0, 3/3, 3/3; tail very short; hoofs broad and rounded; nose naked; fawns spotted: 3 species in the United States.

C. canadensis Erxleben. Wapiti; elk. Color dark chestnut brown on the head, neck and under parts; back and sides yellowish gray; a large whitish patch on the rump; length 2,800 mm.; tail 200 mm.; hind foot 650 mm.; height at shoulders 1,220 mm.; weight 700 to 1,000 lbs.; length of antlers along outside curve 1,655 mm.; Rocky Mountain region from New Mexico and Arizona to British Columbia; formerly eastward in the Canadian, Transitional and Upper Austral zones to the Atlantic; related to the red deer of Europe, *C. elephus* L.

Subspecies of C. canadensis

C. c. occidentalis (Hamilton Smith). Size larger; head, legs and neck black: coastal forests from British Columbia south into northwestern California.

C. merriami Nelson. Color yellowish brown: White Mountains, Arizona and Mogollon Mountains, New Mexico; nearly extinct.

C. nannodes Merriam. Color pale buffy gray; length 2030 mm.; tail 140 mm.; hind foot 620 mm.; legs short: Kern County, California.

2. Odocoileus Rafinesque. Antlers present in the male alone, the first prong being directed upwards and not over the brow; dentition 0/4, 0/0, 3/3, 3/3; tail rather long, thickly haired beneath; hoofs narrow; young spotted: about 20 species, 7 in America.

Key to the United States Species of Odocoileus

a₁ East of the Great Plains.
    b₁ Eastern States, north of the Gulf States....................*O. virginianus.*
    b₂ Gulf States..*O. osceola.*
a₂ Great Plains to the Pacific.
    b₁ In the Rio Grande region.................................*O. texanus.*
    b₂ In northwestern Minnesota and Canada ....*O. vigultus.*

b₃ In New Mexico and Arizona............................*O. crooki.*
                                             O. couesi.
b₄ Texas to Dakota and westwards.......................*O. hemionus.*
b₅ On the Pacific slope........................*O. leucurus; O. columbianus.*

O. virginianus (Boddært). Virginia deer; white-tailed deer (Fig. 184). Color reddish chestnut in summer and grayish in winter; tail white beneath; length 1,800 mm.; tail 280 mm.; hind-foot 520 mm.; height at shoulder 925 mm.; length of antlers, outer curve, 600 mm.; average weight of buck 200 lbs.; extreme weight 400 lbs.: eastern and central States; common in many forest regions, where it feeds on grasses, leaves, buds, small shrubs, acorns, etc.; pairing time in the fall; fawns, usually 2 in number, born in May.

Subspecies of O. virginianus

O. v. virginianus (Bod.). Eastern States from Ontario to Florida and Louisiana; westward to the Missouri River; Austral zone.

O. v. borealis (Miller). Size larger; color gray in winter: eastern States and Canada; Canadian zone.

O. v. macrourus (Rafinesque). Size smaller; color paler: the Great Plains; westward to the Rockies, and to Oregon and Washington.

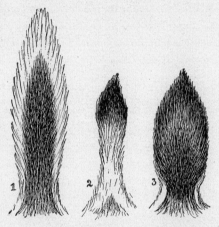

FIG. 37—Typical Tails.

1. Whitetail.
2. Mule-deer.
3. Coast Blacktail.

FIG. 184.—The tail (upper surface) of 1, *Odocoileus virginianus;* 2, *O. hemionus;* 3, *O. columbianus (from Seton).*

O. v. louisianæ (G. M. Allen). Size large; length 2,000 mm.; color pale; antlers high and heavy: lowlands of Louisiana.

O. osceola (Bangs). Florida white-tail. Color dark brown above; flanks cinnamon; under parts white; length 1,600 mm.; tail 280 mm.: Florida.

O. texanus (Mearns). Texas white-tail. Color pale yellowish white; black line from crown to tail; under parts white; ear with black edge; length 1,585 mm.; tail 265 mm.; height at shoulder 880 mm.: southwestern Texas and Mexico.

O. leucurus (Douglas). Size small; colors pale: lower Columbia River basin.

O. crooki (Mearns). Crook's black-tail deer. Color reddish fawn; tail long, flattened, black above and white beneath; length 1,440 mm.;

tail 195 mm.; height at shoulder 650 mm.: mountains of western New Mexico and of Arizona; only 2 specimens ever taken.

O. couesi (Coues and Yarrow).   Arizona white-tail.   Color pale fawn or gray above; sides tawny or brownish; tail white beneath; size small; height at shoulder 812 mm.; ear without black edge: southwestern New Mexico and southern Arizona.

O. hemionus (Raf.).   Mule deer (Fig. 184).   Color dull yellowish or tawny in the summer and gray in the winter, with a dark brown patch on the forehead; rump and tail white, the latter with a black tip; body heavy; ears very long; lengh 1,760 mm.; tail 205 mm.; height at shoulder 1,000 mm.; average weight 200 lbs.; length of antler along the curve 600 mm.; number of young at a birth 2 or 3: mountains and high plateaus of the west from North Dakota to Texas and into Mexico; westward into Washington, Oregon and California.

Subspecies of O. hemionus

O. h. californicus (Caton).   Size smaller; a dark middorsal stripe present: Coast Range south of San Francisco.

O. h. canus Merriam.   Smaller and paler: southwestern Texas, New Mexico and Arizona.

O. h. eremicus (Mearns).   Size large; color very pale: deserts at head of the Gulf of California.

O. virgultus (Hallock).   Smaller, darker underneath: northwestern Minnesota and Canada.

O. columbianus (Richardson).   Black-tail deer (Fig. 184).   Color brownish gray, darkest on the back; tail black above, white beneath; body stocky; ears large; length 1,650 mm.; tail 225 mm.; height at shoulders 863 mm.: Sierra Nevada and Cascade Mountains and the coastal forests from Alaska to central California.

O. c. scaphiotus Merriam.   Color paler; ears much larger: coastal region from San Francisco southwards.

3. Alces Gray.   Moose.   Size very large; antlers borne by the male alone and broadly palmate with numerous prongs projecting upwards; muzzle very broad, with a very convex contour; upper lip long and prehensile; legs very long; shoulders higher than the hips; tail very small; dentition 0/4, 0/0, 3/3, 3/3: 3 species, circumpolar; 2 species in America, 1 in the United States.

A. americana (Clinton).   Color black above, dark reddish brown on the sides; gray beneath; legs below the knees gray; a mane of stiff hairs on the neck; a pendent brush of hair called the "bell" on the throat; length 2,600 mm.; tail 65 mm.; height at shoulders 1,800 mm.; weight

800–1,400 lbs., and more: forests of North America from northern Maine and New Brunswick to northern Michigan and North Dakota; northward to Hudson Bay and Alaska; in the Rockies into Montana and Idaho; a near relative of the European elk, *A. alces.*

A. a. shirasi Nelson. Smaller, with small hoofs; color pale brown along the back; ears pale: Yellowstone Park region.

4. Rangifer H. Smith. Antlers large and borne by both sexes, palmate near the tips; one or both brow-prongs palmate and extending over the face; dentition 0/4, 1/0, 3/3, 3/3; legs and tail short: 12 species, 1 in Asia and Europe, the reindeer *R. tarandus* (L.), and 11 in northern America which range throughout the Canadian, Hudsonian and Arctic zones; 2 species in the United States.

R. caribou (Gmelin). Woodland caribou. Color dark brown, sometimes reddish, on the back, head, sides and outsides of legs; under parts, rump and a band around each foot pure white; in winter, neck white, body gray; length 1,800 mm.; tail 100 mm.; weight 280 lbs.; height at shoulders 1,200 mm.: forests of northern Maine and New Brunswick; northward to Great Slave Lake and Hudson Bay; much less gregareous than the Barren-ground caribou (*R. arcticus* Richardson), which ranges over the Arctic barrens to beyond the Arctic Circle.

R. montanus Seton. Color dark brown; under parts grayish white; length 2,413 mm.; tail 177 mm.; height at shoulders 1,397 mm.; weight 500 lbs.: Rocky Mountain region from Alaska into Idaho, Washington and Montana.

Subdivision 2. Cavicornia. Ruminants with hollow horns, composed of horn, in both sexes, which are never shed, except in *Antilocapra:* 2 families.

Key to the Families of Cavicornia

a_1 Horns branched...1. *Antilocapridæ.*
a_2 Horns not branched.......................................2. *Bovidæ.*

Family 1. Antilocapridæ.—Antelopes with erect horns, each with a short branch in front, which are shed each summer; ears long and pointed; lateral hoofs absent, digits 3 and 4 only present; dentition 0/4, 0/0, 3/3, 3/3: 1 genus.

Antilocapra Ord. With the characters of the family: 1 species.

A. americana (Ord). Prong-horn antelope. Color light yellowish brown; under parts, rump, sides of head and spot behind ears white; length 1,350 mm.; tail 138 mm.; height at shoulder 850 mm.; weight 125 lbs.; length of horns 250 mm.; number of young at a birth usually 2: Great Plains and deserts from the Saskatchewan into Mexico; westward to the Rockies and into eastern Oregon and California.

Family 2. Bovidæ.—Cattle; sheep; goats; antelopes. Ruminants with unbranched horns, in most cases in both sexes, which are not shed; lateral hoofs usually present: numerous species, mostly in Asia and Africa; about 10 species in America, including the buffalo, mountain sheep, mountain goats and muskox.

Key to the United States Genera of Bovidæ

a₁ Body very large and stout; nose not hairy; buffalo..............1. *Bison.*
a₂ Body smaller; nose hairy; sheep and goats.
   b₁ Horns compressed anteroposteriorly; sheep..................2. *Ovis.*
   b₂ Horns compressed laterally; goats........................3. *Oreamnos.*

1. Bison H. Smith. Head large; shoulders high; hind quarters low and weak; fore quarters covered to the knees with a shaggy mane; horns thick at the base and curved; hoofs broad; tail long; dentition 0/4, 0/0, 3/3, 3/3: 1 species.

B. bison (L.). Buffalo. Color dark brown, lighter on the rump; hoofs, nose and horns black; length 3,300 mm.; tail 500 mm.; height at shoulder 1,700 mm.; weight 1,800 lbs.: North America, formerly between the Alleghanies and the Rockies north of the Mexican Boundary, now extinct, except a few preserved herds in the Yellowstone Park and elsewhere, and a few wild herds in northern Canada.

Subspecies of B. bison

B. b. bison (L.). Plains buffalo. From the Rio Grande into Alberta and Saskatchewan; eastwards from the Rockies, formerly to western New York.

B. b. athabascæ Rhoads. Wood buffalo. Larger and darker in color: the Mackenzie region, Canada.

2. Ovis L. Sheep. Body stout; legs short; nose narrow and hairy, except a small naked space between the nostrils; horns very large and heavy, curving backward and then downward; dentition 0/4, 0/0, 3/3, 3/3: numerous species in all continents except Australia and South America; about 11 species and subspecies in northern America.

O. canadensis Shaw. Mountain sheep; bighorn. Color grayish brown, lighter in winter; large white rump patch; length 1,600 mm.; tail 125 mm.; height at shoulders 1,000 mm.; length of horn up to 1,250 mm. in the male, curving outwards and forming often a circle; horns in female short and straight; number of young at a birth 1 or 2: high mountains from the Mexican boundary into Canada and Alaska: 7 subspecies.

Subspecies of O. canadensis

O. c. canadensis Shaw. Arizona and New Mexico north into Canada, and eastern Oregon and Washington.

O. c. californiana (Douglas). Color darker: Cascade Mountains.

O. c. auduboni Merriam. Size large; skull and horn massive: Bad Lands district of the upper Missouri.

O. c. gaillardi Mearns. Size small; color ecru drab; feet very small: low desert ranges in the Austral zone south of the Gila River, Arizona.

O. c. sierræ (Grinnell). Much paler; length 1,450 mm.; tail 120 mm.; hind foot 375 mm.: southern California.

O. c. texiana Bailey. Color dull buffy brown; rump patch pure white; length 1,530 mm.: Guadalupe Mountains, Texas and New Mexico.

O. c. nelsoni (Merr.). Color pale brown; rump patch white; length 1,280 mm.; tail 100 mm.; hind foot 360 mm.; height at shoulder 830 mm.: desert mountain ranges of southern California, Nevada and Mexico.

3. Oreamnos Rafinesque. Body stout; legs short; horns small, curving slightly backwards; chin with a beard; nose hairy; hair long: 2 species in northern America, 1 in Alaska.

O. americanus (Blainville). Mountain goat. Color yellowish white; horns and hoofs black; length 1,650 mm.; tail 160 mm.; height at shoulder 1,000 mm.; length of horns 250 mm.; dentition 0/4, 0/0, 3/3, 3/3; number of young at a birth 1 or 2: high Rockies and Cascades to Alaska.

BIBLIOGRAPHY

ALLEN, HARRISON. A Monograph of the Bats of North America. Bull. U. S. Nat. Mus., No. 43, 1893.

ALLEN, J. A. A Revision of the Genus Didelphis. Bull. Am. Mus. Nat. His., Vol. 14, p. 149, 1901.

ANTHONY, H. E. Field Book of North American Mammals. New York, 1928.

AUDUBON, J. J. AND BACHMAN, J. The Quadrupeds of North America, 1852.

BAILEY, VERNON. The Prairie Ground Squirrels or Spermophiles. Bull. No. 4, U. S. Dep. Agric., 1893.

BAILEY, VERNON. A Revision of the Genus Microtus. North Am. Fauna, No. 17, 1900.

BAILEY, VERNON. Biological Survey of Texas. North Am. Fauna, No. 25, 1905.

BAILEY, VERNON. Life Zones and Crop Zones of New Mexico. North Am. Fauna, No. 35, 1914.

BAILEY, VERNON. A Revision of the Genus Thomomys. North Am. Fauna, No. 39, 1915.

BEAN, TARLETON H. The Fishes of New York. Bull. 60, N. Y. State Mus., 1903.

BLANCHARD, F. N. A Revision of the King Snakes, Genus Lampropeltis. Bull. 114, U. S. Nat. Mus., 1921.

BLANCHARD, F. N. Key to the Snakes of the United States, Canada and Lower California. Papers of the Mich. Acad. of Sci., Arts and Letters. 1925.

BRAUER, A. Suesswasserfauna Deutschlands, Heft 1, 1909.

BROWN, A. E. A Revision of the Genera and Species of American Snakes north of Mexico. Proc. Acad. Nat. Sci. Phila. p. 10, 1901.

CARY, M. A Biological Survey of Colorado. North Am. Fauna, No. 33, 1911.

CARY, M. Life Zone Investigations in Wyoming. North Am. Fauna No. 42, 1917.

COPE, EDWARD D. The Batrachia of North America. Bull 34, U. S. Nat. Mus., 1889.

COPE, EDWARD D. The Crocodilians, Lizards and Snakes of North America. Ann. Rep. U. S. Nat. Mus., 1898.

CORY, CHARLES B. The Mammals of Illinois and Wisconsin. Publ. 153, Field Mus. Nat. Hist. Zool. Ser. Vol. 11, 1912.

COUES, E. Synopsis of the Muridæ of North America. Proc. Acad. Nat. Sci. Phil., p. 173, 1874.

COUES, E. Monograph of North American Rodentia, No. 1, Muridæ. Rep. U. S. Geol. Sur. Terr., Vol. 2, p. 1, 1877.

CREASER, CHARLES W. AND HUBBS, CARL L. A Revision of the Holarctic Lampreys. Occ. Papers of the Mus. of Zool. Univ. Mich. No. 120, 1922.

DICKERSON, MARY. The Frog Book. 1906.

DITMARS, R. L. The Reptile Book. 1907.

DITMARS, R. L. The Snakes of the World. New York, 1931.

DITMARS, R. L. Reptiles of the World. 1933.

DUNN, EMMETT REID. Reptiles and Amphibians collected from the North Carolina Mountains, with special reference to Salamanders. Bull. Am. Mus. Nat. Hist. Vol. 37, p. 593, 1917.

DUNN, EMMETT REID. A preliminary List of the Reptiles and Amphibians of Virginia. Copeia, No. 53, 1918.

DUNN, EMMETT REID. Collection of Amphibia Caudata of the Museum of Comparative Zool. Cambridge. Vol. 62, p. 445, 1918.

DUNN, EMMETT REID. The Salamanders of the Genera Desmognathus and Leurognathus. Proc. U. S. Nat. Mus. Vol. 53, p. 393, 1918.

DUNN, EMMETT REID. Some Reptiles and Amphibians from Virginia, North Carolina, Tennessee and Alabama. Proc. Biol. Soc. Wash., Vol. 33, p. 129, 1920.

DUNN, EMMETT REID. The Salamanders of the Family Plethodontidæ. 1926.

ELLIOT, DANIEL GIRAUD. Synopsis of the Mammals of North America and the Adjacent Seas. Field Colum. Mus. Zool. Ser. Vol. 2, 1901.

ELLIS, MAX M. AND HENDERSON, JUNIUS B. The Amphibia and Reptilia of Colorado. Univ. Color. Stud. X. No. 2, p. 39, 1913. Also, XV, No. 6, p. 153, 1915.

EMERSON, E. T. General Anatomy of Typhlomolge rathbuni. Proc. Bost. Soc. Nat. Hist. Vol. 32, p. 43, 1905.

EVERMANN, BARTON WARREN. List of the Species of Fishes known to occur in the Great Lakes, etc. Bull. Bur. Fish. Vol. 21, p. 95, 1901.

EVERMANN, BARTON WARREN. The Golden Trout of the High Sierras. Bull. Bur. Fish. Vol. 25, p. 3, 1905.

EVERMANN, BARTON WARREN. The Fishes of Kentucky and Tennessee, etc. Bull. Bur. Fish. Vol. 35, p. 293, 1915.

EVERMANN, BARTON WARREN, AND HILDEBRAND, SAMUEL F. Notes on the Fishes of east Tennessee. Bull. Bur. Fish. Vol. 34, p. 433, 1914.

EVERMANN, BARTON WARREN, AND SMITH, HUGH M. The Whitefishes of North America. Rep. U. S. Fish. Comm., p. 283, 1894.

FORBES, STEPHAN A. AND RICHARDSON, ROBERT E. The Fishes of Illinois. Nat. Hist. Sur. State Lab. of Nat. Hist., 1908.

FOWLER, HENRY W. The Fishes of New Jersey. Ann. Rep. N. J. State Mus., 1905.

FOWLER, HENRY W. The Amphibians and Reptiles of New Jersey. Ann. Rep. N. J. State Mus., 1906.

FOWLER, HENRY W. A Supplementary Account of the Fishes of New Jersey. Ann. Rep. N. J. State Mus., 1906.

FOWLER, HENRY W. An annotated List of the Cold blooded Vertebrates of Delaware County Pa. Proc. Delaware County Inst. Sci. Vol. 7, 1915.

FOWLER, HENRY W. AND DUNN, EMMETT R. Notes on Salamanders. Proc. Acad. Nat. Sci. p. 7, 1917.

GAGE, SIMON HENRY. The Life History of the Vermilion Spotted Newt. Am. Naturalist, Vol. 25, p. 1084, 1891.

GAGE, SIMON HENRY. The Lake and Brook Lampreys of New York. Wilder Quarter Century Book, p. 421, 1893.

GOLDMAN, EDWARD ALPHONSO. A Revision of the Woodrats of the Genus Neotoma. North Am. Fauna, No. 31, 1910.

GOLDMAN, EDWARD ALPHONSO. A Revision of the Spiny Pocket Mice. North Am. Fauna, No. 34, 1911.

GREENE, CHARLES WILSON. The Migration of Salmon in the Columbia River. Bull. Bur. Fish. Vol. 29, p. 129, 1909.

GRINNELL, JOSEPH AND CAMP, CHARLES, L. A Distributional List of the Amphibians and Reptiles of California. Univ. Cal. Pub. Zool. Vol. 17, p. 127, 1917.

HAHN, WALTER LOUIS. The Mammals of Indiana. Rep. of State Geol., 1908.

HAY, OLIVER PERRY. Batrachians and Reptiles of Indiana. 17th Rep. Geol. Sur., p. 412, 1892.

HAY, OLIVER PERRY. A Revision of Malachemmys, etc. Bull. U. S. Bur. Fish. Vol. 24, p. 3, 1904.

HENSHALL, J. A. A List of the Fishes of Montana. Biol. Bull. Univ. Mont., No. 34.

HENSHAW, SAMUEL. Fauna of New England. List of Batrachians. List of Reptiles. Occas. Papers Bost. Soc. Nat. Hist. No. 7, 1904.

HERRICK, CLARENCE L. The Mammals of Minnesota. Bull. 7, Geol. and Nat. Hist. Sur. 1892.

HOLLISTER, NED. Remarks on the Long-tailed Shrews, etc. Proc. U. S. Nat. Mus., Vol. 40, p. 377, 1911.

HOLLISTER, NED. A systematic Synopsis of the Muskrats. North Am. Fauna, No. 32, 1911.

HOLLISTER, NED. A systematic Account of the Grasshopper Mice. Proc. U. S. Nat. Mus., Vol. 47, p. 427, 1914.

HOLLISTER, NED. A systematic Account of the Prairie Dogs. North Am. Fauna, No. 46, 1916.

HORNADAY, WILLIAM T. Notes on the Mountain Sheep of North America, etc. Fifth Ann. Rep. N. Y. Zool. Soc. p. 77, 1901.

HORNADAY, WILLIAM T. The American Natural History, 1910.

HOWELL, ARTHUR H. Revision of the Skunks of the Genus Chincha. North Am. Fauna, No. 20, 1901.

HOWELL, ARTHUR H. Revision of the Skunks of the Genus Spilogale. North Am. Fauna, No. 26, 1906.

HOWELL, ARTHUR H. The American Harvest Mice. North Am. Fauna, No. 36, 1914.

HOWELL, ARTHUR H. Revision of the American Marmots. North Am. Fauna, No. 37, 1915.

HURTER, JULIUS. Herpetology of Missouri. Trans. Acad. Sci. St. Louis. Vol. 18, p. 11, 1909.

JACKSON, H. H. T. A Review of American Moles. North Am. Fauna No. 38, 1915.

JORDAN, DAVID STARR. Guide to the Study of Fishes, 1905.

JORDAN, DAVID STARR. The Genera of Fishes. Leland Stand. Univ. Pub., 1917.

JORDAN, DAVID STARR. A Manual of the Vertebrate Animals of the Northern United States, 1914.

JORDAN, DAVID STARR AND EVERMANN, BARTON WARREN. The Fishes of North and Middle America, 1896–1900.

JORDAN, DAVID STARR AND EVERMANN, BARTON WARREN. American Food and Game Fishes, 1900.

JORDAN, DAVID STARR AND EVERMANN, BARTON WARREN. A Review of the Salmonoid Fishes of the Great Lakes, etc. Bull. Bur. Fish. Vol. 29, p. 1, 1909.

JORDAN, DAVID STARR, EVERMANN, BARTON WARREN AND CLARK, HOWARD WALTON. Check List of the Fishes and Fishlike Vertebrates of North and Middle America north of the Northern Boundary of Venezuela and Columbia. Rep. of the U. S. Comm. of Fish, for the Fiscal Year 1928. Document No. 1055, 1930.

KENDALL, WILLIAM, C. Notes on some Fresh water Fishes from Maine. Bull. Bur. Fish. Vol. 22, p. 355, 1902.

KENDALL, WILLIAM C. The Rangeley Lakes, etc. Bull. Bur. Fish. Vol. 35, p. 489, 1915.

LANTZ, DAVID E. Meadow Mice in Relation to Agriculture and Horticulture. Yearbook Dept. Agric. p. 363, 1905.

LANTZ, DAVID E. Coyotes in their Economic Relations. Biol. Sur. U. S. Dept. Agric. No. 20, 1905.

LANTZ, DAVID E. A List of Kansas Mammals. Trans. Kans. Acad. Sci. Vol. 19, p. 171, 1906.

LANTZ, DAVID E. Additions to the above. Ditto, Vol. 20, p. 214.

LANTZ, DAVID E. An Economic Study of Field Mice. Bull. 31 U. S. Dept. Agric. 1907.

LANTZ, DAVID E. Raising Deer and other large Game Animals in the United States. Bull. No. 36, U. S. Dept. Agric., 1910.

LEUNIS, JOHANNES. Synopsis der Thierkunde, 1883.

MEARNS, EDGAR ALEXANDER. Mammals of the Mexican Boundary of the U. S. Bull. U. S. Nat. Mus. No. 56, 1907.

MERRIAM, C. HART. Results of a Biological Survey of the San Francisco Mountain Region and Desert of the Little Colorado, Arizona. North Am. Fauna No. 3, 1890.

MERRIAM, C. HART. Synopsis of the Am. Shrews of the Genus Sorex. North Am. Fauna No. 10, 1895.

MERRIAM, C. HART. Monographic Revision of the Pocket Gophers. ·North Am. Fauna No. 8, 1895.

MERRIAM, C. HART. Revision of the Shrews of the American Genera Blarina and Notiosorex. North Am. Fauna No. 10, 1895.

MERRIAM C. HART. Synopsis of the Weasels of North America. North Am. Fauna No. 11, 1896.

MERRIAM, C. HART. Preliminary Synopsis of the American Bears. Proc. Biol. Soc. Wash. Vol. 10, p. 65, 1896.

MERRIAM, C. HART. A Revision of the Coyotes, etc. Proc. Biol. Soc. Wash. Vol. 11, p. 19, 1897.

MERRIAM, C. HART. Life and Crop Zones of the United States. Bull. No. 10, U. S. Dept. Agric. Biol. Sur., 1898.

MERRIAM C. HART. Results of a Biological Survey of Mount Shasta, California. North Am. Fauna No. 16, 1899.

MERRIAM, C. HART. Preliminary Account of the North Am. Red Foxes. Proc. Wash. Acad. Sci. Vol. 2, p. 661, 1900.

MERRIAM, C. HART. Revision of the Pumas. Proc. Wash. Acad. Sci. Vol. 3, p. 577, 1908.

MILLER, GERRIT S., JR. The Genera and Subgenera of Voles and Lemmings. North Am. Fauna No. 12, 1896.

MILLER, GERRIT S., JR. Revision of the North Am. Bats of the Family Vespertilionidæ. North Am. Fauna No. 13, 1897.

MILLER, GERRITT S., JR. Key to the Land Mammals of Northeastern North America. Bull. N. Y. State Mus. No. 38, Vol. 8, 1900.

MILLER, GERRITT S., JR. Families and Genera of Bats. Bull. No. 57, U. S. Nat. Mus., 1907.

MILLER, GERRIT S., JR. List of North American Land Mammals in the U. S. Nat. Mus., 1912.

MILLER, GERRIT S., JR. The Names of the large Wolves of northern and western North America. Smiths. Miss. Coll. Vol. 59, 1912.

MOORE, J. PERCY. Leurognathus marmorata. Proc. Acad. Nat. Sci. Phila, 316, p. 316, 1899.

MORSE, MAX W. Ohio Batrachians and Rept. Proc. Acad. Sci. Vol. 4, p. 91, 1904.

MURPHY, ROBERT CUSHMAN. Long Island Bats. Mus. Brooklyn Inst. Arts & Sci. Vol. 2, 1913.

NELSON, EDWARD W. Squirrels of Mexico and Central America. Proc. Wash. Acad., Sci. Vol. 1, p. 15, 1899.

NELSON, EDWARD W. The Rabbits of North America. North Am. Fauna No. 29, 1909.

NELSON, EDWARD W. Wild animals of North America. Geog. Mag. November and May, 1918.

NOBLE, G. K. Biology of the Amphibia, 1931.

ORTENBURGER, A. J. The Whip Snakes and Racers, Genera Masticophis and Coluber. 1928.

OSGOOD, WILFRED H. A Revision of the Genus Perognathus. North Am. Fauna No. 18, 1900.

OSGOOD, WILFRED H. A Revision of the Genus Peromyscus. North Am. Fauna No. 28, 1909.

OVERTON, FRANK. The Frogs and Toads. Long Island Fauna and Flora. Sci. Bull. Brooklyn Inst., etc. Vol. 2, 1914.

PALMER, T. CHALKLEY. Delaware County Frogs. Proc. Del. County Inst. of Sci. Vol. 4, p. 12, 1908.

PALMER, THEODORE S. The Jack Rabbits. Bull. No. 8, U. S. Dept. Agric., 1896.

PARKER, H. W. A Monograph of the Frogs of the Family Microhylidæ. London, 1934.

PAULMEIER, FREDERICK C. New York Reptiles and Batrachians. Bull. 51, N. Y. State Mus., 1902.

PEARSE, ARTHUR S. The Food of the Shore Fishes of certain Wisconsin Lakes. Bull. Bur. Fish. Vol. 35, p. 245, 1915.

POWERS, JOSEPH H. Morphological Variation and its Causes in Ambystoma tigrinum. Univ. of Neb. Studies, Vol. 7, p. 197, 1907.

PREBLE, EDWARD A. A Revision of the Jumping Mice of the Genus Zapus. North Am. Fauna No. 15, 1899.

REESE, ALBERT M. The Alligator and its Allies. 1915.

REGAN, C. T. Systematic Study of Hyperoartii. Ann. Mag. Nat. Hist. Vol. 7, Ser. 8, 1911.

REHN, JAMES A. G. A Revision of the Genus Mormoops. Proc. Acad. Nat. Sci. Phila. Vol. 54, p. 160, 1902.

REHN, JAMES A. G. A Revision of the Genus Macrotus. Proc. Acad. Nat. Sci. Phila. Vol. 59, p. 427, 1904.

REIGHARD, JACOB. An Ecological Reconnoisance of the Fishes of Douglas Lake, Mich. Bull. Bur. Fish. Vol. 33, p. 215, 1913.

RHOADS, SAMUEL N. Synopsis of American Martins. Proc. Acad. Nat. Sci. Phila. p. 443, 1902.

RHOADS, SAMUEL N. The Mammals of Pennsylvania and New Jersey. 1903.

RITTER, WILLIAM E. AND MILLER, L. H. A Contribution to the Life History of Autodax lugubris. Am. Nat. Vol. 33, p. 691, 1899.

RUTHVEN, ALEXANDER G. Variations and Genetic Relationships of the Garter Snakes. Bull. 61, U. S. Nat. Mus. 1908.

RUTHVEN, ALEXANDER G. The Reptiles of Michigan. Mich. Geol. Biol. Sur. Publ. No. 10, p. 63, 1912.

RUTTER, C. The Fishes of the Sacramento-San Joaquin Basin, etc. Bull. Bur. Fish. Vol. 27, p. 105, 1907.

SETON, ERNEST THOMPSON. Life Histories of Northern Animals. 1909.

SHULL, CHARLES, A. Habits of the Short-tailed Shrew. Am. Nat. Vol. 41, p. 495, 1907.

SMITH, HUGH M. The Fishes of North Carolina. Geol. and Econ. Sur. North Car., 1907.

SNYDER, J. O. The Fishes of the Coastal Streams of Oregon and Northern California Bull. Bur. Fish. Vol. 27, p. 153, 1907.

SNYDER, J. O. Relationships of the Fish Fauna of the Lakes of Southeastern Oregon. Bull. Bur. Fish. Vol. 27, p. 71, 1907.

SNYDER, J. O. The Fishes of the Streams tributary to Monterey Bay, California. Bull. Bur. Fish. Vol. 32, p. 49, 1912.

SNYDER, J. O. The Fishes of the Streams tributary to Tomales Bay, California. Bull. Bur. Fish. Vol. 34, p. 377, 1914.

SNYDER, J. O. The Fishes of the Lahontan System of Nevada, etc. Bull. Bur. Fish. Vol. 35, p. 33, 1916.

STEJNEGER, LEONHARD. Poisonous Snakes of North America. Report U. S. Nat. Mus. 1893, p. 337, 1895.

STEJNEGER, LEONHARD AND BARBOUR, THOMAS. Check List of North American Amphibians and Reptiles, 1917. Third Edition, 1933.

STONE, WITMER. Notes on the Reptiles and Batrachians of Pennsylvania and New Jersey. Am. Nat. Vol. 40, p. 159, 1906.

STONE, WITMER AND CRAM, WILLIAM EVERITT. American Animals, 1913.

STRECKER, JOHN K. Reptiles and Amphibians of Texas. Baylor Bull. 18, No. 4, p. 1, 1915.

SURFACE, HARVEY A. The Removal of Lampreys from the Interior Waters of New York. Bull. Fish. Comm. Vol. 17, 1897.

SURFACE, HARVEY A. Serpents of Pennsylvania. Zool. Bull. State Dept. Agric. Vol. 4, p. 115, 1906.

SURFACE, HARVEY A. Lizards of Pennsylvania. Zool. Bull. State Dept. Agric. Vol. 5, p. 236, 1907.

SURFACE, HARVEY A. Turtles of Pennsylvania. Zool. Bull. State Dept. Agric. Vol. 6, p. 107, 1908.

SWENK, MYRON H. A Preliminary Review of the Mammals of Nebraska. Stud. Zool. Lab. of the Univ. No. 89, 1908.

VAN DENBURGH, JOHN. The Reptiles of the Pacific Coast and Great Basin. Occ. Papers Calif. Acad. Sci. V. p. 1, 1897.

WARREN, EDWARD R. The Mammals of Colorado. Color. Coll. Pub. Vol. 11, p. 225, 1906.

WHIPPLE, INEZ L. The Ypsiloid Apparatus of Urodeles. Biol. Bull. Vol. 10, p. 255, 1906.

WHIPPLE, INEZ L. The Naso-labial Groove of Lungless Salamanders. Biol. Bull. Vol. 11, p. 1, 1906.

WILDER, HARRIS H. Lunglose Salamander. Anat. Anz. Vol. 12, p. 182, 1896.

WILDER, HARRIS H. Desmognathus fusca (Rafinesque) and Spelerpes bilineatus (Greene). Am. Nat. Vol. 33, p. 231, 1899.

WILDER, HARRIS H. The Skeletal System of Necturus maculatus Rafinesque. Mem. Bost. Soc. Nat. Hist. Vol. 5, 1902.

WILDER, INEZ W. The Life History of Desmognathus fusca. Biol. Bull. Vol. 24, p. 251, 1913.

WRIGHT, ALBERT HAZEN. Life Histories of North American Anura. Publ. 197 Carn. Inst. Wash., 1914.

WRIGHT, ANNA ALLEN, AND WRIGHT, ALBERT HAZEN. Handbook of Frogs and Toads. The Frogs and Toads of the United States and Canada, 1933.

LIST OF AUTHORS

This list includes the authors of specific and generic names and also those of the monographs and treatises herein referred to.

ABBOTT, CHARLES C. (1843–1919). American naturalist and archeologist; Trenton, N. J.

AGASSIZ, LOUIS (1807–1873). Swiss-American zoologist and naturalist; professor in Harvard.

ALLEN, HARRISON (1841–1897). American anatomist; professor in the University of Pennsylvania.

ALLEN, JOEL A. (1838–1921). American zoologist; American Museum of Natural History, New York.

ANTHONY, H. E. (1890–). American zoologist; American Museum of Natural History, New York, 1928.

ARISTOTLE (384–322 B.C.). Greek naturalist and philosopher.

ARTEDI, PETER (1705–1735). Swedish ichthyologist.

AUDUBON, JOHN JAMES (1780–1851). American ornithologist and mammalogist, and painter of animals.

BACHMAN, JOHN (1790–1874). American naturalist and clergyman in Charleston, S. C.

BAILEY, VERNON (1864–). American mammalogist; United States Department of Agriculture, Washington.

BAILY, JR., JOSHUA L., Jr. (1889–). American zoologist, San Diego, California.

BAIRD, SPENCER FULLERTON (1823–1887). American zoologist; Director of National Museum; Secretary of Smithsonian Institution.

BANGS, OUTRAM (1863–1932). American zoologist; Museum of Comparative Zoology, Harvard.

BAUR, GEORGE (1859–1898). German-American herpetologist and zoologist; professor in Clark and Chicago.

BEAN, TARLETON H. (1846–1916). American ichthyologist; State Fish culturist, New York.

BEARDSLEE, LESTER A. (1836–1903). American naval officer and naturalist.

BEAUVOIS, PALISAT (1755–1820). French naturalist who traveled in America.

BELL, THOMAS (1792–1880). English zoologist; professor in London.

BENDIRE, CHARLES E. (1836–1897). American ornithologist and army officer.

BENNETT, EDWARD T. (1797–1866). American educator and scientist; professor in Cincinnati.

BIBRON, G. French zoologist; professor in Paris.

BLAINVILLE, MARIE HENRI (1778–1850). French zoologist; professor in Paris.

BLANCHARD, FRANK N. (1888–). American herpetologist; instructor in University of Michigan.

BLATCHLEY, WILLIS S. (1859–). American naturalist; former State geologist of Indiana.

BLOCH, MARCUS (1723–1799). German ichthylogist and physician in Karlsbad.

BLUMENBACH JOHANNES (1752–1840). German zoologist and naturalist; professor in Göttingen.

BOITARD, PIERRE (1787–1859). French naturalist.

BONAPARTE, CHARLES LUCIEN (1803–1857). French zoologist, nephew of Napoleon; lived in Philadelphia from 1822 to 1828.

BORKHAUSEN, MATTHIES (1760–1806). German entomologist and naturalist in Darmstadt.

BOULENGER, GEORGE ALBERT (b. 1858). Belgian-English herpetologist; British Museum.

BRANDT, JOHANN (1802–1879). Russian zoologist; professor in Leningrad.

BRAUER, AUGUST. German zoologist; professor in Berlin.

BRAYTON, A. W. (1848–1926). American naturalist and physician in Indianapolis.

BREVOORT, JAMES C. (1818–1887). American naturalist.

BRIMLEY, CLEMENT S. (1863–   ). British-American naturalist; Raleigh, N. C.

BRISSON, MATHURIN (1723–1806). French ornithologist; professor in Paris.

BROWN, ARTHUR E. (1850–1910). American herpetologist and mammalogist; Academy of Natural Sciences, Philadelphia.

BRYANT, EDWIN (1805–1869). American traveller and Californian pioneer.

CAMP, CHARLES L. (1893–   ). American herpetologist; American Museum of Natural History, New York.

CATON, JOHN D. (1812–1895). American naturalist and lawyer in Chicago.

CHAPMAN, FRANK M. (1864–   ). American ornithologist; American Museum of Natural History, New York.

CLARK, H. WALTON (1870–   ). American zoologist; Biological Station, Fairport, Iowa.

CLARK, HUBERT LYMAN (1870–   ). American zoologist; Museum of Comparative Zoology, Harvard.

CLINTON, DE WITT (1769–1828). Governor of New York; builder of the Erie Canal.

COPE, EDWARD DRINKER (1840–1897). American zoologist and paleontologist; professor in Haverford College and the University of Pennsylvania.

COPELAND, EDWIN B. (1873–   ). American botanist; professor in Manila.

COUES, ELLIOTT (1842–1899). American ornithologist and army surgeon.

CREASER, CHARLES W. (1897–   ). American zoologist; Museum of Zoology, University of Michigan.

CUVIER, FERDINAND (1773–1838). French zoologist; professor in Paris; brother of Georges Cuvier.

CUVIER, GEORGES (1769–1832). French zoologist, paleontologist and comparative anatomist; professor in Paris.

DAUDIN, FRANÇOIS (1774–1804). French zoologist.

DEKAY, JAMES E. (1782–1851). American naturalist and physician; Oyster Bay, Long Island.

DESMAREST, ANSELM (1784–1838). French zoologist; professor in Aalfort.

DICKERSON, MARY C. (1866–1923). American herpetologist; New York.

DITMARS, RAYMOND L. (1876–   ). American herpetologist; New York Zoological Park, New York.

DIXON, JOSEPH S. (1884–   ). American mammalogist; University of California Museum.

DUMERIL, ANDRÉ (1774–1860). French physician and naturalist; professor in Paris.

DUNN, EMMETT REID (1894–   ). American herpetologist; professor in Haverford College.

DYBOWSKI, BENEDICT (1834–   ). Polish zoologist; professor in Lemberg.

EIGENMANN, CARL H. (1863–1927). German-American ichthyologist; professor in Indiana State University.

ELLIOT, DANIEL G. (1835–1915). American mammalogist; Field Columbian Museum, Chicago.

ELLIS, MAX M. (1887–   ). American zoologist; professor in University of Missouri.

ERXLEBEN, JOHANN (1744–1777). German naturalist; professor in Göttingen.

ESCHSCHOLTZ, JOHANN FRIEDRICH (1793–1831). Esthonian zoologist and physician; professor in Dorpat.

EVERMANN, BARTON WARREN (1853–1928). American ichthyologist; director of the Museum of the California Academy of Sciences, San Francisco.

FABRICIUS, JOHANN CHRISTIAN (1745–1808). Danish zoologist; professor in Kiel.

FISCHER, GOTTHELF (1771–1853). German zoologist; professor in Moscow.

FITZINGER, LEOPOLD (1802–1884). Austrian zoologist; Vienna.

FLEMMING, JOHN (1785–1857). Scotch zoologist; professor in Edinburg.

FORBES, STEPHEN A. (1844–1930). American zoologist; professor in the University of Illinois.

FOWLER, HENRY W. (1878–   ). American zoologist and naturalist; Academy of Natural Sciences, Philadelphia.

GAGE, SIMON HENRY (1851–   ). American anatomist and naturalist; professor in Cornell.

GAIGE, HELEN THOMPSON (1889–   ). American herpetologist; University of Michigan.

GAIRDNER, WILLIAM T. (1824–1907). English physician and naturalist; professor in Glasgow.

GAMBEL, WILLIAM. American physician and naturalist in Philadelphia.

GARDEN, ALEXANDER (1730–1791). American naturalist and physician in Charleston, S. C.

GARMAN, SAMUEL (1846–1927). American zoologist and ichthyologist; Museum of Comparative Zoology, Harvard.

GEOFFROY SAINT-HILAIRE, ÉTIENNE (1772–1844). French zoologist; professor in Paris.

GERVAIS, PAUL (1816–1879). French zoologist and paleontologist; professor in Paris.

GIBBES, ROBERT W. (1809–1866). American naturalist and physician in Charleston, S. C.

GIBBONS, JAMES S. (1810–1892). American naturalist and banker in San Francisco.

GIGLIOLI, HENRI (1844–1909). Italian naturalist.

GILBERT, CHARLES H. (1859–1928). American ichthyologist; professor in Stanford.

GILL, THEODORE N. (1837–1914). American zoologist and ichthyologist; professor in Washington.

GILLIAMS, JACOB (1784–1868). American physician in Philadelphia.

GIRARD, CHARLES (1822–1895). French-American zoologist; Smithsonian Institution.

GMELIN, JOHANN (1748–1804). German naturalist; professor in Göttingen; editor of 13th edition of Systema Naturæ.

GOLDMAN, EDWARD A. (1873–   ). American zoologist and naturalist; United States Biological Survey.

GOODE, GEORGE BROWN (1851–1896). American ichthyologist; United States National Museum, Washington.

GRAVENHORST, JOHANN (1777–1857). German zoologist; professor in Breslau.

GRAY, GEORGE ROBERT (1808–1872). English naturalist; British Museum.

GRAY, JOHN EDWARD (1800–1881). English naturalist; British Museum; brother of George.

GREEN, WYMAN R. (1881–   ). American zoologist; professor in Drew University.

GREENE, CHARLES W. (1866–   ). American physiologist; professor in the University of Missouri.

GRIFFITH, ROBERT E. (1798–1850). American naturalist and physician in Philadelphia.

GRINNELL, JOSEPH (1877–   ). American zoologist; professor in California.

GÜLDENSTÆDT, ANTON (1745–1781). Russian naturalist; professor in Petrograd.

GÜNTHER, A. K. (1830–1914). German-English ichthyologist and zoologist; British Museum.

HÆCKEL, ERNST (1834–1918). German zoologist; professor in Jena.

HALDEMAN, SAMUEL S. (1812–1880). American naturalist; professor in the University of Pennsylvania.

HARLAN, RICHARD (1796–1843). American naturalist and physician in Philadelphia.

HAY, OLIVER P. (1846–1930). American naturalist and paleontologist; Carnegie Institution of Washington.

HAYDEN, FERDINAND V. (1829–1887). American geologist and naturalist; United States Geological Survey.

HECKEL, JOHANN (1790–1857). Austrian ichthyologist.

HENDERSON, JUNIUS B. (1865–   ). American jurist and naturalist, professor in University of Colorado.

HENSHAW, SAMUEL (1850–1930). American zoologist; Museum of Comparative Zoology, Harvard.

HERRICK, CLARENCE L. (1858–1904). American zoologist; president of the University of New Mexico.

HOLBROOK, JOHN E. (1794–1871). American ichthyologist and herpetologist; professor in South Carolina College.

HOLLISTER, NED (1876–1924). American mammalogist; Zoological Park, Washington.

HORNADAY, WILLIAM T. (1854–   ). American naturalist; director of the New York Zoological Park.

HOWELL, ARTHUR H. (1872–   ). American mammalogist and ornithologist; United States Biological Survey, Washington.

HUBBS, CARL L. (1894–   ). American ichthyologist; Zoological Museum, University of Michigan.

HUXLEY, THOMAS HENRY (1825–1895). English zoologist and naturalist; professor in London.

ILLIGER, JOHANNES (1775–1815). German zoologist; director Zoological Garden, Berlin.

JACKSON, HARTLEY H. T. (1881–   ). American naturalist; United States Biological Survey, Washington.

JARDINE, WILLIAM (1800–1874). Scotch zoologist.

JENKINS, OLIVER P. (1850–   ). American ichthyologist; Stanford University.

JORDAN, DAVID STARR (1851–1931). American ichthyologist and naturalist; Stanford University.

KAUP, JOHANN JACOB (1803–1873). German naturalist in Darmstadt.

KENDALL, WILLIAM C. (1861–   ). American ichthyologist; United States Fish Commission.

KERR, ROBERT (1750–1814). Scotch surgeon and naturalist in Edinburg.

KIRTLAND, JARED P. (1793–1877). American naturalist and physician; professor in Cleveland.

KUHL, HEINRICH (1797–1821). German naturalist.

LACÉPÈDE, ÉTIENNE (1756–1825). French zoologist; professor in Paris.

LAMARCK, JEAN BAPTISTE PIERRE ANTOINE DE MONET DE (1744–1829). French zoologist, botanist and evolutionary philosopher.

LATREILLE, PIERRE (1762–1833). French zoologist and entomologist; professor in Paris.

LATROBE, BENJAMIN H. (1764–1820). American naturalist in Philadelphia.

LAURENTI, JOSEPH. Austrian herpetologist and physician in Vienna; latter half of 18th century.

LEACH, WILLIAM E. (1790–1836). English zoologist; British Museum.

LECONTE, JOHN EATON (1784–1860). American naturalist and army engineer; brother to Lewis.

LeConte, John Lawrence (1825–1883). American entomologist and physician in Philadelphia; a son of John E.

LeConte, Joseph (1823–1901). American geologist; professor in the University of California; a son of Lewis.

LeConte, Lewis (1782–1838). American naturalist and physician; brother to John Eaton.

LeSueur, Charles Alexander (1794–1857). French zoologist who lived in Philadelphia from 1817 to 1825.

Leuckart, Friedrich Sigismund (1794–1843). German zoologist; professor in Freiburg; uncle of Rudolf.

Leuckart, Rudolf (1822–1898). German zoologist; professor in Leipzig; nephew of Friedrich.

Leunis, Johannes (1802–1873). German zoologist; professor in Hildesheim.

Lichtenstein, Martin (1780–1857). German zoologist; professor in Berlin.

Linck, Johannes (1674–1734). German zoologist; professor in Leipzig.

Link, Heinrich Friedrich (1767–1851). German biologist; professor in Breslau.

Linnæus, Carolus (1707–1778). Swedish naturalist; professor in Upsala.

Lord, John K. (1818–1872). English zoologist.

Matthes, Francois E. (1874–   ). Dutch-American geologist and naturalist; United States Geological Survey.

McMurtrie, Henry (1793–1865). American educator and physician in Philadelphia.

Mearns, Edgar A. (1856–1916). American naturalist and army surgeon.

Meek, Seth E. (1859–1914). American ichthyologist and herpetologist; Field Columbian Museum, Chicago.

Merrem, Blasius (1761–1824). German naturalist; professor in Marburg.

Merriam, C. Hart (1855–   ). American naturalist, formerly chief of the Biological Survey; Smithsonian Institution.

Miller, Gerrit S., Jr. (1869–   ). American mammalogist; United States National Museum.

Mitchill, Samuel L. (1764–1831). American ichthyologist and naturalist, and physician in Philadelphia.

Monkhaus, William J. (1871–   ). American physiologist and naturalist; professor in Indiana State University.

Moore, J. Percy (1869–   ). American zoologist; professor in the University of Pennsylvania.

Morse, Max W. (1880–   ). American physiologist; professor in the University of West Virginia.

Müller, Johannes (1801–1858). German anatomist and physiologist; professor in Berlin.

Murphy, Robert Cushman (1887–   ). American ornithologist and naturalist; American Museum of Natural History, New York.

Nelson, Edward W. (1855–1934). American naturalist; chief of the United States Biological Survey.

Nilsson, Sven (1787–1883). Swedish zoologist; professor in Lund.

Oken, Lorenz (1779–1851). German zoologist; professor in Munich.

Ord, Edward O. C. (1818–1883). American soldier and naturalist.

Ortenburger, A. I. American herpetologist; professor in the University of Oklahoma.

Osgood, Wilfred H. (1875–   ). American mammalogist; Field Columbian Museum, Chicago.

Pallas, Peter Simon (1741–1811). German zoologist who lived long in Russia.

Palmer, T. Chalkley (1860–1934). American naturalist and manufacturer in Philadelphia, president of the Academy of Natural Sciences.

Palmer, Theodore S. (1868–   ). American zoologist; United States Department of Agriculture.

PAULMEIER, FREDERIC P. (1873–1906). American zoologist; State Museum, Albany.

PEALE, REMBRANDT (1778–1860). American naturalist and portrait painter in Philadelphia and Baltimore.

PEARSE, ARTHUR S. (1877–   ). American zoologist; professor in Duke University.

PETERS, WILHELM (1815–1883). German traveller and zoologist; professor in Berlin.

PICKERING, CHARLES (1805–1878). American naturalist on the Wilkes Exploring Expedition.

POEY, FELIPE (1799–1891). Cuban naturalist and ichthyologist; professor in Havana.

POWERS, JOSEPH H. (1866–   ). American zoologist; University of Nebraska.

PRATT, HENRY S. (1859–   ). American zoologist; professor in Haverford College, Pa.

PREBLE, EDWARD A. (1871–   ). American mammalogist and ornithologist; United States Department of Agriculture, Washington.

PUTMAN, FREDERIC W. (1839–1915). American naturalist and anthropologist; professor in Harvard.

RAFINESQUE, CONSTANTINE (1784–1842). French-American naturalist; Lexington, Kentucky, and Philadelphia.

REESE, ALBERT M. (1872–   ). American zoologist; professor in the University of West Virginia.

REHN, JAMES A. G. (1881–   ). American mammalogist; Academy of Natural Sciences, Philadelphia.

REICHENBACH, HEINRICH (1793–1879). German zoologist and botanist; professor in Dresden.

REIGHARD, JACOB (1861–   ). American zoologist; professor in the University of Michigan.

RHOADS, SAMUEL N. (1862–   ). American naturalist, Philadelphia.

RICHARDSON, JOHN (1787–1865). Scotch naturalist and traveller in Arctic America.

RITTER, WILLIAM E. (1856–   ). American zoologist; professor in the University of California.

RUTHVEN, ALEXANDER G. (1882–   ). American herpetologist; professor in the University of Michigan.

SABINE, EDWARD (1788–1883). English naturalist and Arctic traveller.

SAY, THOMAS (1787–1834). American zoologist; Academy of Natural Sciences, Philadelphia.

SCHLEGEL, HERMANN (1804–1884). German zoologist.

SCHNEIDER, JOHANN (1750–1822). German zoologist; professor in Breslau.

SCHŒPFF, JOHANN (1752–1800). German zoologist and physician in Ansbach.

SCHRANCK, FRANZ (1747–1835). German botanist and zoologist; professor in Munich.

SCHREBER, JOHANN (1739–1810). German zoologist; professor in Erlangen.

SCHWEIGGER, AUGUST (1783–1821). German naturalist; professor in Königsberg.

SEALE, ALVIN (1873–   ). American ichthyologist; Steinhart Aquarium, San Francisco, California.

SETON, ERNEST THOMPSON (1860–   ). Canadian naturalist; Greenwich, Conn.

SHAW, WILLIAM T. (1873–   ). American zoologist; professor in Washington State College, Pullman.

SHUFELDT, ROBERT W. (1850–   ). American ornithologist and army surgeon.

SHULL, A. FRANKLIN (1881–   ). American zoologist; professor in the University of Michigan.

SLACK, JAMES. American naturalist and physician in Philadelphia.

SMITH, HAMILTON. English army officer and zoologist.

SMITH, HUGH M. (1865–   ). American ichthyologist; United States Commissioner of Fisheries.

SNYDER, JOHN O. (1867–   ). American ichthyologist; professor in Stanford University.

SPIX, JOHANN (1781–1826). German naturalist and traveller.

STEJNEGER, LEONHARD (1851–   ). Norwegian-American herpetologist and naturalst; United States National Museum, Washington.

STONE, WITMER (1866–   ). American zoologist; Academy of Natural Sciences, Philadelphia.

STORER, TRACY I. (1889–   ). American zoologist and naturalist; Museum of the University of California.

STORR, GOTTLIEB (1749–1821). German zoologist; professor in Tübingen.

SUCKLEY, GEORGE (1830–1869). American traveller, naturalist and physician in New York.

SURFACE, HARVEY A. (1867–   ). American zoologist; Selinsgrove, Pa.

SWAIN, JOSEPH (1857–1927). American ichthyologist; emeritus president of Swarthmore College.

SWARTH, HARRY S. (1878–   ). American ornithologist and mammalogist; Museum of the University of California.

SWENK, MYRON H. (1883–   ). American zoologist; professor in Nebraska.

TAYLOR, WALTER P. (1888–   ). American zoologist and mammalogist; United States Biological Survey.

THOMAS, CYRUS (1825–1910). American naturalist and ethnologist.

THOMPSON, ZADOC (1796–1856). American naturalist; professor in the University of Vermont.

TROSCHEL, FRANZ (1810–1882). German zoologist; professor in Bonn.

TROUSSART, EDOUARD LOUIS (b. 1842). French zoologist; professor in Paris.

TRUE, FREDERIC W. (1858–1914). American zoologist; United States National Museum, Washington.

TSCHUDI, JOHANN JACOB (1818–1889). Swiss zoologist and traveller.

TURTON, WILLIAM (1762–1835). English naturalist and physician in Swansea.

VALENCIENNES, ACHILLE (1794–1863). French zoologist; professor in Paris.

VAN DENBRUGH, JOHN (1872–   ). American herpetologist; California Academy of Sciences, San Francisco.

VIGORS, NICHOLAS (1785–1840). Irish ornithologist and naturalist; British Museum.

VOIGT, JOHANN (1725–1810). German physician and naturalist.

WAGLER, JOHANN (1800–1832). German herpetologist; professor in Munich.

WAGNER, JOHANN (1797–1861). German zoologist; professor in Munich.

WALBAUM, JOHANN. German zoologist; latter part of 18th century.

WARREN, EDWARD R. (1860–   ). American zoologist; Colorado Springs, Colorado.

WATERHOUSE, GEORGE R. (1810–1888). English naturalist.

WHIPPLE, INEZ L. (Mrs. H. H. Wilder) (1871–1929). American zoologist; professor in Smith College.

WIED, MAXMILIAN (1782–1867). German naturalist and traveller in North and South America.

WIEGMANN, AREND (1802–1841). German zoologist; professor in Berlin.

WILDER, HARRIS H. (1864–1928). American zoologist and anthropologist; professor in Smith College.

WILSON, ALEXANDER (1766–1813). Scotch-American ornithologist and naturalist; Philadelphia.

WOODHOUSE, SAMUEL W. American naturalist and army surgeon.

WRIGHT, ALBERT HAZEN (1879–   ). American herpetologist; professor in Cornell.

YARROW, HARRY C. (b. 1840). American herpetologist and physician in Washington.

ZIMMERMAN, EBERHARD (1743–1815). German zoologist and geographer.

GLOSSARY OF TECHNICAL WORDS AND TERMS

Abdomen. The belly; the ventral portion of the posterior region of the trunk.

Abdominal. Pertaining to the abdomen; applied to the ventral fins of a fish when they are posterior in position.

Abortive. Incomplete; undeveloped.

Acrodont teeth. Teeth which are situated along the edge of the jaw bone.

Acuminate. Tapering to a point.

Acute. Sharp-pointed.

Adipose. Fatty; thick.

Adipose fin. A fleshy, spineless fin back of the dorsal fin in certain fishes.

Adnate. Grown together; a fin which is attached along its lower edge as well as by its base.

Adult. A mature, sexual animal.

Adventitious. Coming from without; foreign.

Æstivate. To pass the summer in a torpid condition.

Air bladder. A large sac filled with air or some other gas lying beneath the backbone in the body cavity of most fishes.

Albinism. A more or less complete lack of pigment in the integument and eyes of an animal; opposed to melanism.

Allantois. The embryonic respiratory organ of the higher vertebrates.

Alveoli. Deep pits in a bone; the sockets of the teeth.

Amnion. The protective envelope of the embryo of the higher vertebrates.

Amniota. Those vertebrates possessing an amnion.

Amniotic. Pertaining to the Amniota.

Amphicœlous. Biconcave vertebræ.

Amphioxus. One of the most primitive chordate animals.

Anadromous. Marine fishes which run up rivers to spawn.

Anal. Occupying a position near the anus.

Anal fin. The median fin just behind the anus.

Anal glands. Glands in connection with the anus which secrete an odoriferous fluid.

Anal plate. The plate immediately in front of the anus in snakes.

Analogous. Having a similar function.

Anamnia. Those vertebrates which do not possess an amnion.

Anchylosed. Grown firmly together.

Anteorbital plate. The plate in front of the eye in snakes.

Anterior. Toward the front end of an animal.

Anus. The hinder opening of the digestive tract.

Aorta. The main artery which carries blood away from the heart.

Aplacental. Not having a placenta.

Apodous. Without feet.

Appendage. A projection from some part of the body, usually applied to the locomotory appendages, the legs.

Appendicular. Pertaining to the locomotory appendages.

Aquatic. Living in the water.

Arboreal. Living in trees.

Arciferous. Referring to the pectoral girdle of toads, the cartilaginous elements of which overlap midventrally.

Articulate.   Jointed.

Artiodactyle.   Even-toed, of ungulates.

Ascidians.   Very primitive chordate animals.

Atrophy.   The state of being undeveloped.

Attenuate.   Long and slender and drawn to a point.

Auburn.   Dark reddish brown.

Auricle.   One of the chambers of the heart.

Azygos plate.   A plate just back of the rostral plate on the head of some snakes.

Balanoglossus.   A very primitive chordate animal.

Barbel.   A long, slender projection on the head of certain fishes and turtles.

Basal.   At or near the base.

Bicolor.   Two-colored.

Bicuspid.   Having two terminal points.

Bifid.   Forked.

Bilateral symmetry.   Having the right and left sides alike.

Bister.   A dark brown color.

Branchial.   Pertaining to the gills.

Branchiostegals.   The bony rays which support the branchiostegal membrane on the under side of the head of a fish.

Buccal.   Pertaining to the mouth.

Buccal funnel.   The depressed plate with the mouth in its center at the front end of a lamprey.

Caducous.   Shedding or falling off early.

Cæcum.   A sac-like appendage of the digestive tract; a blind-gut.

Canine teeth.   Elongate, conical teeth; in mammals those next to the incisors.

Carapace.   The upper shell of a turtle; the shell of an armadillo.

Carinate.   Keeled; with a median ridge.

Carnassial teeth.   The flesh-cutting teeth of a carnivorous mammal.

Carnivorous.   Flesh-eating.

Carpal bones.   The wrist bones.

Carpus.   The wrist.

Caudal.   Pertaining to the tail.

Caudal fin.   The tail fin of fishes.

Caudal peduncle.   The slender body region just in front of the caudal fin in fishes.

Cavernous.   Containing cavities.

Cervical.   Pertaining to the neck.

Cheek.   The part of a fish's head beneath and behind the eye.

Chordate.   Pertaining to animals belonging to the Phylum *Chordata*, being those animals possessing a notochord, such as vertebrates, ascidians, etc.

Cinereous.   Ashen; light gray.

Cinnamon.   Intense dark brown.

Cirri.   Filamentous, sensory appendages.

Clavicle.   The collar bone, the ventral, anterior portion of the shoulder girdle.

Cloaca.   The tubular organ receiving the discharges of the digestive, urinary and reproductive systems, in certain vertebrates.

Cochlea.   A portion of the inner ear in mammals which is spiral in shape.

Compressed.   Flattened laterally.

Condyle.   A bony projection which is an articulating surface.

Coracoid.   The ventral, posterior portion of the shoulder girdle in the land vertebrates; the principal bone of the shoulder girdle in fishes.

Costal folds.   Vertical folds of the skin in salamanders which show the number of the muscle segments.

Costal grooves.   The vertical grooves between the costal folds.

Costals. The lateral plates of a turtle's carapace.

Cranial crests. A pair of longitudinal ridges between the eyes on the head of toads.

Cranium. The portion of the skull which encloses the brain.

Cruciform. Cross-shaped.

Ctenoid. Fish scales which have a pectinated or roughened posterior margin.

Cusp. A sharp projection.

Cuspidate. Ending in one or more sharp points.

Cycloid. Fish scales which have a smooth posterior margin.

Cyclostomate. Round-mouthed; a group of primitive fish-like vertebrates.

Deciduous. Temporary; characterized by falling off at a certain time.

Decurved. Curved downwards.

Dentate. Notched.

Dentine. The very hard, inner substance of a tooth; ivory.

Dentition. The number of each of the four kinds of teeth of a mammal.

Depressed. Flattened dorso-ventrally.

Depth. The dorso-ventral height of a fish's body at the widest place.

Dermal. Arising in the dermis of the skin.

Dermis. The inner layer of the vertebrate skin or integument.

Dextral. Pertaining to or situated on or towards the right hand.

Diaphragm. The muscular septum between the thoracic and abdominal cavities in mammals.

Dicromatic. Two-colored; applied to animals having two color phases.

Digit. A finger or toe.

Digitigrade. Walking on the toes instead of on the flat of the foot.

Dimorphic. Characterized by dimorphism.

Dimorphism. Existing in two distinct forms.

Distal. Away from the point of attachment; opposed to proximal.

Diurnal. Appearing or active during the day.

Diverticulum. A sac-like projection of a tubular organ.

Dorsal. Pertaining to the back.

Dorsal fin. The median fin on the back of a fish or amphibian.

Dorsals. The median plates of a turtle's carapace.

Dorso-lateral ridges. A pair of glandular ridges on the back of most frogs.

Ear-ossicles. The three minute bones in the middle ear of mammals.

Ecru. Coffee-color.

Ectoderm. The outermost layer of cells in the body of an embryo.

Elapine snakes. Snakes which have a pair of short rigid poison fangs in the front of the upper jaw.

Elasmobranch fishes. Sharks and skates.

Emarginate. Slightly forked or notched.

Embryo. A young animal which is passing through its developmental stages, usually within the egg-membranes or in the maternal uterus.

Enamel. The very hard outer covering of a tooth.

Endoskeleton. The inner bony or cartilaginous framework of the body.

Entire. Not divided or split.

Entoderm. The embryonic cell layer which forms the mucous membrane of the digestive tract.

Epidermal. Arising in the epidermis of the skin.

Epidermis. The outer layer of the vertebrate skin or integument.

Eustachian tube. A canal joining the middle ear with the pharynx.

Exoskeleton. The hard parts, as the nails, scales, feathers, hair, etc., on the outer surface of the body.

Extremities. The paired locomotory appendages of the body, as the legs, wings, etc.

Falcate. Scythe-shaped; elongate, slender and curved.

Falciform. Scythe-shaped.

Fauna. The animals inhabiting a region.

Femoral. Pertaining to the thigh.

Femoral pores. A row of pores on the thigh of many lizards.

Ferruginous. Reddish brown.

Filament. A thread-like structure.

Filiform. Thread-like in form.

Fin-rays. The small bony or cartilaginous projections of the gill arches.

Firmisternal. Referring to the pectoral girdle of frogs, the cartilaginous elements of which are fused midventrally.

Flipper. The fin-shaped legs of certain aquatic turtles and mammals.

Fontanelle. An unossified space in a bone.

Foramen. An opening.

Forficulate. Deeply forked.

Frontal bones. The bones forming the top of the head in front.

Frugivorous. Fruit-eating.

Fulcra. Spine-like projections of the fin-rays in certain fishes.

Fulvous. Reddish-yellow; tawny.

Furcate. Forked.

Fuscous. Dusky.

Fusiform. Spindle-shaped; tapering towards ends.

Ganoid. A representative of the Ganoidea.

Ganoid scales. Rhombic scales of many ganoid fishes.

Gastrosteges. The transverse plates which cover a snake's belly; the ventral plates.

Gills. The organs of respiration of a fish and of many amphibians.

Gill-arches. The bony or cartilaginous arches which support the gills.

Gill-clefts. The openings between the pharynx and the outside in which the gills are located.

Gill-rakers. A series of projections along the inner margin of certain of the gill-arches.

Gill-slits. The gill-clefts.

Glottis. The opening from the pharynx into the trachea.

Granulate. Roughened; with granular prominences.

Grinders. The molar and premolar teeth of rodents and some other mammals, the surfaces of which grind the food.

Gular. Pertaining to the upper part of the throat.

Hazel. Dark brown.

Height. The vertical dimension of an animal.

Heterocercal fin. An unsymmetrical caudal fin of a fish, the upper lobe being usually longer than the lower and containing the backbone.

Hibernate. To pass the winter in a torpid condition.

Hirsute. Shaggy.

Homocercal fin. A symmetrical caudal fin of a fish, the backbone ending at the base of the fin and not entering it.

Homologous. Having a common origin.

Hyoid. The bones which support the tongue.

Ichthyopsida. Fish-like vertebrates, those that breathe in the water at some time of their lives.

Imbricate. Overlapping, like the shingles on a roof.

Incised. Cut into; deeply notched.

Incisors. The front teeth.

Inferior. In a lower position.

Infraoral lamina. The toothed plate or ridge posterior to the mouth of a lamprey.

Integument. The skin.

Interfemoral membrane. The portion of the flying membrane of bats which connects the hind legs and includes a part of the tail.

Intermaxillaries. The premaxillaries; the middle portion of the upper jaw, except in mammals.

Internasals. The plates on a snake's head which connect the two nostrils.

Interopercle. The opercular bone between the preopercle and the branchiostegals.

Interorbital. The space between the eyes.

Interparietal. A median bone sometimes present between the posterior portion of the parietals.

Interspinals. Spine-like bones inserted between the neural spines in fishes, often for the support of the fins.

Isthmus. The midventral space lying between the right and the left gill-clefts of a fish.

Jugular. Applied to the ventral fins of a fish when they are anterior to the pectorals.

Keel. A longitudinal ridge along the middle of a scale or other organ.

Keeled. Having a ridge along the middle.

Labials. The scales lying along the lips of a snake or lizard.

Lamella. A leaf- or plate-like structure.

Lamellate. Composed of or provided with lamellæ.

Lamina. A plate-like process.

Larva. A young, immature animal which has not yet acquired the form and appearance of the adult.

Lateral. Toward either the right or the left side.

Lateral line. A sensory line on the lateral surface of most fish, extending usually between the head and the tail-fin.

Lenticular. Doubly convex.

Longitudinal. Lengthwise.

Loreal plate. The plate between the eye and the nostril on the head of a snake or a lizard, just in front of the preocular when it is present.

Lumbar. Pertaining to the region of the body between the thorax and the sacrum.

Lunate. Crescent-shaped; with the form of the new moon.

Mammæ. The nipples on the ventral surface of a mammalian female.

Mammary glands. The milk-secreting glands of the mammalian female.

Mandible. The lower jaw.

Marginals. The marginal plates of a turtle's carapace.

Marsupial pouch. The pouch on the belly of the marsupial female in which the young are kept.

Marsupium. The marsupial pouch.

Mastoid region. The region just behind the ear.

Maxilla. The upper jaw.

Maxillaries. The lateral bones of the upper jaw.

Median fins. The unpaired fins.

Melanic. The tendency to develop melanism.

Melanism. An unusual or abnormal accumulation of black pigment in the integument and eyes of an animal; opposed to albinism.

Membrane bone. A bone which forms in a superficial membrane and not in cartilage.

Meroblastic. Eggs the germinal disc of which alone undergoes segmentation.

Metabolism. The sum of all the vital processes of an animal's body.

Metachrosis. The attribute of changing the body color under the influence of some sensory stimulus.

Metameric. Pertaining to the body segments; segmental.

Metamorphosis. The developmental changes which go on in a young animal's body up to the time when it becomes adult.

Molars.   The hindermost teeth in the mammalian jaw; crushing teeth of certain fishes.

Monozygotic.   The several offspring which may develop from a single fertilized egg, such as identical twins.

Murine.   Mouse-like.

Naked.   Without external coverings, such as hair, scales, etc.

Nape.   The back of the neck.

Nares.   The nostrils, both those opening on the outer surface of the head and the inner ones opening into the mouth cavity.

Nasal.   Pertaining to the nose or the nostrils.

Nasal plate.   The plate in which the nostril is located in snakes and lizards.

Naso-labial groove.   A glandular groove connecting the nostril and the lip in certain salamanders.

Nictitating membrane.   The eye-lid at the inner corner of the eye of certain vertebrates, which moves across the surface of it.

Nocturnal.   Being active in the night-time.

Nose-leaf.   A complicated membrane at the end of the snout in certain bats.

Notochord.   A cylindrical rod which extends the length of the body in chordate embryos and forms the basis of the backbone.

Nuchal plate.   The median anterior marginal plate in the carapace of turtles.

Obscure.   Indefinite in appearance.

Obsolescent.   Gradually disappearing.

Obsolete.   Scarcely visible.

Obtuse.   Blunt.

Occipital.   Pertaining to the hinder part of the head.

Occipital condyle.   The bony prominence by which the skull articulates with the backbone.

Ochraceous.   Light brownish yellow in color.

Œsophagus.   The portion of the digestive tract between the pharynx and the stomach.

Olivaceous.   Yellowish green.

Omnivorous.   Eating all kinds of food.

Opercle.   The gill cover; the movable flap on the side of a fish's head which covers the gill clefts.

Opercular bones.   Membrane bones which support the opercle.

Opercular flap.   The posterior prolongation of the opercle in certain fishes.

Operculum.   The opercle.

Opisthocœlous vertebræ.   Those which are concave behind and convex in front.

Opisthoglyph snakes.   Snakes which have poison fangs in the rear of the mouth.

Orbicular.   Circular or nearly so.

Orbit.   The socket of the eyes.

Orientation, Organs of.   The special sense organs.

Oviparous.   Egg-laying.

Ovoviviparous.   Animals producing large eggs which hatch while still in the mother's body.

Paired fins.   The pectoral and ventral fins of a fish.

Palate.   The roof of the mouth.

Palatines.   Membrane bones supporting the rear portion of the roof of the mouth.

Palmate.   Spreading; broad and flat, with finger-like projections.

Papilla.   A minute, fleshy projection.

Papillose.   Covered with papillæ.

Parasphenoid.   The membrane bone supporting the roof of the mouth in amphibians.

Parotoid.   A glandular organ just back of the ear in toads.

Parietal bones.   A pair of membrane bones forming a portion of the top of the skull.

Pectinate.   Having teeth like a comb.

Pectoral. Pertaining to the breast.

Pectoral fins. The anterior paired fins in fishes.

Pedicle. A stalk.

Pelagic. Living in the surface waters of the sea or a lake.

Pelvis. The bony girdle by which the skeleton of the hind legs is joined with the vertebral column; the pelvic girdle.

Pencil. A tuft of hair or feathers.

Penicillate. Tipped with a tuft of hairs.

Pentadactylous. Five-fingered or five-toed; pentadactyle.

Perforate. Pierced.

Peritoneum. The lining of the abdominal cavity.

Phalanges. The bones of the finger and toes.

Pharyngeal bones. Bones behind the gill arches in fishes which usually bear teeth.

Pharynx. The anterior portion of the digestive tract, that just back of the mouth.

Phylum. One of the main subdivisions of the Animal Kingdom; a Sub-kingdom.

Pigment. Coloring matter.

Pineal eye. A rudimentary median eye on the top of the head of certain lizards.

Placenta. The organ by which the fetus of the higher mammals is nourished.

Placoid scales. The scales of sharks and skates.

Plantar. Referring to the under surface of the foot or hand.

Plantigrade. Walking on the sole of the foot.

Plastron. The lower portion of the turtle's shell.

Pleurodont teeth. Teeth which are situated along the inner margin of the jaw bone.

Plicate. Folded; wrinkled.

Plumbeous. Lead-colored.

Pneumatic duct. A duct joining the air bladder with the pharynx in fish.

Postanal. Back of the anus.

Posterior. Toward the hinder end of the animal.

Postnatal. Occurring after birth.

Postorbital plate. The plate behind the eye in snakes and lizards.

Postorbital processes. The bony processes which form the hinder part of the orbit.

Precoracoid. The anterior, ventral portion of the shoulder girdle in amphibians.

Prefrontal plate. The plate on the head of snakes and lizards in front of the frontal.

Prehensile. Adapted for grasping and holding.

Prehension, Organs of. Organs fitted for seizing.

Premaxillaries. The bones which support the front portion of the upper jaw; in fishes they extend also along the side.

Premolar teeth. The teeth in the mammalian jaw between the canines and the molars.

Preocular plate. The plate on the head of snakes and lizards just in front of the eye.

Preopercle. The membrane bone forming the anterior portion of the opercle in fishes.

Presacral vertebræ. Those anterior to the sacrum.

Proboscis. An elongation of the snout or lips for purposes of prehension.

Procœlous vertebræ. Those which are concave in front and convex behind.

Protractile. Capable of being thrust forward.

Proximal. Toward the point of attachment; opposed to distal.

Pseudobrachiæ. Small gills on the inner surface of the opercle.

Pterygoid bones. Bones in the roof of the mouth.

Pubic bones. Plate-like bones on the belly of sticklebacks just in front of the anus.

Pubis. The ventral, anterior portion of the pelvis.

Pulmonary. Pertaining to the lungs.

Punctate. Dotted with minute points.

Punctulations. Dots.

Pustulate.   Having minute pimple-like elevations.

Pyloric cæca or appendages.   Elongated, blind sacs opening into the intestine at the point where it joins the stomach in fishes.

Quadrate bone.   The bone which joins the lower jaw, on each side, with the cranium, in the lower vertebrates.

Recurved.   Curved upwards.

Reticulate.   Marked with a net-work of lines.

Retractile.   Capable of being drawn in.

Rhombic.   Diamond-shape.

Rostral.   Pertaining to the end of the snout.

Rostral plate.   A plate on the head of snakes and lizards at the tip of the snout.

Rudimentary.   Undeveloped.

Rufous.   Reddish; yellowish red.

Rugose.   Roughened or wrinkled.

Ruminant.   Chewing the cud.

Russet.   Reddish or yellowish brown.

Sacral.   Pertaining to the sacrum or the sacral region.

Sacrum.   The dorsal portion of the pelvis.

Sanguivorous.   Blood-sucking.

Sauropsida.   Reptilian-like vertebrates.

Scalation.   Pertaining to the scales.

Scapula.   The shoulder-blade.

Segmental.   Arranged in definite segments.

Selachian fish.   Sharks and skates.

Sepia.   Light brown.

Septum.   A partition separating two spaces.

Serræ.   Notches; serrations.

Serrate.   Notched; jagged, like the teeth of a saw.

Sessile.   Attached by the base and not stalked.

Setaceous.   Bristly.

Shoulder girdle.   The bony girdle by which the skeleton of the fore legs is joined with the trunk.

Sinistral.   Pertaining to or situated on or towards the left hand.

Soft rays.   Fin rays which are jointed and not stiff and sharp.

Spatulate.   Shaped like a spatula; more or less spoon or trowel-shaped.

Sphenoid.   One of the basal skull bones.

Spine.   A sharp projecting point.

Spinous.   Composed of spines.

Spiracles.   Openings of the head in certain fish and amphibians for the passage of respiratory water.

Spiral valve.   A spiral fold in the intestine of certain fish.

Sternum.   The breast-bone.

Striate.   Striped or streaked.

Subcaudal plates.   The ventral plates of a snake's tail; the urosteges.

Subconical.   Imperfectly conical.

Subcylindrical.   Imperfectly cylindrical.

Subfusiform.   Imperfectly fusiform.

Subopercle.   The membrane bone just beneath the opercle in fishes.

Suborbital plate.   The plate beneath the eye in snakes and lizards.

Subrhombic.   Imperfectly rhombic.

Subspecies.   A geographic race, which differs from the typical form of the species but which cannot be completely separated from it.

Sulcate.   Grooved.

Superciliary plates. The plates just above the eye in certain snakes and lizards.

Superior. In a higher or more elevated position.

Supplementary maxillary bone. A small bone just above the maxillary in certain fish.

Supraoccipital process. A dorsally situated bony crest at the hinder end of the skull in fish.

Supraoral lamina. The toothed plate or ridge anterior to the mouth of a lamprey.

Supraorbital. Above the eye.

Symphysis. The firm union of two bones.

Tail. The postanal portion of the body.

Teleost. A representative of the Teleostei; a bony fish.

Temporal. Pertaining to the temples or the side of the head.

Terminal. At or toward the end.

Terrestrial. Living on or near the surface of the ground.

Tessellated. Marked with a checkered, mosaic-like arrangement.

Tetrapodous. Four-footed.

Thoracic. Pertaining to the thorax, or the anterior portion of the trunk; applied to the ventral fins of a fish when they are just beneath the pectorals.

Thorax. The anterior portion of the trunk.

Trachea. The wind-pipe.

Tragus. A projection in the external ear of bats.

Transverse. In a plane at right-angles to the longitudinal plane.

Tricuspid. With three terminal points.

Truncate. Ending abruptly, as if cut squarely across.

Tubercle. A small elevation.

Tympanum. The ear-drum.

Typical. Of a character usual to a particular group.

Ultimate. The last or terminal member of a number of structures.

Unguiculate. Having claws.

Ungulate. Hoofed.

Unicolor. Of a single color.

Unicuspid. With a single terminal point.

Urosteges. The ventral plates of a snake's tail; the subcaudals.

Urostyle. A bone extending back from the pelvis in frogs and toads.

Ventral. Pertaining to the under side.

Ventral fins. The posterior paired fins of a fish.

Ventral plates. The tranverse plates on the belly of a snake; the gastrosteges.

Ventricle. The posterior portion of the heart.

Vermiform. Shaped like a worm.

Vertebræ. The bones which form the spinal column.

Vertical. A dorso-ventral position.

Vertical fins. The median fins.

Vertical plate. The central plate on the snake's head.

Vesicle. A small or minute cavity.

Vesicular. Composed of vesicles.

Villiform teeth. Teeth of certain fishes which are small, slender and crowded together.

Villose. More or less covered with short, finger-shaped projections.

Viperine snakes. Snakes which have a pair of long movable fangs in the front of the upper jaw.

Viscera. The internal organs of an animal.

Visceral arches. The bony or cartilaginous arches which support the mouth and gills of fishes.

Visceral skeleton. The portion of the skull which forms the frame-work of the jaws, tongue and gill arches.

Viscous. Slimy.

Viviparous.   Bringing forth the young alive.

Vomer bones.   The membrane bones forming the roof of the anterior portion of the mouth

Weberian ossicles.   A series of small bones connecting the air-bladder with the ear in certain fishes.

Ypsiloid cartilage.   A Y-shaped cartilage which projects forward from the pubis in certain salamanders.

Zygomatic bone.   The cheek bone.

INDEX

Specific names begin with small letters and are accompanied each by the name of its genus in parentheses; all other names begin with capital letters. Synonyms are in italics.